Finding Your Way

A Practical Guide for Family Caregivers

250 Real Life Questions
& Commonsense Answers

Dr. Linda Rhodes

Pascoe Publishing, Inc.

Rocklin, California

Some columns in this book appeared in,
Should Mom be Left Alone? Should Dad be Driving? by Dr. Linda Rhodes, New American Library (2005)

Cover Design – KB Designs
Page Design & Layout – KB Designs

Pascoe Publishing, Inc.
Rocklin, California
www.pascoepublishing.com

ISBN: 978-1-929862-73-3

11   12   13
10   9   8   7   6   5   4   3   2   1

Printed in China

Dedicated to my brother, Paul Michael Colvin.

Cancer deprived him of growing old with his children, Lindy and Riley.
They would have lovingly cared for him.

Table of Contents

SECTION TWO
Nursing Homes, Hospice & Home Health

PART II : NAVIGATING LIFE

SECTION ONE
Staying Well

SECTION TWO
Family Conflicts & Relationships

SECTION THREE
Lifestyle

PART III : NAVIGATING LEGAL & MONEY MATTERS

SECTION ONE
Money Matters & Insurance

SECTION TWO
Legal Issues

SECTION THREE
Benefits & Resources

Introduction

It started at the water cooler. One of those Monday morning conversations not about football, but about everyone they knew coping with some type of issue facing a parent growing older. If they were having a hard time – editors of a very large newspaper – how were their readers navigating the rough waters of caregiving?

Within weeks of that conversation, John A. Kirkpatrick, former editor and publisher of *The Patriot-News*, Pennsylvania's "capitol newspaper," had me writing a weekly newspaper column, *Our Parents, Ourselves*, and has featured it ever since on the front page of the Living Section on Monday mornings. Six years later, the columns have now become this book. I am extremely grateful to John for his foresight in "reading" the needs of his public and giving me the opportunity to give them a helping hand as they care for their aging parents and spouses.

Over the years, I've heard from hundreds of caregivers who've sent questions to me through my website (www.lindarhodescaregiving.com). They have kept me grounded as to the everyday struggles that families face while they try to help a loved one get well, stay well, cope with chronic conditions and independently remain at home for as long as possible.

While I was Secretary of Aging for Pennsylvania, I had the honor of launching one of the first Family Caregiver Support programs in the country. Through the experiences of thousands of families in this program – and caring for my children's great grandmother in our home – I learned to appreciate the quiet, heroic efforts so many people make every day caring for an aging spouse, parent, relative or friend. Being better informed makes the caregiving road easier to travel and can save you from stressful detours and costly dead ends.

This book is divided into three parts: Navigating Health Care, Navigating Life, and Navigating Legal and Money Matters. Among them are ten sections that cover over 250 questions and answers that are chock full of resources, contact information and action steps to help you tackle the wide-range of challenges family caregivers face.

So, take this book and treat it like your own personal navigator to help you find your way through the world of caregiving.

Dr. Linda M. Rhodes
www.lindarhodescaregiving.com

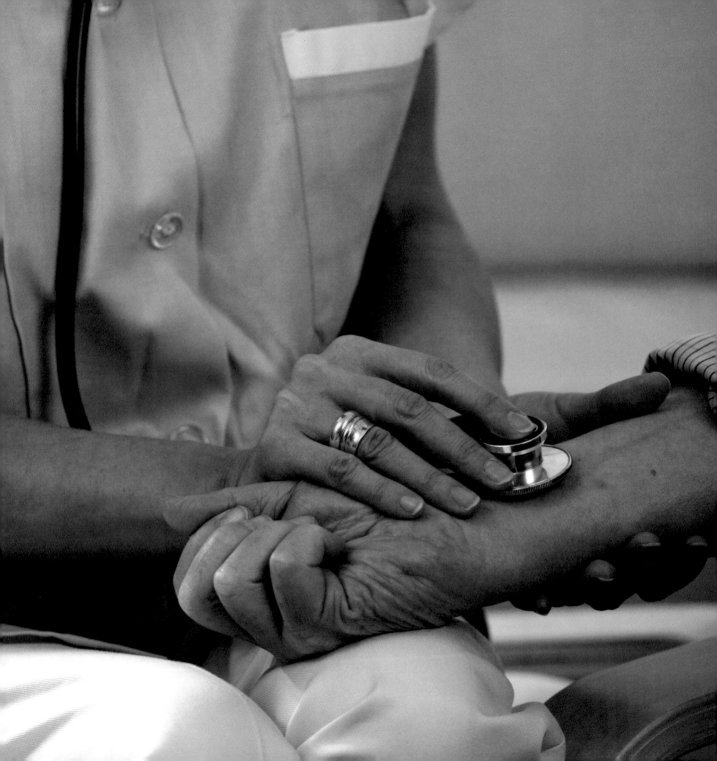

PART I

Navigating
Health Care

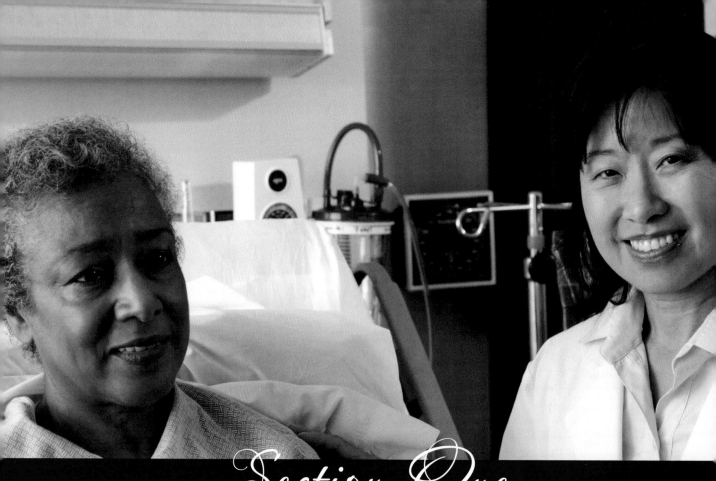

Section One
Hospitals, Clinical Trials & Ambulance Services

Q: Should my Dad just sign all those hospital consent forms or actually question them?

A: If your hospital stay is planned, the hospital will often send their blanket consent forms in advance so that you can go over them. If not, call and request them. If the hospital stay is unexpected, you could sign the form and simply write on the bottom, *"I am signing this on a temporary basis so that my parent can be admitted."* This gives you some added time to thoroughly review the consent form without holding up your parent's much needed admittance. Depending upon the type of procedure or surgery that your parent will have, your parent (or you, if they are not legally competent) will be asked to sign a consent form that identifies the specific risks related to that type of surgery.

Several years ago I had to have neck surgery. My eyes couldn't get past "paralyzed from the neck down" as just one of the risks listed on the consent form. But it is important and right that hospitals lay out the cold, hard facts on the risks that any surgery presents. You and your parents need to weigh the benefits against the risks. No matter how minor the procedure, it isn't risk-free! Many people don't realize that you can make changes on the consent form. My surgery was performed at a very fine teaching hospital and I searched for the best neurosurgeon

in the state. I wanted him to do the actual surgery and no one else. I didn't mind other young doctors learning from him by being alongside of him during the surgery. But that's where I wanted them to be—at his side. So, on the section of the consent form where it said I gave permission for the surgery to the "surgeon or those under his supervision," I crossed out "**or those under his supervision**." You can do the same, if this is a concern of yours.

Besides the surgeon, the other critical person to your Dad's surgery is the anesthesiologist—the one who will put him to sleep during the surgery and monitor him throughout it. Anesthesiologists are physicians who administer anesthesia to relieve pain and manage vital life functions, including breathing, heart rhythm, blood pressure, and brain and kidney functions during surgery. They also manage and treat any medical problems that may be present before surgery or that may develop during or immediately after surgery. Anesthesia requires very sophisticated skills, especially when it's administered to elderly patients. Changes in their physiology and conditions like heart problems, multiple medications or diabetes can cause unexpected complications with geriatric patients. It's very appropriate for you to ask about this person's credentials.

He or she should be Board Certified; this means that they passed a comprehensive test to receive certification, providing you with an added measure of their qualifications. There are also Nurse Anesthetists; make sure they have CRNA after their name (meaning they are certified) and ask about the qualifications of the physician anesthesiologist who will be supervising them.

The anesthesiologist should have a face-to-face meeting with your Dad before the surgery. Hopefully, you, your Mom and/or a sibling is sitting alongside of him. They'll be asking him questions that he's probably answered before. That's okay. They're doing this to double check. Don't mind the repetition.

: What is a hospital Patient Advocate?

: Every hospital is required by law to employ Patient Advocates, also known as Patient Representatives, to resolve patient concerns. Look in the hospital directory or ask the receptionist at the Information Desk to give you the name and number. Hospitals are also required by law to present each patient upon admission a copy of the Patient Bill of Rights, which frequently provides that contact information.

Patient Representatives focus on the needs of the patient and their families. They will listen to your concerns, respond to a complaint, explain hospital policies and procedures, provide information on community services, provide information on insurance coverage and broker a dispute between you and the medical team. Their goal is to resolve conflicts so that the remainder of a patient's stay can be purely focused on getting well.

Hospitals, medical care and insurance have become very complex and it's easy to become overwhelmed by the hospital environment, while at the same time responding to your parent's recovery. Add to the mix the nursing shortage that makes it difficult for nurses to find enough time to communicate with families and patients–you can see how misunderstandings quickly evolve. So, the sooner you talk to a Patient Advocate, the better. Their goal is to resolve a patient's concern during their hospital stay, so that patients can concentrate on their recovery.

Patient Advocates can also help you if you think that your Mom or Dad is being discharged too quickly, or assist in identifying home health care and community services. And they can explain coverage issues regarding Medicare. If they can't resolve the issue within the hospital system, call the Medicare Beneficiary Hotline at 1-800-322-1914 and ask them to connect you with the agency contracted by them to handle a complaint against an early discharge.

Communication is key, so be sure to stay informed on your parent's condition; make a list of questions when you talk to the doctor and nurse in charge of his or her care and share the answers with other family members. It's also helpful to the nursing staff to appoint one family member to become the spokesperson for the whole family. The family spokesperson, in turn, can then inform all of the other members of any new developments or information on your parent's condition. You don't want to bombard the nurse's station with questions and calls from every relative. They'll be very appreciative.

Q: My Mom was told to see a specialist by her family doctor. Is it her doctor's responsibility to set up the appointment?

 Some doctors who make referrals to specialists do make appointments on their patient's behalf and others do not. Those who don't report that the overload of paperwork and high volume of patient visits prevents them from making calls for appointments that a patient can do for themselves. All that may be true and understandable, but there's fall-out from patients being responsible for tracking down a specialist: half never get there according to an alarming study by the Regenstrief Institute and the Indiana School of Medicine. There are a host of reasons for the specialist disconnect: the patient never followed-through, they lacked transportation, they felt too sick to go, the specialist couldn't see them for a month or more, so they gave up, or the doctor's office faxed the referral to the wrong office, or the specialist's office didn't get the fax or someone forgot to confirm the appointment with the patient.

Dr. Weiner, lead author and Professor of Medicine at the Indiana School of Medicine, advises that you should always ask your doctor, "why are you referring me to this specialist and what is it that you want to learn from him or her?" Then ask your doctor, "what's the process in getting an appointment and who handles the follow-up once I've seen the specialist you referred me to?" And then, make the appointment!

Want to secure an appointment with a specialist? Take these steps:

1. If your doctor's office makes the appointment for you, then ask if you can remain in the waiting area while they make it so you won't have to wonder if the appointment was made or not.

2. If your doctor gives you the name of a specialist to call, ask for the name of a second specialist in case the first referral no longer accepts new patients or if the wait is too long to receive an appointment.

3. Even if the appointment is months away, take the first available appointment, but also ask if they would place you on a waiting list for a cancellation. If they don't have a waiting list, ask what number you should call in the mornings to find out if there is a cancellation so you can get in sooner.

4. If the specialist cannot see you for an extended period of time and your doctor felt you should be seen quickly, then call your doctor's office back and let them know. Ask if they think the wait is acceptable or if they should intervene and get the appointment moved up.

If you need to cancel an appointment, be sure to call ahead so someone else who wants to be seen quickly may be given the opportunity.

 : My family physician told me that whenever I'm hospitalized, he won't be seeing me. Instead I'll be seen by a *hospitalist*. Who is that?

 **:** This new type of doctor is really taking off in the medical field. A hospitalist is a physician whose primary practice is to oversee and tend to the care of hospitalized patients. Once you're admitted, a hospitalist will be in charge of your case from start to finish. They often see patients in the ER, admit them to the hospital, order tests, coordinate

care with other specialists, prescribe medications, consult with the patient's primary care physician, create a discharge plan and make arrangements for discharge. You'll likely see your hospitalist a few times a day.

Most hospitalists are trained in internal medicine, with about 15 percent being trained in a specialty most likely in pulmonary (lung) or critical care. There are over 15,000 hospitalists in practice today, which is the same number of neurologists or gastroenterolgists. But, within the next three years that number is expected to double.

Many patients who experience a hospitalist, report liking the frequent contact and the feeling that amidst all of the health care people coming in and out of their room – one familiar face seems to be in charge.

Here are a few other reported advantages:

➤ Hospitalists are more familiar with the hospital's system, and as a result, they can be more effective in getting things done on a patient's behalf.

➤ They know the members of the health care team and can better coordinate them with their consistent presence.

➤ Since they follow you throughout your hospital stay even right after discharge, you're less likely to fall through the cracks; most medical errors occur during the classic hand-off.

➤ They should also have more advanced training and experience in treating common inpatient conditions like severe pneumonia, strokes and heart failure.

So, even though you might feel like your family doctor isn't paying attention to you when you need him or her the most, you should know that this development could really be in your best interest. That said, a quality hospitalist experience is highly dependent upon good communication and not juggling too many cases (15 patients at once is considered a reasonable number). Here is what I suggest you ask to make sure that both the hospitalist and your doctor are talking:

What to ask your doctor:

➤ What procedures does your practice have in place to coordinate my care with a hospitalist?

➤ How soon do they contact you to let you know I've been admitted to the hospital? How often do you talk to the hospitalist while I'm in the hospital? Such as, is there a daily update or do they just call if there is a problem?

➤ Do they know how to get a hold of you?

➤ What information do you share with the hospitalist?

➤ Will you let them know about my medical history, prescriptions and allergies?

‣ Do they send you a copy of my discharge summary and tests results? How soon?

‣ Will your office call me to set up a follow-up visit when I'm discharged, or do I call you?

What to ask the hospitalist: (First, find out who your hospitalist is.)

‣ Have you informed my primary care physician that I've been admitted?

‣ Have you received my medical history from him or her?

‣ Is there anything else you need to know?

‣ How often do you plan on speaking to my physician while I am here?

‣ Upon discharge, ask: Have you sent my discharge summary and tests results to my physician?

‣ If I have any questions about my discharge directions, should I call you or my physician?

I'd also recommend that you write down the name of your hospitalist should you need to mention him or her to your physician during your follow-up visit. You should also be aware that some Medicare managed care plans require members to use hospitalists rather than reimburse your primary care physician to oversee your care in the hospital.

: Hospital mistakes scare me. How do you prevent them?

You might have heard about a report by the Institute of Medicine, a member of the non-profit National Academies studying health and medicine, in which they found that medical errors kill some 44,000 people a year in U.S. hospitals. Another study said the number was closer to 98,000. Most of the medical errors are not the result of individual recklessness, but of basic flaws in the way the health care system is organized. Deadly mistakes can derive from the illegible handwriting of doctor's orders, for example, or the practice of stocking medicines at toxic, full-strength levels, thereby increasing the risk that a hurried technician will administer it without diluting it first. Even though most hospitals run tight ships and your parent's surgery could save his life, he's still at risk.

So here's a crash course on how you can become your parent's personal patient advocate:

1. Read up on his condition and the surgical procedure. Familiarize yourself with the terms. Create a little "cheat sheet" so you can refer to it when you're talking with the nurses and doctors.

2. Get to know the nurses at the nurses' station and choose one or two members of your family to act as the liaison between the nurses and the rest of the family to give updates on your Mom or Dad's condition. The staff will appreciate not being bombarded by five or six family members.

3. Don't be afraid to insist on speaking with the doctor. Many doctors make their rounds early in the morning, so ask the nurses when the doc is due and make it a point to be there. If you can't, have the doctor paged as soon as you arrive so he or she can call or stop by your parent's room.

4. During the first few days following surgery, make sure that someone is with your parent at all times. If he complains of feeling dizzy, nauseated or in pain, you can immediately go to the nurse rather than expect him to hit the call bell and wait for someone to attend to him.

5. If you are concerned that something isn't "right" about your parent's recovery, ask to see the registered nurse on the shift and express your concerns to her. Don't assume that everyone wearing white is a registered nurse. With today's nursing shortages, many hospitals have hired nursing assistants to provide care. They are not trained to make sophisticated, diagnostic decisions that warrant calling in the doctor.

6. If your parent is allergic to certain medications, post a sign on his headboard listing his allergies. Yes, this data should be on his charts, but people die each year because they've been given the wrong drug. So be extra careful.

7. Don't be embarrassed to ask anyone caring for your parent–especially the technicians who take blood samples–to clean their hands in your parent's room. (This goes for you and all visitors, too). If someone comes in with gloves on, tell him you'd feel more comfortable if he'd put a new pair on. Why? The Centers for Disease Control and Prevention reports that during one year alone, nearly one million people will contract a hospital-borne infection. It's one of the biggest problems hospitals face.

The bottom line on being a patient advocate is to ask questions. Be as informed as a college student cramming for a test and as persistent as a 4-year old running around asking, "Why?"

Q: My Dad has been in the hospital for almost a week and he still has a catheter. Should I say something to his doctor?

A: If you ask Sanjay Saint, M.D., M.P.H, lead author of a major study on catheter use in hospitals, he would tell you to definitely approach your Dad's physician. "Doctors are responsible for ordering the removal of catheters," explains Saint, "but research has shown that many of them forget which patients have catheters and how long they have them." Dr. Saint is Director of Patient Safety Enhancement at the VA Ann Arbor Healthcare System and a professor at the University of Michigan Medical School. About one out of every four patients in hospitals is prescribed a urinary catheter during a hospital stay. Many experts contend that large numbers of these patients have them longer than necessary, increasing their risk for urinary tract infections (UTI). Infections in the urinary tract account for forty percent of all hospital acquired infections and catheters are the most likely culprit. A UTI can develop into a very painful bladder infection and, in extreme cases, a blood infection that can prove fatal. Having a catheter in place for more than two days, according to the researchers, increases the likelihood of an infection at a rate of 5 percent each day. So, you certainly have a reason to raise your concern to your father's doctor.

Saint and his colleagues tested a reminder system by having a nurse check the medical records of patients every day while they were hospitalized. After a catheter was in place 48 hours, she attached an "order" to remove the catheter, placing a "Sign Here" sticker for the doctor to sign. If the doctor didn't sign it, she'd page him or her just to make sure that they wanted the patient to retain the catheter. About two-thirds of the doctors signed the order to remove the catheter, and as a result, the number of days patients spent using catheters dropped by 25 percent – and so did the rate of infections.

Dr. Saint advises all hospital patients, after using a catheter for 48 hours, to ask their doctor if they still need the catheter. Ask every single day he or she comes in to examine you. If you're uncomfortable asking, then have a family member ask or request your nurse to inquire on your behalf. Hospitals are extremely busy and so are physicians; not removing a catheter may simply be an oversight in the midst of assessing more complicated issues about your care or juggling a hundred others. Go on the offense – ask!

: How do I find out about the track record of my Dad's surgeon?

 : I've usually found that very good doctors don't mind you asking about their credentials, and they understand your need to be comfortable with their level of expertise. It's important for a physician to earn your trust, not to think that you'll just blindly hand it over to him or her. If you've never met the physician, and your Dad is about to put his life in this stranger's hands, then asking questions is just plain common sense.

Our parents' generation is inclined to think that it's impolite to question a doctor. I know my own father gets nervous when I insist on getting a second opinion for any major procedure. He thinks his doctor will get angry. But most doctors, given today's malpractice environment, prefer patients who have done their homework and have realistic expectations. A second opinion, for example, validating what the doctor has told your Dad, will contribute to the trust between doctor and patient, rather than working against it. Let your Dad know that, nowadays, good doctors expect questions from their patients.

So, what do you do? The most important thing you want to know is how competent and skilled this physician is to perform your Dad's surgery. Getting the answer requires some research and a candid, yet polite conversation with the physician.

First, the research: thanks to the internet and a few publications, you can gain access to basic background information about physicians and learn whether they've been cited for malpractice, civil and/or criminal violations. Here's how:

> ▸ **"Doctor Finder"** (www.AMA-Assn. org) is offered by the American Medical Association. Click onto *Doctor Finder* and you can check out basic data on every licensed physician in the country. You can find out where they went to school, when they graduated, where they practiced their residency and whether they are board-certified in their specialty. Doctors who are board-certified have at least 3 to 5 years of post-medical training in a specialty. They have passed a difficult exam and have been approved by a specialty board of highly accomplished physicians in that field. It's a good quality marker when searching for a doctor.

> ▸ Your state's **Doctor Disciplinary Board**. You can find out if any disciplinary action has been taken against any state-

licensed physician by your state licensing board for health professionals. Most states have a Professional Licensure Board affiliated with their Health Department, which is responsible for taking and reporting disciplinary action on health professionals. You can find your state's medical board website by going to the Federation of State Medical Board's directory at: www.fsmb.org/directory_smb.html.

Now that you've done your homework, you're ready for a conversation with the physician. You can start with something like, "I know you'd want to do the best by your father; I'm trying to do the same for mine. So, if you could help me out by just answering a few questions, I'd really be thankful."

Here's what I suggest asking:

- Are you board-certified? Could you explain what that entailed?

- How many times a year (or month) do you perform the procedure you're recommending for my Dad? (It's important that he or she perform this procedure frequently.)

- Where do you hold hospital privileges?

- Do you consult with other doctors on difficult cases?

- What are the risks for my Dad if he has this surgery?

- What are the risks for my Dad if he does not have this surgery?

- Have you ever been professionally disciplined or had your hospital privileges revoked?

That last question might be a little difficult to ask. But this is your Dad's life at stake. If you ask it sincerely and in a friendly tone, no doctor should be offended.

 How can I compare hospitals as to their quality?

 Comparing hospitals from a consumer's perspective recently got easier with the addition of the "Survey of Patients' Hospital Experiences," offered by the Centers for Medicare and Medicaid Services (CMS) Hospital Compare website. More than 2,500 hospitals now survey random samples of discharged patients treated for a wide range of conditions. The new patient survey taps people's reactions to their hospital care, asking such questions as, "How often did nurses explain things in a way you could understand? How often did doctors listen carefully to you? How often was your pain well-controlled? After you pressed the call button, how often did you get help as soon as you wanted it? And, how often did hospital staff tell you what the medicine was for?"

Patients are also asked if it was quiet near their room at night and whether or not their room was clean. But, the most telling question of the survey is based on the power of word of mouth: patients are asked, "would you recommend this hospital to your friends and family?" Nationally, nearly seven out of ten patients said they would recommend the hospital and 63 percent gave their hospital a nine or ten positive rating on a scale of zero to ten. Three out of four patients report that hospital staff gave them information about what to do during their recovery at home. But, on average, hospitals fell short in a number of areas. Only half provided patients quiet rooms at night and 42 percent of the time the staff did not explain the medications they were giving to patients. One third of patients did not feel their pain was well-controlled. Eight out of ten doctors "always communicated well" with their patients and three out of four nurses did– that's the good news. However, Dr. Carolyn Clancy, director of the Agency for Healthcare Research and Quality is alarmed that 20 to 25 percent of patients did not feel health care professionals communicated well with

them. "Poor communication is a major source of medical errors," claims Clancy, "affecting hundreds of thousands of people each year."

Review the results of all 28 questions at www.hospitalcompare.hhs.gov for hospitals in your area and compare up to three at a time. You are also shown how your hospital ranks compared to state and national averages. If you do not have access to the internet, call Medicare at 1-800-633-4227 and say "Other Choices" at the end of the menu options. Then, ask for an "Agent" and when you speak to them, tell them you want to compare hospitals through "Hospital Compare." Besides patient experience results, you can also learn how hospitals perform in treating heart attacks, heart failure, pneumonia and recovery from common surgeries, known as "Process of Care" measures. Mortality rates for key conditions within 30 days of hospitalization are also provided.

Q: You hear about medical mistakes in hospitals, but what about at your doctor's office?

A: The odds are mounting that you will be on the receiving end of a medical mistake resulting from your doctor's office visit. If you want to weigh the odds, consider this: for every eight people who are admitted to the hospital, nearly 30 times that number visit a physician's office. The average family physician sees 100 patients every week, spending about seven minutes to listen, examine, diagnose and treat you. Two out of every three office visits result in giving patients pills and four out of ten physicians order some type of diagnostic test (prescription mistakes and testing slip-ups are the leading causes of medical errors in doctor's offices).

It's not just the likelihood that you'll be visiting a doctor's office that places you at risk, there are not enough primary care physicians, appointments are getting shorter, and patients are seeing more and more doctors who specialize in body parts with no one coordinating their care. Most of the new safety practices and technologies to prevent medical errors have zeroed in on the hospital setting, not the doctor's office.

A report in 2008 sponsored by the U.S. Agency for Healthcare Research and Quality, along with the American Academy of Family Physicians, uncovered just how high how the odds are for medical errors at the doctor's office. Here is what they found from 243 clinicians who reported close to **one thousand errors** in a 32-week period:

› Nearly one out of every five mistakes caused some type of physical or emotional harm to the patient, of which half caused pain and suffering.

› The vast majority of cases (80 percent) led to extra time and expense, but did not adversely affect the patient's health.

› Most mistakes were made in the process of ordering, performing and reporting test results. For example, the wrong tests were ordered, misfiled, lost, misinterpreted, not done properly or no one told the physician and/or patient the results.

So, if you want to reduce your odds, take these steps:

› When your doctor orders a test (e.g. blood, x-ray, EKG), always ask what is the name of the test, what is it for, when will you receive the results and by what means?

Never accept, "If you don't hear from us, then assume everything is okay" from your doctor or nurse. Tell them you want to know the results, whether normal or abnormal.

 If you have not heard from your doctor's office on the test results when he or she said they should be done, call and ask for the results.

 Always take a current list of your medications or, better yet, take the pill bottles of all the current medications you are taking to the doctor's office to prevent prescription errors.

 Ask for a copy of your test results and check them against what the doctor told you he ordered.

 Don't be afraid to ask your doctor about the results and, if you are making major decisions on cancer treatment or surgery based on test results, ask your doctor about having another pathologist or radiologist look at your tests for a second opinion.

Medical care these days is more complex and overburdened. Despite all of this, most of the time your doctor is treating you mistake-free, but it doesn't hurt to become a safety-check partner, so you both can beat the odds.

 : You've talked before about the hazards of "body parts medicine." What do you mean?

 : What I call "Body Part Medicine & Disconnected Care" is in reaction to a national survey released by the Campaign for Better Care. The survey of over one thousand adults 50-plus years found that older people who are struggling with one or more chronic conditions also struggle with poor care coordination and inadequate communication among the doctors who treat them. It's happening, in large part, as a result of specialized medicine.

It's not uncommon for those in their sixties to juggle doctor's appointments for two or more chronic conditions. Diabetes, heart disease, high blood pressure and arthritis can catapult a rather "healthy person" into a world of blood tests, self-administered blood pressure and glucose readings, along with a multitude of medications. In all likelihood, specialists will treat each of these conditions. For example: a cardiologist for heart disease, rheumatologist for arthritis, endocrinologist for diabetes and an internist to monitor blood pressure and diagnose any new problems or make referrals to other specialists.

Each of them will likely order tests like x-rays, blood work, CT scans, MRIs and they'll prescribe medications to treat each condition. Unless all of these doctors practice within the same health care system, they can't access the results of each other's test results. And, in some cases, unless the patient speaks up, they'll order repeat tests, unaware that it was ordered by some other treating physician. Or, if the patient doesn't share his or her complete list of medications, a doctor may prescribe a medication that should not be taken with another drug or they may prescribe the same medication as has another physician. Thus, a patient may unwittingly wind up taking twice the dosage. Sometimes this happens when a patient thinks a drug in a generic form is different from a drug written under the brand name, yet it's actually the same drug. Patients using multiple pharmacies are more at risk for this to occur because the pharmacist is less likely to pick up the duplication.

Here are some key findings of the survey that may alarm you:

› On average, 40 percent of the respondents reported that their doctors do not talk to them about potential interactions with other drugs or over-the-counter medications when prescribing new medications.

› Forty percent of those with multiple chronic conditions act as the chief communicator among the doctors they see because the physicians don't talk to each other.

› Three out of four respondents really wish their doctors would speak to each other to better coordinate their care.

› One in eight respondents had to retake a test or procedure because the doctor or hospital did not have the earlier results.

› Three-quarters of heavy users of the health care system have left a doctor's office or hospital confused about what to do at home.

› Three-quarters of adults ages 50 and older say they are worried that the quality of health care services they receive will get worse in the future.

› Twenty percent reported that they had to unravel conflicting information from different doctors.

So, what about you? Do you have a story to tell or suggestion to make on how patients and doctors can better sort this out? Go to my blog at www.give-emhealth.com to post a comment.

In the meantime, always keep an updated list of your medications and bring it to every physician visit to share with your doctor. Also, ask for copies of your test and procedure results and bring those with you to every doctor visit. Let the doctor know of your other medical conditions and the names of those physicians treating you. Bottom line? It's all about you. **You** are in charge of your health care.

Q: I can't stand hearing medical staff calling elderly people "sweetie" and the like. Am I overreacting?

A: Sounds like they have touched a nerve and, rest assured, you're not alone feeling this way. Too often, in an attempt to be friendly or show they care, health care providers, retail clerks, hair dressers and restaurant servers, just to name a few, will address an elderly person in "elderspeak." People use this form of language when they assume that the older person isn't all there and probably can't hear well, either. In no time, the conversation has been "dumbed down" to baby talk. If you're wondering what elderspeak sounds like, here are some examples offered up by respondents on the *New Old Age* blog of *The New York Times*:

› When asking someone their age, they ask: "How many years young are you?"

› Salutations often begin with "Hi sweetie, cutie, or honey."

› Actions, as simple as taking a pill, are evaluated like a grade school child with "Good job!" or "good girl" or "good boy."

› A woman clearly in her seventies or older is referred to as "young lady."

› The nurse or doctor who asks her patient, "How are we feeling?"

› Rather than asking about a career or current interests, an older person is asked, "Who were you or what did you used to be?"

› Greeting older people by their first name, as they would a teenager.

The overall tone of elderspeak is usually patronizing, overbearing and spoken slowly in a loud voice using simple words. The speech sends the subliminal message that the older person is incompetent. And here's the thing: People pick up on it–even those with Alzheimer's disease–and they don't like it. They see it as insulting and a form of bullying.

New research shows that elderspeak, no matter how well-intentioned by the speaker, is a lot more than an annoyance for those on the receiving end. Dr. Kristine Williams, an associate professor at the University of Kansas School of Nursing, analyzed hundreds of videotaped interactions between staff and residents who suffered from mild to moderate dementia. They identified as to whether or not the staff used elderspeak, spoke normally, or said nothing at all while they helped a resident bathe, dress, or groom, and then rated how residents reacted to the exchange. What the researchers found was sobering: When nurse aides used elderspeak, the residents resisted by physically pulling back, saying no, grimacing, grabbing the person or clenching their teeth. The more the residents became uncooperative, the more the staff resorted to talking to them like misbehaving children.

So, to answer your question: No, you are not overreacting, and it would be appropriate for you to share with the staff helpful ways in which they can best relate to your parents. Here are some suggestions on how to correct elderspeak toward yourself or your parents; when it comes to professional health care providers, you could approach it in one of two ways. First, let them know how much you appreciate the care they provide you and, in that spirit, you'd like to share with them ways in which they can best communicate and relate to you. At this point, tell them how you like being acknowledged, (for example, by Mr. or Mrs., or by your first name). If you need to speak up for a loved one who's a patient, perhaps you might explain that they would respond best to a combination of a salutation along with their first name, such as "Miss Linda" or "Mr. Eric." Ask that they place this information on your loved one's chart, so that everyone will know how to greet them.

What elderspeak words or phrases get on your nerves? Let me know at www.give-emhealth.com.

 : The hospital says that Medicare will not pay the bill for my father's surgery. Now what?

The hospital should have given your Dad an Advance Beneficiary Notice form before his surgery stating that Medicare would probably deny payment for the specific surgery, the reasons why, and that, if you proceed with the service, then your Dad would be fully responsible for the payment if Medicare does, in fact, deny the payment.

Right away there are two things to note: First, there are a number of procedures that Medicare will cover only when performed in an outpatient facility rather than a hospital; second, hospitals don't have to give you an Advance Beneficiary Notice for services that already are excluded from Medicare, such as routine dental care, vision and hearing services. So, always ask first! Don't assume Medicare will cover whatever your doctor prescribes as treatment.

If your Dad did not receive the ABN form, then he definitely should not pay this bill and should immediately call the Fiscal Intermediary for Medicare in his state. These are private companies that contract with Medicare to pay Medicare Part A bills (hospital and skilled nursing care). Call Medicare at 1-800-Medicare (1-800-633-4227) to find out who is assigned as your Dad's Fiscal Intermediary. The number should also appear on the denial letter. Be sure to explain that no one told your father that Medicare might not cover his surgical procedure in a hospital and he never saw or signed an ABN Form (CMS-R-131).

ABNs also are used for Medicare Part B services, which cover physician, lab, home health and outpatient services. If you have a question or complaint about a Medicare denial with Part B services, you'll need to talk to the Fiscal Intermediary that covers Part B. Advance Beneficiary Notices are meant to protect consumers from unexpected financial liability in cases where Medicare will likely deny payment. It gives you the opportunity to decide whether you want to receive the service (this also applies to medical supplies and equipment).

If you receive an ABN from your doctor or a provider, absolutely take the time to read it. You can then decide, for example, whether to find another doctor who could safely perform the surgery on an outpatient basis, which would be covered by Medicare.

According to the Centers for Medicare and Medicaid Services, if a consumer receives an ABN, they should choose one of two options on the form:

‣ **Option 1.** If you check this option, then you indicate YES: You want to receive the service or item and your claim will be sent to Medicare. You might be billed while Medicare is making its decision. If Medicare pays, you will be refunded any payments you made that are due to you. BUT, if Medicare denies payment, then you will be personally and fully responsible for payment. You will have the right to appeal Medicare's decision. Medicare will not decide whether to pay unless you receive the service or item and have a claim submitted.

‣ **Option 2.** If you check this option, then you indicate NO: You will not receive the service or item, and your claim will not be sent to Medicare. You will not be able to appeal the supplier's, physician's or provider's opinion that Medicare won't pay.

Please note that the only way you can appeal the decision is to take your chances and say "Yes" on the ABN form. Medicare needs an actual claim for services in order to deny it. If you don't want to take the risk, then seek second opinions from other physicians and providers to see whether they can meet your needs and the eligibility requirements of Medicare.

The bottom line: Always question a bill that you think should have been covered by your insurance and/or Medicare. The Fiscal Intermediaries are paid by Medicare to resolve these issues – so make use of the service.

Q: How can I stop the hospital from discharging my Dad too quickly?

A: Once the physician decides that your father's health is stable enough to no longer need acute hospital care, she'll authorize his discharge. This doesn't mean that your Dad is completely recovered and can resume a normal life. He might need other forms of care before he can go directly home and be on his own. That's where the discharge planners come in: Their job is to make sure that arrangements have been made before your Dad leaves the hospital to assure that his discharge is, according to Medicare, "safe and adequate."

The discharge planner may be a nurse, a social worker or other professional who will be your primary contact in making plans for your Dad's transition from the hospital to his next level of care. Perhaps your Dad will need short-term care in a nursing home, rehab center, or assisted living facility or he'll need home health care nurses to provide care in his own home.

What's meant by "safe and adequate" is up to you, the doctor and discharge planner to determine. You really need to be involved in deciding whether or not your Dad can safely make a transition to another level of care outside of the hospital. The discharge planner will surely ask whether or not your Dad lives alone. If he does live with your mother, but your mother is not well enough to take care of him, you need to speak up. Plans for discharge must be realistic.

The discharge plan is immediate and short-term. It's not a plan for the long run. It's to get your Dad past his most immediate health issues and onto the road to recovery. These first steps, however, should lead to a sound, feasible long-range plan to keep your Dad healthy. To best assess his needs, ask the doctor to tell you exactly what your Dad will be capable of doing once he leaves the hospital and what type of health care he will need. For instance, if he is recovering from a stroke you'll want to ask questions like: At what level are his thinking skills? Will he need assistance with bathing, eating, using the toilet, grooming, dressing, or taking medications? Will he need physical and occupational therapy (how much and how often)? Answers to these questions determine whether or not you can take him home using home health care or whether or not he needs care in a facility.

You might disagree with the physician's decision to discharge your parent. Perhaps you believe he is not well enough or that releasing him without adequate care will jeopardize his already precarious condition. You can do something. Your father's rights are clearly worded in the "An Important Message from Medicare" statement that the hospital must provide to you. It tells you that your parent has the right to receive all of the hospital care he or she needs and necessary follow-up care after leaving the hospital. The hospital will also give you a written notice known as a "Hospital-Issued Notice of Non-coverage," also referred to as a HINN. On that form, check out the phone number of the Quality Improvement Organization  (QIO). Call them and tell them you want to file an appeal to delay your father's discharge. Until the QIO makes a decision, the hospital can not force your Dad to leave or force you to pay for his continuing care in the hospital.

The best defense against scrambling to find alternative care when the hospital is asking your parent to leave is planning in advance. It's really worth your time to engage in what I call the "If" game with your parents. You play it while they're well. Start by telling them you want to do what's best for them in the event they can't take care of themselves. So…"If you had a stroke and needed to recuperate before they let you back home, where would you like to go? If you had a heart attack, what hospital would you like to go to? If you broke your hip and could go home only if you had home health care, who would we hire? If you had cancer, would you want to try alternative treatment or opt for chemotherapy and radiation, and would you want us to call hospice?" Frankly, most people will not have ready answers to these questions, so ask your parents to start visiting and researching potential facilities, so you'll know where to turn. The goal is to keep them in charge and to make smart, informed decisions when "heads are cooler" than in the heat of an emotional crisis.

 : My Mom is in the hospital and now my Dad's health seems to be failing. What's going on?

 : Your father is reflecting what a group of researchers learned studying over a half million couples who experienced the hospitalization of a spouse: it's extremely stressful and can pose very serious health risks for the "well" partner. In fact, it can even place the spouse at greater risk of death. The study, sponsored by the *National Institutes of Health* and led by Harvard

researcher, Nicholas Christakis, M.D., reviewed Medicare claims and mortality rates of the couples over a nine year period. Turns out, the first month of a sudden hospitalization is the most risky for spouses and this may be why your Dad is having such a hard time. The psychological stress of seeing a partner seriously ill, fragile and dependent may cause a spouse to feel that their world has been turned upside down. And, it many ways it has: The well spouse is confronted with an anxiety-producing health care maze of specialists, technicians, confusing medical terms and decisions, while maintaining a vigil at their spouse's bedside. Whatever daily routine your father had before your mother's hip fracture is now tossed aside. Meal times, social activities, naps, and bedtime are quickly disrupted. The daily commute to and from the hospital, especially if the spouse is driving, becomes draining. Nutrition takes a back seat to missed meals or grabbed on the run, medications may be forgotten, alcohol or cigarette use increases and loss of sleep becomes a nightly hassle.

All of this psychological and physical stress weakens the immune system and makes any current chronic conditions suffered by the non-hospitalized spouse all the more vulnerable to further decline. Now that we've established that what your father is experiencing is very real and is placing him at risk for his own health, let's take a look at what you can do to keep him well:

> Intervene quickly to create a support system for your Dad; he's at greatest risk the first thirty days.

> Organize family members to share a visitation schedule so that your mother has someone with her throughout the day and evening. Find out your Dad's daily routine and get others to visit during those times so your Dad can preserve some of his former "life" while not feeling like he's abandoning your mother.

> Offer to be available whenever the doctor and therapists meet with your mother to go over her treatment and care, so that you can help with the follow-through and become her patient advocate.

> Find out what doctor's appointments your Dad has scheduled and make sure he doesn't miss them. Also, check on his daily regimen of medications, so those aren't missed either.

> Talk with your mother and ask her to encourage your Dad to take some time off from being at her bedside (But, make sure she is comfortable with this and that her needs are met when your Dad is not there.).

> If your father drives back and forth to the hospital, arrange for someone or yourself to take him so he doesn't have to park or deal with busy traffic or night time driving.

> If family and friends offer to help, give them assignments like delivering

meals so he'll always have something healthy to eat, picking up groceries and prescriptions or provide transportation.

▸ If someone in your family or a trusted friend is good at dealing with insurance, let them help organize all the paperwork that will soon pile up or may require a response to process a claim or gain authorization for treatment.

▸ If your parents don't have the service, treat them to housecleaners while your Mom is in the hospital and while your Mom recuperates at home.

▸ Your Dad may find it exhausting to keep everyone updated on your Mom's

condition. You could set up a telephone relay among family and friends so he only has to let one person know everyday. Or, he could leave a taped "Daily Report" on his answering machine. This might be the time to get him a cell phone, if he doesn't already have one.

Let his friends know what is going on and share with them how they can help. If your parents belong to a church or synagogue, give them a call, as many faith-based groups offer friendly visitors to hospitalized members. You can also find out what respite care may be available for your Dad by calling your local Area Agency on Aging (1-800-677-1116).

Q: A friend who has Parkinson's benefited from something called "palliative care." What is it?

Palliative care (pronounced pal-lee-uh-tiv) focuses on relieving pain and the symptoms of serious illnesses. Patients who receive this kind of care will find that the "care team" is all about helping them gain a better quality of life by preventing and easing their suffering. And, not only is the patient the center of attention, so are family members. They recognize that loved ones are also affected by the illness and that everyone's daily life is

altered when a life-limiting illness enters the picture.

Living with Parkinson's, cancer, congestive heart failure, ALS, or Alzheimer's brings about major life changes for both those suffering from the disease and their loved ones who care for them. Besides coping with physical symptoms, the emotional toll often exacts a high price from both the person with the disease and family members. Relieving stress is also part of the palliative care package.

Typically, you'll find that palliative care is provided by a team that includes doctors, nurses and social workers who work as partners with your primary doctor. The team will help you and your family better understand your condition, learn what to expect as to how the disease will progress and aid you in sorting out all of the treatment options being presented to you. Their goal is to improve your ability to handle your medical treatments, manage your pain and make informed choices during different stages of the illness.

Not making informed choices can lead to a lot of regrets later. And, that's where a good palliative care team can step-in. "We really help people not to second-guess their decisions," is how Maureen Asper, Coordinator of Palliative Care at Holy Spirit Hospital in Camp Hill, Pennsylvania explains what they do. As a clinical nurse along with a team of doctors and social workers, she helps families gain a full understanding of the condition, so they can make choices that preserve the quality of life they choose during each stage of the illness, all the while relieving the pain.

People who are struggling with uncontrolled physical and emotional symptoms such as pain, anxiety, fatigue, nausea, shortness of breath, loss of appetite, depression, or sleeplessness due to a serious illness will benefit from palliative care. So would a spouse or other family members who find themselves unable to cope with the emotional strain of watching their loved one suffer from the debilitating effects of their condition and how it has altered their lives.

So, how do you get palliative care? It's rather new, so you may have to ask for it. If you think that you or your loved one suffering from a serious illness would benefit from this type of care, ask if the physician treating you would prescribe it. Many hospitals provide the care during a hospitalization, but again you may need to ask for it. Medicare and most insurance policies will cover it during a hospital stay. And some hospitals are offering palliative care clinics on an outpatient basis, as well, and through home health care agencies. Just be sure to ask if they are certified in palliative care. For individuals who are faced with a life-ending illness, hospice programs also offer palliative care during the late stages of the disease. In fact, they've lead the way in providing holistic care and managing pain.
You can find out more about palliative care and if there is a provider near you at www.getpalliativecare.org or call your local hospital to see if they offer the service.

Q: How can my Mom NOT get an infection during her hospital stay?

A: Recently, the Institute of Medicine, the prestigious non-profit advising the nation and government on matters of health, reported that up to 98,000 people die every year from infections they acquire in hospitals – most of which could have been prevented. Hospitals, of course, are places for very sick people, and very sick people have germs. Doctors, nurses and technicians who care for these very sick people come in contact with them in the most intimate of ways: via blood, urine and bodily contact. It doesn't take much for germs to travel from one person's hands to dozens of people every day. The problem for patients, however, is that their immune systems are weakened. If they've had surgery, the site of the wound is a prime destination port for germs.

In response to this infection crisis, the American Hospital Association (AHA), the American Medical Association (AMA), and the National Patient Safety Foundation (NPSF) have created an excellent patient education brochure, titled *Preventing Infections in the Hospital – What You as a Patient Can Do*. The following ten action steps are listed in their brochure as effective ways for patients to protect themselves from getting a hospital-acquired infection:

1. Wash your hands carefully after handling any type of soiled material – especially after you have gone to the bathroom.

2. Do not be afraid to remind doctors and nurses about washing their hands before working with you.

3. If you have an intravenous catheter, keep the skin around the dressing clean and dry. Immediately tell your nurse if the dressing becomes loose or wet.

4. Similarly, if you have a dressing on a wound, let your nurse know right away if the dressing becomes loose or wet.

5. If you have any type of catheter or drainage tube, let your nurse know if it becomes loose or dislodged.

6. If you have diabetes, be sure that you and your doctor discuss the best way to control your blood sugar before, during, and after your hospital stay. High blood sugar increases the risk of infection noticeably.

7. If you are overweight, losing weight will reduce the risk of infection following surgery.

8. If you are a smoker, you should consider

a smoking cessation program. This will reduce the chance of developing a lung infection while in the hospital and may also improve your healing abilities following surgery.

9. Carefully follow your doctor's instructions regarding breathing treatments and getting out of bed.

10. Ask your friends and relatives not to visit if they feel ill. Make sure that all visitors clean their hands when they come to visit and after they use the bathroom.

You might also want to ask if the hospital participates in the Centers for Disease Control's voluntary infection monitoring program – the NNIS system. This stands for National Nosocomial Infection Surveillance; the term "nosocomial" means "hospital-acquired." Hospitals that participate in this program report significantly lower infection rates than those who don't participate. If your parent does acquire an infection, ask the doctor for the exact name and spelling of the infection. Also ask to see someone from the Infection Control Unit (every hospital must have one). Ask for an explanation of the nature of the infection, and what best practices are being used to treat it.

Q: My husband just had major surgery and has "post operative cognitive dysfunction," which makes him delirious. What's going on?

A: This is the question I posed to my father's doctor when, at age 87, my father had emergency surgery for a herniated colon. He was doing just fine initially, however, on the third day he started seeing things in his room. He kept warning me to stand out of the way because trucks were coming at us, he saw his grandson hiding under the bed and was absolutely convinced that the hospital took over his house and was only letting him stay in this one tiny room. It was frightening to watch my

very independent, active father, who had no signs of cognitive decline prior to his surgery, acting as if he were in the throes of advanced dementia. Would he come out of it?

My father was experiencing an episode of acute delirium which is one of the complications of Post Operative Cognitive Dysfunction (POCD). Besides delirium, people can also experience short and long term decline in their thinking abilities (cognitive). It is suspected that the effect of anesthesia is a major contributing factor. The older you are, the more likely it may occur, especially among people in their eighties. According to one study, "Postoperative Cognitive Dysfunction After Cardiac Surgery" (CHEST, 2005), a team of physicians reported that up to 40 percent of their heart patients over sixty years old experienced some form of POCD after surgery. It would usually present itself a few days after the operation. Delirium lasts a few days to a week, while the effects of cognitive decline could last up to three months for about ten percent of patients. Some form of cognitive decline could become permanent. Most other reports that I read on the subject describe similar results, however, surgeries not related to the heart show less incidence.

So, what do you do? If your loved one starts seeing things, becomes paranoid, anxious, unaware of his or her surroundings, and has trouble performing common tasks, tell the nurse immediately and share this information with the doctor. They will need to monitor your loved one's behavior and determine if he or she is at risk of hurting themselves. In my father's case, he became delirious in the middle of the night and pulled out both of his IVs, a nasal gastrointestinal tube and his catheter. For the next three days, I or another family member was constantly with him and at night, the doctor ordered a "Safety Sitter" (a personal care aide employed by the hospital) to remain with him through the night.

I also found it helpful to go along with my father's delirium rather than argue with him. For example, he kept telling me there was paint on him and asked if I'd get him a wash cloth so he could wipe it off. I'd lightly wet the cloth and he would spend an hour "wiping it off" and feel better after having done so. When he would become frightened, I would calmly explain that the anesthesia was causing him to see things in his mind and – even though what he was seeing seemed very real – it wasn't there and he was safe with me.

After three days, my father began to recover and a neuropsychologist was called in to examine his cognitive ability. Though he functioned less than what he did prior to his surgery, we found that, once he was home, he recovered much faster. For the first two weeks, either I or my sister stayed with him. He is now back living alone with family looking in on him every day. We preferred trying this approach rather than placing my Dad in a short-term facility after the hospital. It was also very helpful to his recovery that his physician immediately took him off of morphine for pain and chose not to introduce more mind-altering drugs into his system to "calm him down" during his delirium.

I hope what I learned through my father will help you through the same. Because more surgeries are being performed on the elderly with escalating reports of POCD, anesthesiologists are conducting research to determine if different forms of anesthesia are less likely to cause POCD. Given my father's story, it can't happen soon enough.

Q: The emergency department at the hospital would not give me any information on my Dad because of "HIPAA." What were they talking about?

A: It can certainly be frustrating and downright frightening when you are trying to find out what's wrong with a loved one and you're told that you can't be given the information because of privacy rules. What the hospital person should have done was to ask your father if he'd give permission for someone to talk with you. If your father would have said yes, then his oral consent would have been sufficient.

HIPAA stands for "Health Insurance Portability and Accountability Act," but is more commonly known as the HIPAA Privacy Rule. The law was passed over a decade ago and it was designed to protect your health records from getting into the wrong hands (e.g. employers or insurance companies looking for ways to terminate your employment or not cover you) and give you easier access to your own health records.

But, once lawyers for hospitals, doctors, nurses, pharmacies, nursing homes and other health care providers read the law, they became very concerned about possible litigation. So they designed ways to make sure that whoever they were giving information to was absolutely legitimate. That's why whenever you see a new physician or health care provider, you're asked to read three to four pages of small print as to all of your rights under HIPAA. Though the law was well-intended, many consumers find the red tape associated with it to be more trouble than it's worth.

So let's cut through the red tape. When can family members be given information on health conditions and records on loved ones? Here are examples adapted from the "Patient's Guide to the HIPAA Privacy Rule:

1. An emergency room doctor may discuss your treatment in front of a friend or family member when you invite them into the treatment room.

2. While you are recovering from surgery, emergency care or other treatment, a doctor may discuss your present condition with a parent, spouse or adult child.

3. A hospital employee may discuss your bill with a family member or friend who is with you at the hospital should you have any questions about the charges.

4. A physician can speak to someone who is driving you home, for example, after out-patient surgery, as to what instructions

you should follow on the drive home and immediately following your arrival.

5. A doctor can discuss drugs prescribed for you, possible side-effects to watch for and instructions on how to take them with whomever has accompanied you during the appointment.

6. Physicians, nurses and other health care providers cannot discuss your past health history or your long term prognosis without specific instructions from you to do so.

In general, there are any one of three basic rules that a health care provider must follow before they can share information about your health to others: The provider can ask for your permission (this can be in writing or verbally), or tell you that he or she is going to discuss the information about your health with a specific person and you do not object, or decide using his or her professional judgment that you do not object.

The law does not require that your loved one give permission in writing. However, many providers insist upon it. The safest thing you can do, so you are not caught in this situation again, is to ask the hospital(s) where your father will most likely be admitted for a copy of their HIPAA form for him to sign identifying all of those he gives permission to receive information as to his health records and condition. He should do the same for every doctor that he sees. Oftentimes, he will automatically be given these forms at the doctor's office.

Because my parents live out of town, I have a letter which identifies my relationship, address and phone number signed by each of them giving health care providers permission to speak to me. My parents also have a copy on their refrigerator should paramedics ever be called so they can just grab it and give it to staff in the emergency department.

 : When my wife was discharged from the hospital, it wasn't a smooth transition. How can we avoid problems in the future?

 : National accreditation standards and federal law require hospitals to create plans on how and when they will discharge patients. And, they are to involve the patient, along with his or her family, in the process. When patients are discharged, they are to receive written

and verbal instructions on their condition, medications and any care they should receive from family members and health care professionals to help them recuperate. Here are some steps everyone should take to make the trip from hospital to home a smooth ride:

▸ Always keep a list of the medications you take and take it with you to every doctor visit and to the hospital. Have it handy to give to paramedics. For a free, printable form to keep track of your medications go to www.lindarhodescaregiving.com.

▸ When you are being discharged from the hospital, review the list of medications that is given you. If you do not get one, ask for it. Find out how long you are to take those medications and check it against the list of pills you were taking when you came to the hospital. If there are differences, ask why. Be sure to take both lists to your follow-up doctor's appointment.

▸ Ask the doctor or nurse what you should do if a problem occurs once you are home. What signs and symptoms should you be concerned about and who should you call?

▸ Make sure you are given written discharge instructions, read them and ask questions. One of the smartest things you can do is to say to the person discharging you, "Okay, let me see if I got this right …" and repeat back what you believe they have told you.

▸ Days before you are being discharged, it is very likely that a care manager will be speaking to you about what type of services that your physician will prescribe for you once you go home, usually provided by a home health care agency. Oftentimes, the care manager will make the contact for you but, if not, ask for contact information and set up an appointment for them to come to your home within days of being discharged.

▸ All throughout your hospital stay, ask for easy-to-read material on your condition and treatment. A good online resource is: www.medlineplus.gov, or go to a national association that represents a particular disease (e.g. American Heart Association).

▸ Absolutely make and keep your follow-up appointment with your primary physician. Ask him or her to re-explain your diagnosis and treatment along with your test results taken during your hospital stay. Review your medications by bringing all of your prescriptions to that visit rather than taking a chance that you've written down something wrong on your list. One of the most common medication errors people make is to continue taking prescriptions from a hospital stay that should have been stopped.

Q: What are clinical trials and how do you find them?

A: Clinical trials are research studies to determine whether vaccines, drugs, new therapies or new treatments are safe and effective. These trials are offered to humans after researchers have tested various procedures in laboratories and on animals. All clinical trials must be approved by an Institutional Review Board (IRB) that consists of researchers, physicians and consumers who must review the proposed study and assure that it is safe and ethical and that the rights of those being studied are protected. Be aware, however, that the sponsoring institution of the study forms the IRB.

Besides receiving the go ahead from an IRB, pharmaceutical companies must gain approval from the Food & Drug Administration (FDA) that their animal and laboratory studies were successful enough to warrant safe testing of humans. There are basically four phases to clinical trials, with each phase expanding to test more people. For instance, a Phase 1 study will research a small group of 20 to 80 people and by Phase III up to 3,000 people may be involved. The "protocol," which is the plan of study for the research project, describes the types of people who will be tested, the schedule of tests, treatment, medications,

dosages, and length of time in the study. Frequently, patients in clinical trials are assigned either to a study group that receives the new treatment or to a "control" group that receives standard treatment or a placebo (an inactive pill, liquid or powder with no treatment value, such as a sugar pill). It is unethical, however, to give a sick patient a placebo when there is a known beneficial treatment available.

The major benefit of participating in a clinical trial is to gain access to the latest "discovery" and hopefully, the most advanced form of treatment. For someone who is becoming blind, dying of cancer or in great pain, a clinical trial may sound very appealing and may greatly improve their quality of life.

But, there are definite risks. So, do your own research to make sure that the benefits outweigh the risks. Your first step is to check out the National Institutes of Health (NIH) website at www.clinicaltrial.gov, or give them a call (1-800-411-1222). At the website you can simply search by topic, for example, enter *macular degeneration*, and you'll immediately find clinical trials related to the disease being conducted throughout the country, along with their contact information. You can also go to other links for further research on medical conditions and news on clinical trials from disease-related associations (e.g. American Cancer Society).

If you're wondering what you should be asking the doctors who run the clinical trial, NIH and other experts suggests you ask:

- Who is sponsoring this study and who is funding this trial? Do you or the director have a financial stake in this treatment or drug?

- What can you show me to verify the credibility of the group sponsoring this clinical trial?

- What is the purpose of the study?

- How will my safety be monitored?

- Who is going to be in the study?

- Why do researchers believe the new treatment being tested may be effective? Has it been tested before? On how many people?

- What kinds of tests and treatments are involved?

- How might this trial affect my daily life?

- How long will the trial last?

- Will hospitalization be required?

- Who will pay for the treatment?

- Will I be reimbursed for other expenses?

- What type of long-term follow-up care is part of this study?

- How will I know that the treatment is working? Will results of the trials be provided to me?

- Who will be in charge of my care? How can I reach him or her if I have complications?

Always take a family member or friend to the preliminary visit, bring a tape recorder and very carefully read the Informed Consent Form. This form should answer many of the questions listed above and clearly spell out the risks. Be sure to consult with your primary care physician and your specialist, as you will want them to work with the clinical trial team. Ask them their opinion on the risks and benefits as they relate to you or your loved one's particular diagnosis. Remember: you can stop participating in the clinical trial at any time. This is absolutely voluntary. Medicare will pay for qualifying clinical trials, so be sure to ask whether or not Medicare will be covering all of your expenses.

Clinical trials can be literal lifesavers. Just make sure that whoever offers the clinical trial is credible, is part of a highly regarded medical and/or academic institution and is forthright about the risks and who is funding the research study.

Q: What do "phases" mean in clinical trials?
Are they the same as "stages" in cancer?

A: The quick answer is no. Cancer *stages* and clinical trial *phases* are not the same thing. The numbering of phases and stages (even though both use Roman numerals) do not correspond. Now, for the long answer:

Cancer is characterized by four stages. Stage I is the most curable, while Stage IV is the least. Staging is determined by grading the tumor itself, how large it is, whether it's affecting surrounding tissue, whether and to what extent the lymph nodes are involved, and how much the cancer has spread (metastasized).

Clinical trials, which are research studies to determine whether vaccines, drugs, new therapies or new treatments are safe and effective, are divided into four phases.

Phase I Trials are the first tests of the new drug being researched on humans. Researchers investigate findings on dosage, timing, and safety of the new drug or therapy. In this phase of clinical research, the dosage of the drug is gradually increased to identify the safest dose to give humans. Researchers are also looking at how the drug is absorbed, processed, and distributed in the body. At this phase of the trial, clinicians are *not* trying to determine the effectiveness of the drug. These trials are very small – oftentimes no more than 20 patients are involved.

Phase II Trials focus on how the new treatment accomplishes its aim. For example, a cancer trial will look at whether or not the tumor is shrinking and if blood work results are improving. Trials during Phase II usually take two years to complete and again involve a small number of patients, usually not more than 40. In order to proceed to the next phase, researchers must prove that the response rate to treatment is equal to or higher than the conventional standards of practice.

Phase III Trials take this potentially new treatment and compares it against the current standard of care. Now the study group greatly expands in numbers so researchers can better determine if the new treatment is more effective, can be prescribed for shorter periods of time, and/or avoids any negative side-effects. Many times trials during this phase will also look at how the drug fares in combination with other therapies. Patients who participate in Phase III trials are randomized to receive either the new drug or treatment being studied or the conventional one. If a drug has been proven successful in a Phase III trial, then the researchers apply for FDA approval to market their product to the general public.

Phase IV Trials are conducted as an added measure to make sure that the results of Phase III trials apply to the general patient population across age, race, and gender groups.

The National Institutes of Health (NIH) website offers a great resource to help you identify a clinical trial near you at <u>www.clinicaltrial.gov</u>. You can also give them a call at 1-800-411-1222. At the website you can simply search by topic and you'll immediately find clinical trials related to the disease being conducted throughout the country. You can also go to other links for further research on medical conditions and news on clinical trials from disease-related associations (e.g. American Cancer Society). For a list of questions on what to ask a doctor if you are considering participating in a clinical trial, see p. 52.

 : How can my parents be better prepared to deal with an emergency room?

 : Advance planning for the unexpected can be a very smart move for your Mom and Dad. The likelihood of anyone over sixty-five years making one of those dreaded emergency room visits is pretty high. Symptoms of heart attacks and strokes, complications from diabetes and other chronic illnesses, hip fractures, and adverse events from medications all play into rising numbers of elderly needing Emergency Department (ED) care. The latest report on ED visits by the Centers for Disease Control cites a 26 percent spike in emergency room visits frequented by the elderly. Some hospitals are responding by creating specialized emergency geriatric units to handle the unique and complicated needs of older patients.

So, with the odds in favor of your parents needing emergency room services in their future; it would be wise for them to take precautionary steps *now* to get the best results. Here are some excellent tips from David Sherer M.D., author of *Hospital Survival Guide* (Claren Books):

▸ If you have a condition that increases your risk for needing emergency room care (e.g. heart condition), ask your physician which hospital he or she would recommend you go to in an emergency. Some ERs have better results than others in certain specialties and you want to know where your doctor prefers to go.

> Whenever possible, call your physician *before* you leave for the emergency room or have someone do this while you're on the way so that your primary doctor or specialist can begin coordinating your care as soon as you arrive.

> It is critical for paramedics and physicians to know what medications your parent is taking, the dosage and schedule. This information should be on-hand and up-to-date at all times. Write it on a card and place it in a wallet or purse. Don't wait to do this: scrambling to put this together on the way to an emergency room or trusting your memory in a crisis increases the chances of giving faulty information that could prove fatal.

> Wear a medical alert bracelet to alert emergency personnel not only of allergies, but of health conditions as well, such as heart, stroke, diabetes, dementia, asthma or epilepsy. Think of what a paramedic should absolutely know about you if you became unconscious. For Medic-Alert bracelets call 1-888-633-4298 or go to www.medicalalert.org.

> Dr. Sherer advises that you should tell Emergency Department doctors and nurses what you felt like when your symptoms were at their worst. For example, how high was your fever? How severe was the pain? Tell them this even if your symptoms have improved by the time you arrive in the Emergency Room.

> Don't be so stoic! If you continue to feel worse while you are waiting to be seen by a physician, let the Triage Nurse know. Don't hesitate one bit if you are having trouble breathing, your pain is becoming intense, you feel like you're going to faint or your vision is becoming blurred, or you can't move a body part.

> Besides having a list of your medications available, also have a card handy that lists all of your medical conditions (e.g. kidney disease, breathing and lung problems, heart conditions, digestive disease) along with the names of the doctors who treat these conditions and their phone numbers. Getting in touch with one of these physicians can save precious time in giving a complete history to the ER doc and save you from a high-risk guessing game.

> Always carry on your person the names and phone numbers of loved ones to contact in an emergency.

And, of course, don't forget to take your insurance cards.

: Are all ambulance services alike?

 Not at all. There are basically three types of health-related transportation: The most basic is "Wheel Chair Van" transport. These vans are equipped with lifts so that individuals can remain in their wheelchairs, be secured and transported. The second level is a "Stretcher Van," used when a physician determines the patient must remain lying down and be on a stretcher. The van is equipped to lock the stretcher in place, and at the very least, oxygen equipment is on board. The third level is the most sophisticated and it is the "Ambulance Service" you receive when you dial 911. You will see the initials BLS (Basic Life Support) associated with ambulance services. They have the equipment and trained personnel to keep you alive on transport to the emergency room.

You need to know the differences among the three transport services because they are directly related to your health and safety and who will pay for what.
Medicare covers very limited ambulance services: "Ambulance services are covered only if transportation in any other vehicle could endanger your health." It will cover transporting you or your parent in an emergency to a hospital emergency room and if a hospital cannot meet a patient's needs, Medicare may cover the transport to the closest facility that can meet those medical needs. Medicare will not cover transport to a doctor's office.

If a hospital or nursing home offers to call an ambulance to take you or your parent home, check to see if a physician has ordered it, and if it will be covered by Medicare. Otherwise, you could be hit with a pretty hefty bill.

If you or a parent need non-emergency transportation in a wheel chair van or stretcher van, here's what I recommend you ask before you hire them:

1. **What kind of training have your attendants received?** Dave Crossley, an Emergency Medical Services Chief in Pennsylvania told me that, "I'd only feel comfortable putting my loved one on a non-medical transport if the attendants have at **least** a state certification as a First Responder. Your loved one obviously has health problems if he needs the service in the first place, so make sure he's protected." Chief Crossley also wants you to know that wheel chair and stretcher vans are **not** regulated or licensed by the Department of Health or Medicare. Virtually anyone can go into the business and start offering rides.

2. **What kind of background checks do you**

conduct on your employees? For example, driving history, criminal records and employment references.

3. *Do you always have an attendant riding in the van besides the driver?* If only a driver is present, he or she won't be able to deal effectively with an emergency of a passenger.

4. *What type of equipment do you have on the van (e.g. oxygen, safety features)?*

5. *What is your communications system with the driver? Can the driver reach a dispatcher in case of an emergency?*

6. *What are your rates? Do you offer membership programs with discounts?* Be sure to ask around as prices can really vary.

7. *What are my financial responsibilities? Is any of this covered by my insurance?* Most likely it is not, however, some nursing homes cover it as part of their contract with residents. But, make sure first!

8. *Are you a stand-alone company or are you part of a Basic Life Support ambulance company?* Chances are, if they are part of a BLS company, their higher training and standards will spill over to the non-emergency side of the company.

One of the most important questions you need to ask medical personnel is, "Has the mode of transportation been ordered by an attending physician?" Doug Wolfberg, a former paramedic-turned-lawyer and national expert in EMS and public safety, warns consumers to make sure that a physician has determined the safest mode of transport for their loved one, "Say your Dad has just had surgery for a hip replacement; placing him in a wheelchair van rather than a stretcher van during a transfer to a rehab facility could possibly jeopardize his recovery." Make sure a physician is involved in the decision.

Section Two
Nursing Homes, Hospice & Home Health

Q: Who does what in nursing homes?

A: Nursing Homes are fast becoming quasi-hospitals as people need more sophisticated long-term care. If your parent is meeting up with more and more therapists, it's because she needs specialized care and specially trained people are being asked to give her the added care she needs. And that's a good thing. On the other hand, it can seem downright overwhelming. There are five types of therapists you're likely to encounter. Here's a brief run-down on what they do:

› **Physical Therapists (PTs)** restore the mobility and strength of patients who are limited or disabled, oftentimes as a result of strokes. Through exercise, massage and equipment, PTs alleviate pain and restore functioning. They also teach families and patients how to transfer from chairs, beds, and toilets. These therapists are licensed and have post-graduate education and training.

› **Occupational Therapists (OTs)** help your parent perform the activities of daily living (eating, bathing, using the toilet, cooking, dressing, and doing basic household chores). They can assess the home and identify ways to make living at home easier and safer. In the nursing home, they can show you how to use adaptive equipment and devices and get her involved in creative activities to help her with daily functioning. OTs have received special training and are licensed.

› **Respiratory Therapists** (RTs) evaluate, treat and care for patients with breathing disorders. They operate sophisticated equipment to administer oxygen, manage mechanical ventilation for people who can't breathe on their own, administer medications in aerosol form, and manage overall therapy to help patients breathe better. There are two levels of respiratory therapists: the certified therapist and the registered therapist. All RTs are required to have either an associate's degree (two years of college) or a four-year college degree in the sciences. They can then take a national voluntary exam to become a Certified Respiratory Therapist (CRT) or they can take two more exams to become a Registered Respiratory Therapist (RRT).

› **Speech & Language Therapists**, also referred to as speech pathologists, help your parent restore his or her speech, often lost or disabled due to strokes, surgery, or injury. These therapists can also help with breathing, swallowing, and muscle control. They are licensed and have post-graduate training beyond college.

‣ **Nutrition Therapists who are Registered Dieticians (RDs)** assist your parent and professional staff in developing a nutritional plan for certain medical conditions. They, too, are licensed following post-graduate training.

The professional services provided by all of these therapists must be considered medically necessary and be prescribed by a physician in order to be eligible for Medicare coverage. In many cases, Medicare will cover some of the costs while Medi-gap polices will also pay a portion, depending on your parent's plan. Nutrition therapy is covered by Medicare for people with diabetes, kidney disease and for those who have had a transplant. If you have questions about

coverage, be sure to ask the nursing facility's social worker or someone in the finance office.

In most instances, these therapies are also covered by Medicare on an outpatient basis, *but always make sure that your parent meets Medicare's criteria for coverage and that the provider is Medicare-certified before you begin the service.*

It is always helpful to get to know the staff in the nursing facility and learn how you can be supportive of your parent's care. They'll appreciate your interest – and don't forget that a "thank you" will go a long way with dedicated, overworked staff.

 : How can I compare the quality of care among nursing homes?

 : Medicare has just made understanding how to look for quality care in a nursing home a bit easier. They've identified nine basic measures of quality and report it for every nursing home in the country – all 17,000 of them. They also compare the quality measures for each home to state and national averages. As a result, you'll have a better perspective on how each home measures up to their competitors.

The Five Star Quality Rating system is part of Medicare's *Nursing Home Compare* program (www.medicare.gov/nhcompare). The nursing home quality measures are derived from data that nursing homes routinely collect on all residents at specified intervals during their stay at the facility. The quality measures are based upon the care that is provided to the total population of residents in a facility.

Here is a list of each measure and what it means:

1. **Help with daily activities:** Percentage of residents who need more help eating, moving from one chair to another, going to the bathroom alone, changing positions in bed than when they were last assessed.

2. **Infections:** Percentage of residents who have infections (e.g., pneumonia, bladder, urinary tract).

3. **Pain:** Percentage of residents with very bad pain or moderate pain over the last week.

4. **Bedsores:** Percentage of residents with skin wounds caused by constant pressure on one part of the skin (usually bony parts of body, e.g., tailbone, heel, hip).

5. **Lost too much weight:** Percentage of residents who lost too much weight (can indicate malnutrition, not receiving enough help eating).

6. **Physical restraints:** Percentage of residents who are physically restrained daily with any device, equipment or material that prevents them from moving freely.

7. **Improved walking:** Percentage of residents who were admitted for a short-stay (e.g., stroke rehab) whose walking improved.

8. **Short-stay residents in pain:** Percentage of residents who have had very bad pain at any time or moderate pain over the last week.

9. **Short-stay residents with delirium:** Percentage of residents who have problems focusing, being confused and unaware of their surroundings. (This condition can appear suddenly, but can be reversible). Delirium is not senility or dementia – these are memory and learning impairments.

10. **Number of nursing staff per resident per day:** *Nursing Home Compare* also reports the number of hours that a registered nurse, licensed practical nurse and nurse aide spends daily with each resident.

Every home is compared against state and national averages. The more nursing time given a resident, the better.

To get a report, go to www.medicare.gov and scroll to the section titled *Resource Locator*. Click on *Nursing Homes* and follow the prompts. Or call Medicare at 1-800 MEDICARE (1-800-633-4227) and ask for a customer representative to read to you the ratings of a particular nursing home. Another feature at the Nursing Home Compare web page is a report on the number of nursing hours that are spent on each resident at a facility. This is very important to know: The more time that nursing staff spends directly with your parent, the more likely he or she is receiving quality care. Of course, you don't want to just rely on this one report to decide whether or not a nursing home is good for your loved one. You must visit the facility – I suggest once during the day and once during a weekend or night when staffing is lighter. Please don't think that surprise visits are a good idea – privacy and security reasons prevent you from roaming through a facility. Set up an appointment. Be sure to ask what percentage of the nursing staff is from a "temp agency." It's better to have permanent, stable staff providing care since continuity of care is a good quality predictor. Having your parent exposed to new staff every day increases the chances that care plans or routines are being disrupted.

If you'd like a list of questions to ask in an interview and a checklist of what to look for on your tour of the facility, along with research tips, visit my website at www.lindarhodescaregiving.com and print out my free *Nursing Home Navigator.*

 : A friend of mine raved about a nursing home that went through a "culture change" process. What was she talking about?

 : Over the past several years there has been a growing movement known as the "pioneer network" with a mission to move nursing homes away from a medical, institutionalized model toward offering residents an environment that feels more like living in a neighborhood and community. The process that nursing home administrators employ to get them there is known as "culture change." It revamps how they organize their staff, how they offer care, how they relate to their residents and how their staff relates to each other. Everyone from the bottom-up gets involved in the change process and studies are rolling in showing five-star results: nurses and support staff are happier, fewer staffing turn-over rates, care is improved and residents actually feel good about their surroundings.

So, if you are looking for a nursing home for a loved one, ask them if they've gone through culture change and have them show you how their home operates because of it. Here are some of the things you should expect them to tell you:

› We've created neighborhoods and communities within our facility where our residents live in "households" rather than living in certain "wings" or "floors" organized around a nurse's station. No one is called a "patient."

› Residents can wake up when they want and go to bed on their own schedule.

› You'll see our staff knock on doors before entering a resident's room.

- Nurses and nursing assistants will be able to tell you about the lives of each of the residents. They'll know what they did before they retired, if they have children and grandchildren, what their hobbies are, along with their likes and dislikes.

- Residents have decorated their own rooms with belongings from home.

- You'll find our residents petting dogs and cats, birds chirping in bright clean cages, aquariums in the lobby and plants galore throughout the facility.

- Our residents order from menus, no one is forced to wear a bib and some days we use china and crystal. We dine in small areas rather than in a large cafeteria-like room.

- Residents get to choose when they want a bath or shower. We really encourage them to be in charge of their care and daily routine.

- We use "Person Directed Care Planning" known as "I" Plans. In other words, residents have care plans written in language that everyone can understand, focusing on an individual's strengths and how they hope to maintain or improve their health. Whenever possible, the resident participates in designing her care plan with our team. So rather than seeing something like "CVA (stroke), unable to remember time and place, prescribe reality orientation three times a week," you'll see the care plan written in the first person, "I have a problem with my memory because of a stroke. When I get up in the morning and after my nap, please show me my clock and calendar to help me get back on track."

- We have gathering places scattered throughout the facility so people can read, visit with each other, watch television, play games or just sit and enjoy the ambience.

- You won't find an authoritative chain of command; we believe that each person can make a difference and we work as a team.

- We believe that relationships among our staff, residents and families must be continuously nurtured and are vital to quality care.

- We respond to the human spirit along with mind and body.

Most people will tell you that you can immediately "feel" the difference of a nursing home that has undergone the life-affirming process of culture change. And that "feeling" is a good thing.

: When I make a site visit of a nursing home, what should I look for?

: I suggest visiting the homes twice, once during a weekday and once in the evening or on a weekend. It's really *not* to your advantage to make a surprise visit. The residents have a right to privacy, and the home will not allow you to simply roam the halls. After you've done your research on the facility, it's time to trust your senses and instincts when you visit. Here's my list of what to look for:

- When you visit a resident's room, does it feel like home? Are there personal effects in the room?

- Is the staff interacting in a friendly manner with one another and the residents?

- Is the home free of odors? Is it clean? Well-lighted?

- Is the temperature comfortable? Stop by a few rooms to see.

- Are the residents well-groomed? Are they dressed appropriately for the time of day?

- Where are the residents? In halls? Involved in group activities or staring at

TV for great lengths of time? Or, are they in their rooms appearing isolated?

- Is there a wandering alert system?

- Is there an activity calendar? Are there pictures on the bulletin boards showing recent activities? Are the activities interesting and varied?

- How many volunteers do they have? Is there an active volunteer corps?

- Are the lavatories clean?

- Are food trays left sitting out? Do you see a lot of leftover food on the trays?

- Are call buttons left unanswered for long periods of time?

- Ask to see the menus. Does the food sound appetizing? Ask about the qualifications of the person who oversees the menus. Taste the food, if possible.

- Does the equipment look up-to-date and in good condition?

- Is the outdoor area secure so that no one can wander off into an unsafe area?

- Go to the dining room. Are residents

enjoying themselves? Is it pleasant? Is the staff interacting with the residents?

- Are the bed linens and towels cleaned daily? Ask what the laundry department does to prevent bedsores. (Poorly cleaned, starchy sheets and certain detergents can cause skin breakdown.)

- Are soiled linens piled up in the hallways or in residents' rooms?

- Are the showers clean? Look for safety devices to prevent falls.

- Is there fresh water on night stands easily accessible for residents?

You might want to make a copy of this list and check off each item as you go through the facility. Then, combine this information with the research you've done on survey reports, fall and incident reports, and conversations with the local ombudsman.

 : How do I stay on top of my Mom's nursing home care?

 : Nursing homes are very busy places and the nursing staff is in high demand. So, one way you can help your Mom is to become her very own "Patient Advocate" by staying on top of her care.

You do not need to be a doctor or nurse to pick up telltale signs that something's amiss. What follows is my list of what to look for every time you visit. Share this with other family members, and if you live out of town, share it with your mother's friends or with a volunteer who will visit her regularly and stay in touch with you.

- Check for any redness or bruises on the skin, especially near bony areas, such

as the tailbone, heels and elbows. You're checking for bed or pressure sores. You can do this while you give your Mom a massage or place lotion on her skin.

- Check for weight loss, changes in appetite, sores in her mouth, problems with dentures or chewing or extreme thirst. You're checking for malnutrition and dehydration. Make sure there's always fresh water at her bedside.

- Check for any ingrown toenails, infections, bunions and uncut nails on her feet. You're checking for potentially serious infections and problems in walking, especially if your parent is diabetic. These could be signs of poor care.

- Check for poorly kept hair or beard, clothing not clean or pressed, body odor, wet adult briefs, unclean sheets. These are signs of poor care and can lead to pressure sores, infections and depression.

- Check out how long it takes for call bells to be answered. And note if aides frequently tell you, "We're short-staffed today." Are meal trays served late? Is there rarely fresh water in the room? These are signs of lack of staff, which can lead to poor care.

- Check to see if your Mom's clothes or belongings are missing.

- Check for high staff turnover. Does it seem like every time you turn around there's a new director of nursing or head nurse, or your Mom has a different nurse aide from one week to the next? Does staff morale seem pretty low? It won't take long for high staff turnover rates to spill over into poor care.

If you think there is a problem, report your concerns to the ombudsman. His or her job is to help solve problems among residents, their families and staff in long-term care facilities. Most ombudsmen are employed by Area Agencies on Aging; their name and phone number should be posted on a bulletin board in the lobby of the nursing home. You also can call the Eldercare Locator at 1-800-677-1116 for a nationwide listing. Research has shown that residents who are visited regularly by family and friends fare better in nursing homes. So, always stop by and let a staff member know you were there and give them an update on your Mom. And take a minute to let them know how much you appreciate their help.

Q: What kind of evacuation plans should be in place at my mother's nursing home?

 One of the toughest decisions a nursing home administrator will ever make in a disaster is whether or not to stay by "sheltering in place" or evacuate residents to a safer haven. Moving residents who have complicated health conditions and those with severe dementia can also place the resident in harm's way. They're exposed to traffic accidents, long rides on jammed highways and possibly bad weather conditions. If the disaster is community or region-wide, the shelters they reach may be understaffed to meet their needs and place them at even greater risk. In the case of hurricane Katrina, once nursing home administrators decided to evacuate their residents – many found there were no buses, ambulances, or vans to transport them. Everyone was competing for too few vehicles. Even if the home had contracts with transport companies for emergencies – they were nowhere to be found.

So, where does all this leave you and your Mom? The good news is that many nursing homes throughout the country are now taking added measures to develop more comprehensive emergency preparedness plans. This is in response to a major study conducted by the General Accountability Office (GAO) which is the independent, bipartisan investigative arm of Congress that analyzed what went wrong during the evacuation of nursing home residents during Hurricane Katrina. Medicare and the Department of Health and Human Services are also creating new regulations regarding what they'll require of hospitals and long term care facilities in disaster planning.

Even if you live in a region where hurricanes are rare, you are still exposed to tornadoes, power outages, chemical spills, nuclear plants, bioterrorism and the forecasted flu pandemic. After reviewing the GAO report and guidelines for disaster planning of groups that accredit nursing homes and hospitals, here are my suggestions of what to ask nursing home administrators and directors of assisted living facilities:

The Plan. Do you have a plan? When was it last updated? Does it meet state and federal standards? What guidelines did you follow to create the plan (e.g. an accrediting body or CMS)? Do local first responders (e.g. police, fire department, paramedics and township officials) have a copy of the plan and do you have written agreements with them as to who will do what in an emergency?

Communications. How will you let me know if my mother is being evacuated? What alternative forms of communication do you have when land and cell phones are not working? For example, will there be a central phone number I can call or website that will give continuous updates on the status of residents and any evacuation plans? How will your staff be able to maintain communications with each other? How will responders be informed of my mother's identity, contact information, health conditions and her medication schedule? Will each resident wear an identification tag containing vital information?

Transportation. How will you transport residents, especially those who are in wheel chairs or need ambulance assistance? Do you have contracts with transportation companies to assist in an evacuation? What is your back-up plan if they are overwhelmed by demands of other health care facilities in the event of a mass evacuation?

Staffing. What type of training has your staff received in disaster response and evacuation? How often does your staff review your emergency preparedness plan? When was the last time your staff ran through a practice drill? What type of staff and how many would remain on the premises during a shelter in place scenario? Who will accompany residents to shelters during an evacuation and how long will they remain with the residents? Can family members volunteer to assist? How will you maintain enough staff to care for residents during a flu pandemic?

Mobilization Centers and Housing. Where are the designated mobilization centers and shelters cited by the Red Cross and NDMS in case of an evacuation? Where would I pick up my mother during disaster evacuation? Do you have arrangements with other facilities to provide housing for residents?

Supplies. What type of emergency supplies do you have in reserve and how long will they last (such as food, water, oxygen, flashlights, medications)? Do you have generators and how long can you operate on them? How will supplies be transported with residents during an evacuation (especially personal medications)? Does each resident have a personal emergency supply kit to take with them during an evacuation?

Here's hoping that this is one plan that remains just that – a plan untested by reality.

. What are good holiday gift ideas for residents in nursing homes?

It doesn't matter where you live or how old you are – there's nothing like a cheerfully wrapped present to brighten your spirits. Residents in nursing homes present some unique challenges in gift-giving, so I've created a list that's received the "seal of approval" from those who work in nursing homes. And my guess is they would make any resident feel special during the holiday season.

As you go through this list, consider what it would be like if you and everyone who reads this decided to go out and buy just one extra gift and drop it off (or mail it) to their nearest nursing home to be given to a resident without family or friends.

Gifts to brighten up their room
Picture frames, plants (live or silk), paintings, a calendar marked with birthdays of family members, artificial gold fish bowl or water fall, sun catchers for the window,

framed pictures of the resident in earlier days, a collage of pictures of families and friends – these make great conversation pieces – or an all-season wreath or decorative knocker to hang on their door.

Gifts for pampering
Basket of lotions and talcum powder (be sure to check with the nursing staff on what's best), shaving lotion, favorite perfumes, luscious bath towel and/or robe, gift certificates to the in-house beauty parlor or barber for hair styling and manicures, grooming products.

Gifts for having fun
Buy a very simple-to-use DVD and send new movies every month and videos of family events, large print books, a simple-to-use CD Discman so they can listen to their favorite music without disturbing roommates, low-vision playing cards, large print crossword puzzles or other games appropriate for their cognitive ability, a box of all-occasion

greeting cards with a book of stamps, a digital picture frame, stuffed animals.

Gifts for staying warm
Lap afghans or fleece throws are very popular, cheerful holiday sweaters, sweat suits, no-skid slippers, fun socks that depict the holidays or interest of the resident (e.g. golf, flowers).

Gifts that touch the heart
Hand-made gifts, a framed poem or artwork from grandkids or from you, phone cards to stay in touch and pre-pay long-distance calls. The most cherished gift, however, is a visit from you. If the resident is able, you might offer to take him or her out for an evening ride to enjoy the holiday lights, along with a hot cup of cocoa. And one last idea: make it a New Year's resolution to volunteer at your local nursing home or assisted living facility. A friendly visit to a resident without family is a gift that will make you all the richer for it.

Is assisted living different from a nursing home?

Yes, assisted living is different from a nursing home (also known as a skilled nursing facility or long-term care facility). "Assisted living" means receiving some assistance with the tasks of daily living. "Nursing home care," on the other hand, provides 24-hour nursing care and supervision because their residents need assistance all of the time. Assisted living means just what the term implies: Your parent receives assistance in such daily tasks as bathing, grooming, taking pills on time, housekeeping, getting meals, managing the bills and/or using transportation. You'll often hear these referred to as ADLs, for "activities of daily living."

Sometimes you'll run into other terms that refer to assisted living, such as catered living, personal care homes or boarding homes. Whether assisted living makes sense for your parent will depend on how well she does by herself performing the tasks of daily living. Not all assisted living facilities take people with Alzheimer's disease. If they do, they offer specialized floors with professional and additional staff to accommodate their needs. If you are looking at such a facility, make sure it is qualified to care for someone with dementia by asking to see any certification papers they have received from state regulating bodies and ask them to describe the training their staff have

received to care for people with dementia.

Nursing homes offer skilled nursing care, rehab, medical services, and protective supervision as well as assistance with the activities of daily living. People with long-term mental or physical conditions that require a 24-hour protective environment offering medical and health care services need nursing home care.

Unlike nursing homes, regulations governing assisted living facilities are uneven and determined by each state, so be sure to do your research. Some assisted living facilities have voluntarily gone through an accreditation process and are listed at the website of the Rehabilitation Accreditation Commission at www.carf.org. For a list of nonprofit facilities and tips on what to look for in an assisted living facility, go to the American Association of Homes and Services for the Aging website at www.AAHSA.org.

Q: Does Medicare really pay for the first 100 days of nursing home care?

The answer is a bit more complicated than a simple yes or no. But it is certainly a myth that Medicare covers long term care. Regretfully, it's a myth that

many people believe: in a recent survey conducted by AARP, more than half of the respondents believed that Medicare will cover all of their nursing home costs. It just isn't so.

As of 2010, Medicare will pay for up to 100 days of skilled nursing care in a facility that is certified by Medicare IF the following conditions are met:

> ‣ Placement in a skilled nursing facility (SNF) is within 30 days of a hospital stay.

> ‣ The stay in the hospital was for at least three days – but that doesn't include the day of discharge – so it's really four days.

> ‣ The care is medically necessary, which is usually defined as skilled-nursing or skilled-rehab care.

> ‣ The skilled care is directly related to the medical condition that resulted in the hospitalization.

If all of these conditions are met, Medicare may cover up to 100 days of skilled care. But remember, the care must be skilled, not chronic or custodial care. Skilled care must be medically necessary and prescribed by a physician. The skilled care must improve or maintain the patient's condition and prevent it from further deterioration. The care requires registered nurses, physicians and professional therapists who manage, observe and evaluate the patient's condition. Under this scenario, Medicare will pay 100 percent of your parent's first twenty days in a nursing home. On average, most people need no more than twenty days of skilled care. Where they run into trouble is needing additional days of "chronic care," which Medicare won't cover.

If your parent needs additional "skilled" care beyond twenty days, Medicare will cover all but $137.50, which is your hefty daily co-pay, for days 21 through 100. The good news is that most Medi-gap policies (her supplemental insurance) will cover her co-pay. But after 100 days, there will be no Medicare payments or Medicare supplements.

A beneficiary can collect under this benefit several times over a lifetime. How? A benefit period is not based on an annual or lifetime basis. It begins when your parent enters a hospital and ends when there has been a break of at least 60 consecutive days since her inpatient hospital or skilled nursing care was provided.

The two most important things to remember are: always carry a Medi-gap policy which will cover the gap between what's charged for the care and what Medicare will cover, and never assume that Medicare will cover nursing home care. If, during a hospital stay, your parent is told that she needs to be transferred to a nursing home, make sure you talk with her physician to find out if he or she is prescribing skilled care. If so, also make sure that she's being transferred to a facility that has been certified by Medicare so that she can receive the coverage that Medicare does provide.

If you have any questions, be sure to ask to speak to the hospital social worker prior to discharge. Medicare also has an excellent website that features their downloadable handbook, *Medicare Coverage of Skilled Nursing Facility Care* at www.medicare.gov. Enter *Skilled Nursing Facility Coverage* in the search bar and follow the prompts. You can also call them at 1-800-633-4227.

Q: How do we find a good home health care agency for my Dad?

A: Home health care covers a wide range of services including nursing care, physical, speech, respiratory and occupational therapy, wound care, and medical social services. Your Dad may also be eligible for help from a home health aide to assist him with the activities of daily living, like aiding him with bathing, dressing or getting in and out of bed. To receive Medicare coverage, your father's physician must prescribe the home health care services your Dad will receive.

It's likely that a social worker or discharge planner at the hospital will provide you with a packet of information on home health care that includes a list of Medicare-certified agencies. One of the best ways to determine whether or not the agency offers high quality care is to check out Medicare's relatively new "*Home Health Compare*" tool on their website, www.medicare.gov. Just by entering your father's zip code, you can find out the name and contact information of home health agencies near him, the services each

agency offers, whether or not it is Medicare-certified, and its type of ownership (e.g. profit vs. non-profit).

Once you choose the agencies that offer the services your Dad needs, you can then simply click on each one and find out how each compares in twelve quality measures. You'll even learn how the agency's ratings stack up against other home health care agencies in the state and nation. Under the agency's care, you'll learn the percentage of patients who have less pain when moving around, who get better at taking their medicines, whose bladder control improves, whose wounds improve and heal after surgery, and the percentage of patients who are re-admitted to a hospital, who need urgent, unplanned care or wounds that have gotten worse or new ones emerge.

Just go to www.medicare.gov and on the home page choose the "*Compare Home Health Agencies*," selection. If you don't have internet service, call Medicare at 1-800-633-4227 and ask if they'll give you quality measure information on home health care agencies that you are considering. Also ask them for a free copy of *Medicare and Home Health Care*, an excellent guide for consumers, describing what you need to know in finding and utilizing home health care. You can also download a copy at their website.

The Medicare guide also features a check-list of what you should consider when choosing an agency. Here is what they recommend you ask:

1. Is the agency Medicare-certified? This means that Medicare will reimburse the agency for services they perform.

2. Do they offer the services that your doctor prescribed?

3. Do they offer personal care services (e.g. helping with bathing, dressing, using the bathroom).

4. Will they secure support services for you like Meals on Wheels?

5. Are they recommended by your doctor, hospital discharge planner, or social worker and will they provide references?

6. Do they have staff available at night and weekends for emergencies?

7. Do they conduct background checks on their staff?

8. Have they explained what your insurance covers and what you must pay out of pocket?

9. Will they have the staff available to provide the type of care your doctor prescribed and for the number of hours needed?

With a little bit of homework using the Compare Home Health Agencies tool and asking the right questions, you should be in good shape to find your father an agency that will take good care of him for a smooth and speedy recovery. Be aware that home health care "registries" do not employ the caregiver you will be hiring; they are employment agencies for home health care workers. Thus, you will be responsible for paying the worker's taxes and following health and labor laws. So, be sure to find out whether or not the agency you use actually employs the workers or is a registry.

: What exactly is "Senior Care" and how would I find it for my Mom?

: Senior care companies offer individualized assistance with day-to-day living for older people living at home. I call it "stitch in time" care; they do the little things that can help people stay independent, remain socially engaged and stay in their own home. Companies offering senior care services make it very clear that they provide non-medical services. In other words, they are not in the home health care business. Instead, they offer such services as companionship, meal preparation, medication reminders, light housework, incidental transportation, errands, grocery shopping, pharmacy pick-ups, arranging doctor appointments, mailing bills and letters and providing a stable bathing environment – to name a few.

If you're worried that your Mom isn't getting enough social interaction, they'll even match her up with someone with whom she enjoys spending time and can engage in your Mom's favorite hobby, watch movies, or just enjoy good conversation.

There has been quite a growth in the senior care industry over the last five years. You'll usually find senior care companies listed in the phone book under "Home Care." Some are franchises, such as Home Instead, Wisdom Keepers, Comfort Care, Visiting Angels and Comfort Keepers, while others are independently owned. Home Instead Senior Care is the only national franchise that offers advanced training in Alzheimer's for its caregivers.

In most states these companies are not licensed by a state agency because they are offering non-medical care. So, that means, as a consumer, you need to do your homework. Here is a list of questions that can help you identify the best agency for your parent.

1. Do you conduct criminal background checks on your employees and are they bonded?

2. Are the caregivers your employees or are you a referral agency?

3. Who is responsible for paying the taxes and Social Security of the caregivers?

4. What type of training do your employees go through to be hired?

5. Is your training on-going? Please describe it.

6. Please describe for me the background

of your average caregiver (e.g. part-time homemaker, certified nurse aide, high school graduate, or retiree?)

7. If you provide transportation, have you checked out your employee's driving record?

8. How do you go about making sure that the caregiver will be compatible with my parent?

9. How long have most of your employees worked for you?

10. Are your services covered by long term care insurance and will you process the paperwork?

11. How do you supervise and oversee the quality of care provided by your workers?

12. May I see a sample service agreement and a listing of your prices?

Also check to see if there are any complaints lodged against the company through the Better Business Bureau. You could also ask the ombudsman for your local Area Agency on Aging if he or she knows of any complaints against the company (call Elder Care Locator at 1-800-677-1116 to find your local Area Agency on Aging). I'd also ask if they would allow you to speak with any customers who have used the service. You'll find that prices range from $18 to $25 per hour and there usually is a minimum service requirement of at least three and four hours per day. Services can be arranged for

as many as 24 hours a day for a short term or long term arrangement, including weekends and holidays. This can be especially helpful when families need respite from daily care-giving.

Some long-term care insurance policies do cover non-medical senior care, so be sure to look over your mother's policy if she has one. You may also find volunteer senior care services being provided by faith-based organizations, so if you are financially

strapped, give your local church or synagogue a call to see what they provide. Local senior centers may also be a good resource for finding non-profit groups that offer volunteer senior care.

Q: Any pointers on hiring home health care workers without using an agency?

A: First, methodically think through what your Mom or Dad's day is like and what kind of help he or she needs to get through it. Let's say that we're talking about your mother. Does she need help taking her medications, getting to and from the bathroom, preparing meals, taking a bath or shower, getting dressed, or doing physical exercises? Does she have any medical conditions that require special attention? Are there symptoms that the caregiver must be aware of so that she can alert your mother's physician?

This list will guide you in creating a job description for your mother's caregiver. I'd also advise you to ask your Mom to share her expectations; what she would like the caregiver to do. Once she has shared her expectations, then you should also express yours. The goal is to have everyone in sync, so that you can create a job description that is realistic and will serve your mother's best interests. This will also make it much easier for the caregiver to assess whether or not she is suited for this job. It is a good idea to interview prospective caregivers at a neutral place, like a local coffee shop. This way, especially if your mother lives alone, her vulnerability is not disclosed to a stranger.

Here's a list of interview questions and tips:

1. Inform the caregiver of your mother's medical condition(s) and ask her to describe what she knows about this condition, how she'll respond and whether she has cared for anyone else with this condition.

2. Share the job description list with her and ask her to go over each item on the list, telling you how she'll respond to each of your mother's needs.

3. Ask the worker to tell you what training she has had for each of the tasks described.

4. Ask the caregiver to show you any certificates or educational degrees she has received.

5. Ask for a resume that identifies any schools or training programs she has attended, previous jobs and contact information of all previous employers.

6. If your mother suffers from dementia, find out what specialized training the caregiver has received to work with cognitively-impaired adults.

7. Ask what training she has received in lifting people and how does she go about giving a bath? What safety measures does she use? Ask her to identify any physical demands of caring for your mother and how she will address them.

8. Ask the caregiver to provide you with a copy of the results of a police background check.

9. Ask for a list of references – and call them. Make sure that at least two references are from families who have used the caregiver's services.

Once you've narrowed down your search and checked out their references, then you can invite a potential caregiver to the home and see how the caregiver interacts with your mother.

If you're hiring a certified nurse aide, check their references with your state's Certified Nurse Aide Registry, which is usually run by the state's department of health and/or human services.

Once you've hired the caregiver, ask for a daily phone call to update you on how your mother's doing. As time goes on and you feel very secure with her services, then an update every few days or even once a week may seem reasonable.

I'd also stop by to see how things are going and how well your mother and the caregiver interact. Caregiving is a dynamic and evolving process that must constantly adjust to changes in your mother's health and caregiving needs. Thus, it's important for you to stay involved and monitor the effectiveness of the caregiving services.

 Q: I think my mother has Alzheimer's, but my siblings don't believe me. What should I do?

A: It can seem pretty isolating when you see your Mom deteriorating while your brothers and sisters don't share your view. If they live farther away and don't see your Mom as often as you do, then their view is going to be different because they simply don't see what you see. They may be visiting with Mom or talking to her on the phone during a short period of time where she acts perfectly normal. Some people in the early stages of Alzheimer's, especially if they have good social skills, can be very good at covering up.

The best way to get all of you on the same page is to get to the heart of the matter and find out exactly what's going on with your mother. What may look like Alzheimer's to you could be a side-effect from medication, signs of clinical depression, the results of a mini-stroke or even a B-12 deficiency. Your Mom would do well to receive a geriatric assessment that includes a battery of tests that could determine whether or not she is suffering from some form of dementia or another condition.

Once those tests are completed, it would be helpful if the results can be shared with you and your siblings by your mother's physician. For those who live out of town and can't make the appointment, then make arrangements with the doctor's office for a conference call. If the office doesn't have that capacity, then at least have one other sibling attend with you. You could also bring a cell phone and call another sibling and place them on speaker while the doctor explains your mother's condition. The objective is for at least one of your siblings to hear the same thing you hear from the doctor and for both of you to have the opportunity to ask questions. Following that session, you should share with each other what you heard the doctor say and then jot down notes of what you'll tell your other siblings. By involving your brothers and sisters early in the diagnosis, they'll feel included and they won't have to second-guess whether or not your instincts are correct.

If it turns out to be Alzheimer's or any other serious illness that requires a good deal of caregiving on your part, then it will be important for all of you to understand the course of the disease and what to expect in terms of the care your Mom will need. The more the entire family understands how Alzheimer's progresses, then the more likely you'll be able to act as a team. No matter where each of you lives, each of you could attend a support group offered by your local Alzheimer's Association or local hospital.

One way for other family members to appreciate the caregiving needs of a loved one is to spend two to three days caring for them while the caregiver leaves for a short break. It's also a good idea to keep a journal for a week describing the tasks you perform to take care of your mother. Giving her medications, taking her to doctor's appointments, preparing meals, taking her to adult day care, helping her with exercises, performing household chores, addressing her emotional needs, and keeping her safe are just some of the things you're likely doing all week long. Share the list with your siblings and ask if any of them would like to volunteer to help with any of the items on the list. Even from a distance, someone can make arrangements for doctor's appointments, pay bills, look up information on medications, research medical conditions or make calls to Medicare and insurance carriers. Everyone can pitch in to help pay for a housecleaning service to make your life easier or send some catered meals your way. Reach out to your siblings...caring for Mom is a family affair.

Q: My Mom has Alzheimer's and refuses to move to assisted living. Now what?

A: Sounds like a very tough dilemma: You know it's not safe for your Mom to be left alone and you feel irresponsible if you don't do something. On the other hand, you're trying to respect your Mom's wishes, and you don't want to make her feel that she's been placed under house arrest or traumatically remove her physically from her home.

But because your Mom has Alzheimer's, "reasoning" with her will be very difficult – you don't share the same reality. So, let's look at some steps you can take to get her into a safe and nurturing environment while respecting her self-determination.

I assume that she has had a comprehensive geriatric assessment to arrive at the diagnosis of Alzheimer's. If not, get one by a physician certified in geriatrics. If she's had this, arrange an appointment with her doctor and explain that it's no longer safe for her to be alone. Provide the doctor with a list of examples that show she can no longer perform the tasks of daily living. Also describe your family support system and let the doctor know that you can no longer provide supervision for her at home. Ask the doctor if he could "prescribe" a week at a "center" for necessary treatment for her condition. If this is coming from the doctor in the form of a handwritten prescription rather than from her "overprotective" kids, she might listen.

By making it a temporary situation, you're not backing her into a corner. Also, if her sense of time has been affected, the "week" might easily transition into a permanent solution. Another way of easing her into the idea might be to ask those in charge of the facility if you could bring your Mom over for lunch and eat there as you would in any other restaurant.

Dr. Roger Cadieux, clinical professor of psychiatry at Penn State University, Hershey Medical Center, who practices adult and geriatric psychiatry, had this to say when I asked him how he would handle this situation when he has the hard data from a geriatric assessment, "The approach that I use is to sympathetically but firmly present the findings and then state definitely that there is now a need for a higher level of care. There is usually a great deal of distress but the anger, if any, is directed toward the physician and not the family. I make sure that the patient understands that I am their advocate even though I am imparting difficult information. The trick is for the family to find a physician who can and will take this approach."

Dr. Cadieux recommends giving the patient the opportunity to participate, if possible, in the process of finding a facility that provides a higher level of care. When warranted, he added, medication, especially low doses of antidepressants and/or antipsychotics, can make the difference between easy acceptance or abject refusal of this necessary move.

: What is hospice and how do I find a good one for my Dad?

: Hospice care brings together medical care, pain management and emotional and spiritual support for terminal patients and their families. This care is provided in the patient's home when possible or in an inpatient hospice facility with a home-like setting. The mission of hospice staff and volunteers is to address the symptoms of a terminal illness with the intent of promoting comfort and dignity. They are experts at pain management. Based upon my personal experience with hospice and my professional work training hospice volunteers, I can't emphasize enough how helpful hospice can be to you and your family. They can manage your father's pain, help you understand what he is going through, and help you and other family members cope with your emotions. Many of us are at a loss as to what we should do before and at the time of death. The hospice folks can get you through it at your own pace. They also stay in touch with you following your loved one's death.

Medicare does provide a hospice benefit that covers almost all of the costs of caring for a dying person during his or her last six months of life. To qualify for the Medicare hospice benefit:

> Your Dad must have Medicare Part A.

> Your Dad's doctor and the medical director of the hospice must confirm that your Dad has a life expectancy of less than six months.

> Your Dad must sign a statement choosing hospice care instead of other Medicare-covered benefits to treat his terminal illness. (Medicare will still pay for covered benefits for any health problems that aren't related to your Dad's terminal illness.)

> Your Dad gets care from a Medicare-approved hospice program.

The Medicare hospice benefit covers: skilled nursing services, physician visits, skilled therapy, medical social services, bereavement counseling, the partial cost of prescriptions and short-term respite care. Medicare does not cover 24-hour home care; however, in a medical crisis, continuous nursing and short-term inpatient services are available.

To find a hospice, you can visit the National Hospice Organization website at www.nhpco.com, call Medicare directly at 1-800-633-4227 or look in the Yellow Pages under Hospices. Here's a list of questions you should ask:

> Are you Medicare-certified? (If not, Medicare will not pay).

> Are you a member of any professional organizations or are you accredited?

> Are there certain conditions that patients and families have to meet to enter the hospice program?

> Are you willing to come to the home and conduct an assessment to help us understand if this is the best option for my parent?

> What specialized services do you offer, such as rehab therapists, family counselors, pharmacists, used equipment?

> What are your polices regarding inpatient care? With which hospital(s) do you have a contractual relationship in the event my parent would need to go to the hospital?

> Do you require a primary family caregiver as a condition of admission?

> What are the caregiver's responsibilities as related to the hospice?

> What kind of emergency coverage do you offer? Who is on call? Will a nurse come quickly to the home, if needed?

> What out-of-pocket expenses can we expect?

> Will your staff handle all of the paperwork and billing?

> What are your policies on the use of antibiotics, ventilators, dialysis, and/or nutrients given intravenously?

> What treatments are outside of your hospice's purview?

Take the time to visit with their staff and tour their inpatient facility. The journey you are about to take will leave you with a lifetime of memories. Make sure you feel very comfortable and at peace with the hospice professionals who will guide you along this path of letting go.

Q: When is the right time to call in hospice? My Mom is resisting contacting them for my dying father.

A: I've seen family members get into quite a debate as to whether or not to call in hospice care, even though everyone knows that their loved one is dying. Sometimes the answer lies within the heart and mind of the person who is dying. If your father is aware of his end-of-life condition, which I imagine he is, then perhaps a heart-to-heart conversation with him is in order. Today, oncologists and family physicians are much more open about telling patients the status of their disease, including "how much time they may have left." This is so different from the 1950's when my grandfather died of cancer. Everyone walked around acting like Grandpa would get better – especially around Grandpa. Families and physicians believed it was best to spare the loved one from the agony of knowing. Your Mom, being part of that generation, might still feel that she wants to spare your Dad from the heart-wrenching reality of his impending death. So, she holds off calling hospice because she feels it is a symbol of dying.

Yet, if your Dad knows his illness is terminal, then chances are there are two very strong needs he's internally wrestling with: he wants to be reassured that his dying will be as painless as possible, and that your Mom will be spared from becoming physically ill herself from the toll of caring for him. And I'm sure that your Mom also wants to see your Dad out of his pain.

So, if you stay focused on these two needs and then re-introduce the concept of hospice, your Mom may be more receptive. If she sees hospice as helping with your Dad's pain management and if your Dad sees it as helping your Mom by coordinating all of his care, then they may both see hospice in a new light. You can also reassure your Mom that if your father decides to pursue treatment to extend his life (e.g. chemotherapy or radiation) he can opt out of hospice and go back to the service later.

There is another advantage to hospice care, as Medicare will also cover respite care for your mother as long as your Dad is receiving hospice care. Thus, if your Dad needs to stay in a nursing home, in-patient hospice facility or hospital to provide him palliative care in order for your mother to get a break, Medicare will pay almost all of the cost for his inpatient respite care for up to five days. Your parents may be responsible for a small co-pay for the respite care, depending on the assessment of the hospice medical team.

Q: My Dad is terminally ill. Can you tell me what dying people want?

A: It is terribly difficult to prepare for the death of a loved one. No matter how full a life anyone has had or how much forewarning you've been given, the shock and loss is never really lessened. When the time feels right, or perhaps when your Dad brings it up, ask him how you can be helpful. Besides addressing the standard tasks of how your Dad will distribute his property and assets, and the end-of-life decisions about his medical care, the most lasting memories will come from how you both travel the emotional journey you are about to take.

I'd like to share with you the results of a compassionate and comprehensive study by the Veterans Affairs Medical Center in Durham, North Carolina. They interviewed terminally ill patients, their doctors, social workers, hospice volunteers, chaplains and family members. They asked what makes for a positive end-of-life experience. This is what they learned:

- Preventing pain is the most important issue to patients. Many people fear dying in pain more than dying itself. Doctors can be very helpful in managing pain and reassuring both patients and their families that pain can be controlled.

- Patients want to be involved in making decisions regarding their treatment. Gone are the hush-hush days of "sparing" the patient from the truth. Letting the patient's desires direct decision-making relieves families of guilt and prevents conflicts and debates among family members. What your parent wants becomes the unifying rallying point, even if it isn't what you would have chosen for yourself.

- Patients and families need to know what to expect from the fatal condition and the treatment. This knowledge helps them better prepare for events, symptoms, and treatment outcomes surrounding the impending death. It will also help your Dad feel in control.

- Patients and families search for meaning to their lives and their relationship with each other. They'll seek the solace of faith, review their lives, resolve conflicts, spend time with family and friends and say good-bye. At your Dad's direction, facilitate meeting and talking with loved ones and friends, so that they can gain closure together.

- Patients find satisfaction in contributing to the well-being of others. They find peace in helping their loved ones come to terms with their dying and helping loved ones let go. They also find it satisfying to leave behind the means to care for their loved one's physical and financial needs.

➤ Patients do not want to be seen as a "disease" or a "case" but as a unique, whole person.

I hope this advice from people who've walked in your shoes will be helpful to you. Also be sure to contact your local hospice, which can provide wonderful physical and emotional support.

Section Three
Prescriptions & Alternative Medicine

Q: My Mom takes multiple medications and doesn't qualify for Medicare. How can she cut down her prescription costs?

A: Keeping up with escalating drug costs can seem overwhelming, but there are some proven strategies to control her out-of-pocket expenses. It takes a little bit of homework but she'll like the results:

› Ask if there is a generic equivalent of the drug being prescribed. Generics are less expensive and by law are bio-chemically equivalent to the brand. It's not uncommon to find a generic for at least half the price and more.

› If her physician prescribes a brand new drug on the market – which is usually the most expensive and without a generic substitute – ask if an older version of that class of drug would be feasible to try first. Newer drugs don't necessarily mean they are "improved." Rarely are new drugs tested against the drug they are replacing to see if it is better or safer. Instead, they've been tested against a placebo (a pill containing no medication drug).

› If your Mom is taking a new drug for the very first time, ask for a trial size rather than the 30-day supply. That way, if your mother has an adverse reaction from the new drug, she will not have wasted her money on a month's supply.

› Ask the doctor for drug samples as another means to try out a drug before investing in a 30-day supply.

› If she is taking a maintenance drug – one she has to take for a long period of time to maintain her health – buy the drug in ninety-day supplies, which is cheaper.

› She could also buy maintenance drugs online for a good cost savings. Check out the National Association of Boards of Pharmacy's (NABP) website at www.vipps.info. Click on the left navigation topic of "Find a VIPPS online pharmacy" to see if it is a legitimate pharmacy from which to buy on the internet or call them at 1-847-391-4406. Be very careful not to buy from a site that does not require a prescription and make sure it is a site with the VIPPS trademarked symbol which stands for "Verified Internet Pharmacy Practice Site." This means they have been certified to meet certain safety and quality standards by the NABP. Go to www.destinationrx.com to compare drug prices among internet pharmacies.

- Check out mail order programs with pharmacies or membership groups like AARP which offer the convenience of home delivery and savings.

- Shop around. You'd be surprised at the difference in prices among pharmacies that range from independents, chains, grocery stores and membership clubs like Costco. It's worth making the calls and many pharmacies will deliver to someone who is homebound.

- Cardiologist and author Michael P. Cecil in his book *Drugs for Less*, tells his patients that certain drugs are safe to split with a pill cutter. Some medications are actually "scored" with an indentation down the middle. He explains that "if you take a 40mg. daily dose of a medication and the cost of the 80mg. tablet is identical to the cost of the 40mg. tablet, then you can divide the 80mg. tablet in two parts and cut your costs in half." He gives examples of drugs like Coreg and Celexa as being safe to split in half. However, he cautions that not all drugs can be split in half. If they are a time-released capsule, they can not be split in two nor can certain medications that use different mechanisms to delay the release of the drug. The bottom line is to ALWAYS check with your physician and pharmacist to determine whether or not pill splitting is advisable for the medication you are taking.

You might want to pick up a copy of the *Drugs for Less* book. It's a savvy, smart guide that shows you how to save money on prescriptions and concludes with a listing of 100 top-selling drugs, identifying which of his seven strategies you can use to save money on each.

Q: Are there any free or discounted prescription assistance programs for people who don't qualify for Medicare Part D or Medicaid?

A: Actually, there are a number of programs offered by drug companies for people who are uninsured, have low incomes and do not have any other coverage, such as Medicare Part D, VA benefits, Medicaid or private insurance. And, there are some excellent programs that offer a centralized searching tool to find out what government and non-profit prescription assistance programs you can qualify for, as well. A thumbnail sketch on each is described below.

PROGRAMS OFFERED BY DRUG COMPANIES:

Partnership for Prescription Assistance

The PPARx prescription assistance program is sponsored by the Pharmaceutical Research and Manufacturers of America, the trade association of the drug makers. By visiting the program's website at www.pparx.org, you can easily find free and highly discounted prescription assistance offered by nearly every drug company, non-profit group and government program. By filling out some basic information on the medicines you need and your income, you can quickly find out what you qualify for and can make an immediate application online. You can also call their toll free number at 1-888-477-2669.

RxAssist

RxAssist is a pharmaceutical access information center created by Volunteers in Health Care (VIH), a national resource center for safety net organizations. The center operates out of the Brown University Center for Primary Care and Prevention based at Memorial Hospital of Rhode Island. This robust site also offers a directory with links to all drug company assistance programs available to consumers and allows for online applications. It receives support from the Robert Wood Johnson Foundation. Visit them at www.rxassist.org.

Lilly Cares

This patient assistance program is provided by Lilly Cares Foundation, Inc., a private foundation funded by Eli Lilly and Company. The program assists uninsured patients with incomes less than 300 percent of the Federal Poverty Level. Most Lilly products are available through the program. Applications are available to anyone on their website at www.lillycares.com and must be completed and signed by both the patient and the physician or you can call Lilly Cares at 1-800-545-6962. The medication is shipped directly to the physician's office.

CENTRALIZED SEARCHING TOOLS FOR NON-PROFIT AND GOVERNMENT PROGRAMS:

National Council on Aging (NCOA)

NCOA offers the nation's most comprehensive web-based service, Benefits CheckUp, to screen for benefits programs for seniors with limited income and resources. It includes more than 2,000 public and private benefits programs from all 50 states and the District of Columbia. Besides searching for a wide range of benefits, two are dedicated to searching and identifying prescription benefits: the Prescription Drug Assistance search and Medicare RxExtra Help. By providing basic information on health status, income and your locality, they'll identify prescription benefit programs that you qualify for and link you to online applications. Go to www.benefitscheckup.org.

NeedyMeds

This nonprofit provides information about drug and disease-based assistance programs available to low-income people and their advocates at no cost. The website identifies government, non-profit and drug company programs that are available nationwide. NeedyMeds also features a database on free clinics and an online forum for patient advocates. It does not offer phone assistance. It can be visited at www.NeedyMeds.org.

Q: My parents think that medications they buy over the counter are safe and won't affect their prescription drugs. Aren't they wrong?

A: I don't want to sensationalize the issue, but yes, over the counter (OTC) drugs can cause dangerous interactions with some prescription drugs. In fact, they can also have an adverse side-effect not only with other drugs, but with other medical conditions such as diabetes or Parkinson's. Even vitamins and herbal supplements can interact with prescription drugs. Just because you can buy pills without a prescription doesn't mean it isn't a drug or that it is risk-free. More than 600 OTC drugs contain ingredients and dosages that 20 years ago you couldn't even buy without a doctor's prescription. Every year an estimated 100,000 people die of adverse drug reactions and 2.1 million are injured. Throwing caution to the wind is not a good idea when taking *any* kind of drug.

So, how can your parents be more careful? The Food and Drug Administration has mandated an easy-to-read format known as "Drug Fact Labels" to appear on all packaging of over the counter drugs. The first thing your parents need to do is to read the label. Here is what they'll find:

> **Active Ingredients and Purpose.** An active ingredient, also known as the active pharmaceutical ingredient (or API), is the substance of a drug that essentially makes it work. The purpose will tell your parents what type or category the medication is, such as an antihistamine, pseudoephedrine or antacid. If you take multiple drugs, make sure to look at the active ingredient of each to make sure that you're not taking too much of the same thing.

> **Uses.** This section of the label simply tells you what symptoms the drug can help relieve. It's a good idea to take a drug that is specific to your symptoms rather than take some mega-pill that treats problems you don't even have. This is especially true of flu medications. The more symptoms the pill claims to treat, then the more active ingredients it contains, which increases the risk for side-effects and adverse drug-drug interactions.

> **Warnings.** Here is where you'll learn about medical conditions that may make the drug less effective or not safe for you; under what circumstances the drug should not be taken; symptoms that indicate you should stop taking the drug and when to call a doctor or pharmacist before use.

> **Directions.** This section of the label specifies the dosage of the drug, when you should take it and how often. It also tells you the length of time and the amount of the product that is considered safe to use.

> **Other Information.** Provides required information about certain ingredients contained in the product such as sodium, calcium or potassium and how to store the product.

> **Inactive Ingredients.** These ingredients are components of the drug that bind the compounds together and add coloring. Be sure to check these ingredients if you have food or other allergies.

A new advocacy group dedicated to educating the public about OTC safety is the Consumer Health Education Center (www.CHECforbetterhealth.org). With over 100,000 over-the-counter drugs available to consumers, they know how easy it is to be overwhelmed when trying to make smart choices about medications. Here are a few of their tips that you should find helpful: When it comes to taking cold or flu medicines, select the products that treat **only** the symptoms you have; watch for medications that treat congestion often containing active ingredients of phenylephrine and pseudoephedrine if you have heart disease or high blood pressure; never use more than one pain reliever at the same time unless you are under a physician's instruction to do so and if you are on blood thinner prescription medication be careful of OTC drugs with aspirin ingredients – this can cause a double dose of blood thinning which can lead to hemorrhaging. They also advise older people against self-prescribing for heartburn or indigestion when these could be symptoms of a heart attack.

Bottom line? If you are taking prescription drugs, it's always best to ask the pharmacist if the over-the-counter drug you are about to purchase is really the best choice for you, given your current prescriptions and any pre-existing conditions.

Q: What does it mean when my doctor prescribes a drug "off-label?"

Prescription drugs must undergo a rigorous process to prove the safety, reliability and validity of a drug before it is approved by the Food and Drug Administration for public consumption. Part of the approval process requires that drug manufacturers provide evidence gathered through clinical trials of what specific conditions are treatable by the drug including dosage regimen, duration and what age ranges are appropriate for its usage. The FDA grants its approval based upon this evidence. So, if you are taking a drug that was proven to treat a heart condition and the FDA approved it as such, then the drug company can't also recommend that you use it for stomach ulcers.

The drug company must publish in their drug package inserts the approved uses of the drug, potential complications and a lot of scientific data that consumers rarely understand. These indicated uses of the drug are considered "labeled." In contrast, when a physician prescribes the drug for a use not specifically indicated on the label approved by the FDA, then the physician is prescribing for an "off-label" use. The FDA approves the *label*, also known as the *language* of the drug package insert.

You might wonder why would a doctor prescribe a drug off-label? Once a drug has been on the market and is used by large numbers of people, doctors begin to gather clinical experience on a wide range of drugs. They may find that a drug they've prescribed for one indication had an added benefit to their patients for another condition. They may share their clinical experience in medical journals or with other physicians at conferences and the word spreads. It is not uncommon, for instance, for chemotherapy drugs to be prescribed for off-label indications as physicians try to find a life-saving formula for cancer patients. Sometimes this practice can be life-saving and sometimes it can be life-taking. A six-month study of off-label practices by Knight-Ridder Newspapers found that in 2002 over 100 million prescriptions were written for off-label uses, such as epilepsy drugs given for depression, powerful anti-psychotics given for insomnia, and high blood-pressure pills given for anxiety. The study cited the case of the drug Risperdal, an FDA drug approved to treat schizophrenia, being widely used by family practice physicians to treat dementia. But in April of 2003, after alarming reports of elderly patients suffering strokes after using the drug for dementia, the drug maker Johnson & Johnson was forced to send letters to doctors throughout the country warning them of the increased risk of strokes among the elderly when using the drug off-label.

So, what can you do? You really need to take the time to educate yourself every time you or your parent is given a new prescription drug. It starts with the physician prescribing the medication, so ask your doctor:

> Is this drug approved by the FDA for what you are treating me or is this an off-label prescription?

> What is your reason for prescribing this off-label treatment? On what studies or evidence are you basing this?

> What are the risks and benefits to this treatment? Is there an alternative?

> What is the lowest dose I can take and are you prescribing it?

> How long should I be on this medication as approved by the FDA?

> What side-effects should I be aware of that could indicate I'm having an adverse reaction?

Be sure to take the time to read the drug package insert – that tiny printed tissue paper found in the box packaged with your medicine. You'll know whether or not the drug is being prescribed off-label by reading the section titled, "Indications and Usage" which will tell you what the drug is approved to treat. It is also wise to read about the contraindications which explain when a drug should not be used and the "Warnings and Precautions" section. Don't assume that a pamphlet provided by your pharmacy gives you with the same complete information on the drug as what is on the label. Go to the original source! If it doesn't come with your medicine, ask the pharmacist for a copy. And feel free to ask your pharmacist the same list of questions you've asked your doctor.

Check out the FDA website at www.fda.gov and click onto the *DRUGS* sidebar. You can search for every FDA approved drug in the United States and read the actual approved label (drug package insert) for the drug, an FDA description of the drug and a copy of any Letters to Health Professionals that the

FDA forced the drug makers to send advising them of problems associated with the drug.

Q: Is the FDA banning Tylenol? My husband really needs this drug for his arthritis.

A: No, the Federal Food and Drug Administration (FDA) is not banning Tylenol. However, the FDA will be issuing tougher warnings about the risk of liver damage from taking drugs that contain acetaminophen (a SEET a MIN oh fen). Drugs like Tylenol, Benadryl, Contac, Excedrin, Sudafed, Pamprin – all contain this ingredient, as do many cold and flu medicines. An FDA advisory panel was recently formed to review the safety of acetaminophen and reported that many consumers aren't aware as to how much acetaminophen they take in a day when using over-the-counter drugs (OTC). The FDA recommends no more than 4 grams per day, equal to about 12 tablets of regular strength Tylenol.

The Chairman of the panel, Dr. Lewis S. Nelson, a medical toxicologist, explains: "People often don't know what products contain acetaminophen, so it isn't that hard to go over the 4 gram dose." He gives an example of someone taking five or six acetaminophen tablets throughout the day for arthritis, a Tylenol PM for sleep, and Theraflu for a cold, resulting in twice the limit. Despite five years of warnings about the link between acetaminophen and liver damage, the FDA has seen an increase in cases of acute hepatic failure due to overdose of the drug, landing 42,000 people in the hospital every year and 400 people losing their lives. The panel is also urging the FDA to reduce the acceptable daily limit of the drug down to around 3 grams per day or 8 to 10 regular-strength pills. They are also recommending that extra-strength doses of 1,000 milligrams should only be acquired through a prescription. If you rely on acetaminophen to help control your pain, here is what you can do:

1. Always read the labels of any over-the-counter drug you are taking to determine if you are exceeding 4 grams of acetaminophen. It may be spelled out on the label or it may appear as APAP. Do the same with your prescription drugs.

2. Keep track of how many tablets you are taking every day. It's pretty easy to lose count, so write it down.

3. If you drink more than three alcoholic beverages a day, talk to you doctor first before taking Tylenol.

4. Consider alternatives to controlling pain, such as seeking chiropractic care, acupuncture, massage or physical therapy. Try using heating pads or ice packs and if you are overweight, shed some of the pounds to reduce the load on sore and inflamed joints.

On a personal front, for years I had constant lower back pain and relied on Tylenol and Advil to get through the day. About six months ago, I decided to see a chiropractor and it has greatly improved the quality of my life and I rarely need to take either medication. The answer always isn't in a pill.

And speaking of Advil (ibuprofen), the FDA panel also warned that switching over to this drug and other non-steroidal anti-inflammatory drugs (NSAIDS) poses an even greater health risk. Over 100,000 people are hospitalized each year and an estimated 17,000 people die as a result of gastrointestinal complications, ulcers and internal bleeding associated with NSAIDS.

The bottom line? Acetaminophen can be helpful in reducing pain and the FDA considers it a safe drug, but you must be vigilant as to how much you are ingesting every day you take it. Count the grams and look to see if Acetaminophen (APAP) is an ingredient in any other drugs you are taking. Your liver deserves the added homework.

: What should my Mom *ask* her doctor when he gives her a prescription?

: One of the most dangerous problems that older adults face when taking drugs is how multiple drugs interact with each other. One quarter of the elderly take at least three drugs a day. The older they are, the more drugs they take. The more drugs they take, the greater the risk for an adverse reaction that could land them right into the hospital. That is why it's critical that your

Mom learns to ask questions rather than blindly take every drug given her. A recent study in the Journal of the American Medical Association reported that drug reactions kill an estimated 100,000 people a year in U.S. hospitals. The researchers also claim that another 2.1 million are injured by adverse reactions. The elderly are especially vulnerable because of the number of drugs they take.

Chances are your Mom has more than one chronic condition, so she gets to meet a number of specialists. As she visits one doctor after the next, she might walk away from each visit with a prescription in hand. If she forgets to tell either doctor about what she's taking, she's placed herself in danger of an adverse drug reaction.

Besides taking drugs that may negatively interact with each other, your Mom might also be taking the same drug twice—and not know it. I've seen this happen when one doctor gives a drug in the *generic* name and another in the *brand* name. Because the names are different and the pills don't look alike, your Mom may think she's taking two different medications. If the pharmacist or doctor doesn't pick up on this, the double whammy could set off some pretty significant health problems.

Not all combinations of drugs are bad. For instance, a physician might prescribe an anti-ulcer medication with an anti-inflammatory medication. The doctor is doing this because the anti-inflammatory drug can cause severe irritation to the lining of the stomach. So as a precautionary measure, he or she will prescribe the anti-ulcer drug.

So, back to your original question: Here's my list of questions that I suggest your Mom ask every doctor who gives her a prescription. It's also a list that you can copy and encourage your Mom to ask any time she's given a new medication.

> What is the name of the medication (brand name and generic name)?

> What is the medication supposed to do?

> Why are you recommending that I take this?

> How often should I take the drug?

> For how long should I take the drug?

> When should I take it? (Whenever I need to? Before, during, or after meals? At bedtime?)

> Should I avoid certain foods or alcohol when taking this drug? Should I stay out of the sun?

> Should this medicine be refrigerated?

> If I forget to take it, what should I do?

> What side effects might I expect? Under what circumstances should I call you?

> Is there any written material on this drug in lay terms?

> Is there something else I could try first, such as a change in diet, exercise, or therapy?

> How much does this drug cost? (Let the doctor know if you cannot afford it. Ask if there is a generic substitute, which costs less.)

If you want to get understandable information on the drugs your Mom is taking, the latest news on new drugs, clinical trials and health warnings, check out the U.S. National Library of Medicine's website at www.medlineplus.gov. It offers a guide to thousands of prescriptions, over-the-counter medications and supplements. Just click onto "*Drugs & Supplements.*"

: **What should my Mom *tell* her doctor about the prescriptions she takes?**

: If your Mom doesn't have one general practitioner quarterbacking all of the prescriptions she's taking, then you need to create your own playbook. Make a chart that identifies her name, social security number and allergies, placing this information on the top of the chart. Then add four columns with the following headings: Name of the Drug, Dosage Level (e.g., 15 mg), Number of Pills a Day, and Time of Day. Simply list each medication she is taking and fill out the information for each under the headings.

This chart should be continuously updated and be taken by your Mom to each visit. It's smart to keep extra copies, so that if your Mom becomes hospitalized, you can quickly grab it and give it to the physicians at the hospital or, in the case of an emergency, hand it to the paramedics.

Now, it's your Mom's turn to give information to the doctor. Here's what Mom should tell her:

➤ The name of all prescription drugs she is taking, including how long and how frequently she's taken the drugs.

➤ Any over-the-counter drugs she's taking, such as cough medicine, aspirin or ibuprofen.

➤ Any vitamins she is taking.

➤ All allergies to medications and food.

➤ Any serious side effect she's had to a particular medication.

➤ If Mom has stopped taking a medication, she can't keep it a secret. She might not tell because she thinks it will upset the doctor, however, the physician needs to know since some medications work in combination with other drugs.

▸ Any concern about not being able to afford the medication. (Studies show that 1 in 4 elderly don't take the drugs they are prescribed because they can't afford it.)

▸ If she consumes alcohol frequently (every few days or more).

The reason for all of this information sharing is to prevent serious medical problems for your Mom. Research from the federal General Accounting Office reports that more than 5 million Americans use medications that are either inappropriate or could cause adverse interactions serious enough to warrant hospitalization.

You'll find that your Mom's local pharmacist can be an excellent resource – if you just ask. You and your Mom will find it helpful to ask the pharmacist the same list of questions that you asked the doctor. Hearing it twice and double-checking doesn't hurt. The pharmacist also can advise your Mom about over-the-counter drugs as to how they might interfere with your Mom's medicines or might not be suitable for the geriatric population. Many pharmacies have additional consumer-friendly information on the drugs that they dispense, so ask for a copy.

You can print out a Medication-Minder Sheet for free at my website at www.lindarhodescaregiving.com. And, an excellent website with up-to-date consumer information on both prescription and over-the counter medications can be found at www.medlineplus.gov.

Q: How can I help my mother sign up for the Medicare Part D prescription benefit?

A: The easiest way to determine the best plan for your Mom is to gain access to the internet while you go through her list of medications. If you can't go online with her, make a complete list of each of her prescriptions (make sure you spell each drug correctly). You also need to identify the dosage level of the drug and the number of pills she takes each day of the drug. I also suggest identifying the pharmacy she uses to get her prescriptions filled and how much she is paying for each prescription.

Once you have this information, then you will be ready to use the "Plan Finder" at www.medicare.gov. But, before you do that, go to www.mymedicarematters.org. This website is run by the National Council on Aging and they walk you through seven simplified steps to make an informed decision on what plan is in your best interest. You can then link to the Medicare Plan Finder. If you are currently enrolled in a Medicare Part D plan, then the site will walk you through a different set of steps.

Once you enter your data in the Medicare Plan Finder, it will show all of the plans that cover the prescriptions your mother takes and how much each costs – the annual deductible, co-pay and monthly premium. It also calculates your annual costs including the prescriptions you entered. You can compare several plans at a time, but be aware there are a lot of choices.

If you do not have access to the internet, then give your Area Agency on Aging or local senior center a call and ask who is hosting Part D seminars and individual counseling sessions to help consumers weigh their options. You can also call 1-800-MEDICARE (1-800-633-4227) 24 hours a day, seven days a week. (TTY users call 1-877-486-2048.)

Here is the *Least You Need to Know* about Medicare Part D:

1. Between November 15th and December 31st you can change your Part D Plan if you are currently enrolled in one or sign up for the first time. This is known as the open enrollment period. If you don't sign up for a plan, you will be penalized later by paying higher premiums.

2. Look for any restrictions on the drugs that your mother takes. Plans place drugs in tiers – the higher the tier, then the higher the co-pay, or you may be required to take another equivalent drug.

3. Don't forget about the coverage gap known as the "donut hole," in which you must pay 100 percent of your prescription costs. Up until 2014, Medicare will pay you a one-time check of $250 when you reach the coverage gap and you will receive a 50 percent discount on brand medications during this period. In 2014, there will no longer be a "donut hole."

4. Don't assume that because you like your current plan, you don't have to do your homework and compare plans again this year. Many plans are increasing their premiums or they may have dropped a drug that you are currently taking from their formulary.

If you have a low income, you may qualify for "extra help" to assist you with the costs of premiums, deductibles and co-pays along with coverage during the coverage gap. Check with a Medicare representative to see if you qualify.

Q: I need to organize my Dad's pill taking; what would you do?

A: First of all, it's a good idea to take your father to his primary physician or a physician certified in geriatrics to review all of his medications and give him a thorough physical to see what is going on. I recommend taking all of his prescription bottles to the doctor, so that the physician can see who has prescribed what medication and when it was prescribed. All too often, with our parents seeing so many specialists, one physician may not know what the other has prescribed. I've seen some older people taking the same medication twice because it was prescribed by two different doctors: one prescribing it in the generic form and the other in the brand name. So, your first stop is a review of all medications with his primary physician or a geriatrician. Local hospitals can give you names of physicians certified in geriatrics.

If your father lives alone, you need to set up a system so he will not mix up his medications. Here are some suggestions, some of which I've used for my mother as she can not see very well and is on six different medications:

1. Purchase a "pill organizer" at the pharmacy. These plastic containers are found in a number of sizes: some are for one day, some for each day of the week and some for the entire week. Choose the one that your father will find easiest to use. The one that I prefer, if your Dad needs to take medicines at different times of the day, is organized for 7 days of the week with each day marked on top. Along the side are four rows marked for morning, noon, dinner and bedtime. You simply place the pills for each time of day in its space and he'll open it at the right time and take those pills. Every Saturday, he should fill the organizer for the following week. If he has difficulty seeing, perhaps either you or a friend can assist. Many of the full week pill organizers are designed so that a day's supply can pop out in a smaller container. That way, if he is out for the day, he has a day's supply with him.

2. Buy round plain white stickers at least 1 inch in size and in large print write what the pill is for on it and stick it on top of the pill bottle. For example, if he is taking Lasix (diuretic) write WATER on the sticker, if he is taking a blood thinner like Plavix, write THINNER, or BP for a blood pressure medicine. By doing this, he'll be less likely to confuse the medications, especially given the hard to pronounce names of many generics. If color coding works, like a blue sticker for

a water pill, then create a color coding system.

3. There are more sophisticated systems for dispensing pills, but you'll want to make sure that it is easy for him. Retailers such as Sharper Image and Brookstone, for example, sell an electronic pill organizer with alarms to remind you when to take each pill. You can also purchase a "talking prescription bottle." If your parent is visually impaired, this is a terrific device that offers a digital audio recording on a label placed on the prescription bottle. Ask your local pharmacist if they would recommend a particular brand or you can perform a search on the internet by simply using the keywords "talking prescription bottle" and you'll find a number of companies that sell them.

4. Create a list detailing what medications your father is taking. List the drug, what it is for, who prescribed it, when they prescribed it, the dose and when it is to be taken each day. Your Dad should take this list to every doctor appointment.

5. Keep track of any adverse reactions your father has on any drug (e.g., dizzy, confused, nauseous), so that when he is hospitalized or sees a new physician, he'll be able to alert them to problems he has had in the past with that particular drug. This list is in addition to any known allergic drug reactions.

6. Always talk with your Dad's pharmacist. He or she can be an excellent resource on possible side effects, contraindications and when to take each medication and under what conditions. This information is very important when your father starts taking more than three medications. Read and study those inserts that the pharmacist includes with each prescription. If you don't understand any of the directions or information, then give them a call.

7. Always let the doctor and pharmacist know of any over-the-counter drugs and vitamins your Dad is taking, as these do interact with prescriptions.

 : Just what is alternative medicine, anyway?

 : Complementary and alternative medicine (CAM) offers a wide array of health care practices such as homeopathic, naturopathic and Chinese medicine, biologically based therapies found in nature

(herbs, foods, and vitamins), chiropractic or osteopathic manipulation, and energy therapies.

Getting the mind and body to work effectively with its own natural healing process is the mantra of the alternative medicine crowd. Any parent pursuing this route of care will require a good dose of personal responsibility and initiative. Furthermore, alternative medicine is most successful when it is pursued as a partnership with your parent's physician. So, who's who in the CAM line up? The NCCAM classifies CAM therapies into five categories. This is a brief re-cap of what they describe:

1. **Alternative Medical Systems:** These systems have evolved separately from the conventional medical approaches used in our country. Some of these systems include homeopathic, naturopathic, chiropractic and to some extent, osteopathic medicine. *Naturopathic* doctors (ND) are similar to a general practitioner, as they are trained to use and prescribe a wide range of approaches in CAM to assist their patients that may include dietary, massage, exercise, acupuncture, minor surgery, and various other interventions. *Homeopathic* doctors believe that "like cures like," meaning that small, very diluted quantities of medicinal substances are given to cure symptoms. If, however, these substances were given at greater or more concentrated doses, they would actually cause the very symptoms being treated. *Chiropractic* care focuses on the relationship between bodily structure (especially, the spine) and function, and how that relationship affects and restores health. Chiropractors use manipulative therapy as their integral treatment tool. *Osteopathic* medicine is also seen as a form of conventional medicine. These doctors (DO) believe that, in part, disease arises as a result of dysfunction in the musculoskeletal system and that all of the body's systems work together. Disturbances in one system may affect function elsewhere in the body.

2. **Mind-Body Interventions:** The focus here is to enhance the mind's capacity to affect bodily function and symptoms, including meditation, visualization, prayer, mental healing, and therapies that use creative outlets such as art, music, Yoga or dance.

3. **Biologically Based Therapies:** These therapies use substances found in nature, such as herbs, foods, and vitamins. There are basically two schools of herbalists: Western and Chinese. Both camps believe that herbs can nurture and protect the immune system, especially during chemotherapy treatments.

4. **Manipulative and Body-Based Methods:** These therapies use manipulation and/or movement of one or more parts of the body. Some examples include chiropractic or osteopathic manipulation, and a wide range of massage therapies.

5. **Energy Therapies:** There are two types of energy therapies. The first is Biofield therapies that are intended to affect energy fields that surround and penetrate the human body by applying pressure and/or manipulating the body by placing the hands in, or through, these fields (e.g. qi gong, Reiki, and Therapeutic Touch massage). The second is Bioelectromagnetic-based therapies involving the use of electromagnetic fields, such as pulsed fields, magnetic fields, or alternating current or direct current fields.

Within each of these systems there is a wide array of treatments—far too many to detail in a single column.

 : How do you find a reputable practitioner in alternative medicine?

 : Complementary and alternative medicine (CAM) offers a wide array of health care practices such as homeopathic, naturopathic and Chinese medicine, biologically based therapies found in nature (herbs, foods, and vitamins) chiropractic or osteopathic manipulation and energy therapies, all of which focus on getting the mind and body to work effectively with its own natural healing process. Here are some generic guidelines to follow in finding a qualified CAM practitioner:

1. **Find good referrals.** The first place to start is among family, friends and co-workers whom you respect. Ask if any of them have had a positive experience with a practitioner who has treated your health problem. Call local professional associations, as many offer lists of practitioners who are affiliated with them. Go to local support groups. For instance, your mother might call or go to a breast cancer support group and ask other women if they have had any positive outcomes with alternative medicine and by whom. Local health food stores often become an informal hub for people involved in alternative medicine. They know most of the practitioners in town and they can tell you if there is a formal alternative medicine network or newsletter. Once you start hearing the same name(s) of highly regarded practitioners among all of these sources – you know you have a good lead.

2. **Ask the right questions among your referrals.** In an excellent book, *Five Steps*

to Selecting the Best Alternative Medicine by Mary and Michael Morton, they recommend that you ask your referral sources the following questions: Why did you seek out this particular provider? What were your expectations and were they met? What is the provider's specialty? Did they listen to you and do they communicate well? Are they experts in a particular treatment or health condition? How many treatments did you have? Was it successful? Was their fee reasonable? What is their educational and clinical background?

3. **Ask about their education and clinical training and if they are licensed.** The first thing to know is the difference between someone telling you they are registered, certified or licensed. Registered simply means that they have submitted their name with some entity to have it listed – it by no means is a benchmark that they are qualified. If they are "certified" it usually means that a professional body reviewed their qualifications, set standards that the practitioner had to meet (e.g. graduating from an accredited school, spent a set amount of hours in clinical training), and then required the individual to take an exam to prove their knowledge. This is usually a solid marker of competency, however, you must also research the certifying body. If they are not credible, then neither is the certificate. "Licensed" means that the individual had to take a rigorous exam administered by state law and a state licensing body that also oversees any complaints

and investigations over any licensed professional in the state. A license provides you with extra protection in finding a practitioner but it is not a gold seal.

Not all states license naturopathic doctors (ND). However, all states do license chiropractors (DC) and osteopaths (DO), which both fall under the alternative medicine system. You can check online or call your state's Medical Board, which most likely runs the professional and occupational licensing board to find out if they license any of the CAM professions. Without a licensing guidepost, it is very important for you to ask the provider to tell you where they received their education, if the school is accredited, and how many clinical hours they spent in training. There are several accredited naturopathic colleges, one of which is the well-known Bastyr University of Natural Sciences in Seattle, Washington. Be extremely leery of anyone who received their degree through a correspondence program. This holds true for a conventional doctor with MD behind their name. Just because they are a licensed medical doctor does not mean that they know how to practice holistic, integrative alternative medicine.

4. **Interview the practitioner.** Now that you have done your research, you are in a position to meet with your potential CAM practitioner. Again, Mary and Michael Morton offer some very good sample questions for you:

- After you have described your condition ask them what tests, treatment and techniques they would propose doing for you.

- Then ask: How will I know these treatments are working?

- How often and how many people have you treated with my condition?

- How do you keep informed on the latest research and treatments for my condition?

- What are the side-effects?

- How long will it take for me to expect results?

- Do you have patients who would be willing to talk to me about their experience with your practice?

: What are good consumer resources on alternative medicine?

Complementary and Alternative Medicine offers a wide array of health care practices such as homeopathic, naturopathic and Chinese medicine, biologically based therapies found in nature (herbs, foods, and vitamins) chiropractic or osteopathic manipulation, body work and energy therapies, all of which focus on getting the mind and body to work effectively with its own natural healing process.

The field is exploding and it may seem overwhelming to you, so here are some national resources that can guide you through the world of alternative medicine:

1. **Contact the American Holistic Medical Association (AHMA).** This is the oldest association in the United States representing physicians (MDs) and (DOs) who practice alternative medicine – in fact, the internationally known integrative medicine physician, Dr. Andrew Weil, is a member. You may contact them to find members who practice in your area and those who have become board certified in CAM by requesting a printed directory: Write to them at American Holistic Medical Association, 23366 Commerce Park, Suite 101B, Beachwood, Ohio 44122, or visit their website at www.holisticmedicine.org. The American College for the Advancement in Medicine also provides

referrals to alternative MDs in the United States and they can be reached at 1-800-532-3688 or www.acam.org. If you'd like to find a referral of a Chinese medicine practitioner, then contact the American Association of Oriental Medicine (AAOM) at www.aaaomonline.org or call 1-888-500-7999.

2. **Check out programs at your local hospital.** More hospitals are adding CAM or "integrative" medicine to their list of health care services. Call them to find out if they have any special programs in CAM or any physicians who have trained in the field. A growing number of hospitals are now offering programs in Reiki, Shiatsu, acupuncture, massage, nutrition consultations, meditation, imagery and hypnosis.

3. **The Moss Reports.** Internationally recognized, Ralph Moss Ph.D., has authored eleven books on cancer and alternative medicine and is a founding member of the National Institutes of Health Alternative Medicine Advisory Council. If you want an extensive, in-depth and comprehensive report on your particular cancer detailing conventional and alternative therapies available to you with Moss's top recommendations on the most effective therapies with contact information, then consider ordering a *Moss Report*. Visit his website www.cancerdecisions.com or call 1-800-980-1234.

4. **Websites and Books.** Many CAM practitioners may recommend supplements and other nutrition products. One way of sorting through what claims are valid about these products and which are exaggerations is by visiting www.consumerlab.com. This group provides and posts online independent test results and information to help consumers and healthcare professionals evaluate health, wellness, and nutrition products. The National Foundation for Alternative Medicine (www.NFAM.org) investigates, validates and reports on clinics throughout the world that demonstrate promising treatment options for degenerative diseases. For a solid, commercial website go to www.naturalsolutionsmag.com, connecting you to many of the developments in the field. This group has also published a book, *Cancer Diagnosis: What to do Next* by W. John Diamond, M.D. and Lee Cowden, M.D. And finally, another top notch resource is *Healing Outside the Margins: The Survivor's Guide to Integrative Cancer Care* by Carole O'Toole and Carolyn Hendricks, M.D. Research your medical conditions (www.mayoclinic.com) and let them know if certain foods make matters worse. Most chronic illnesses benefit from a special diet.

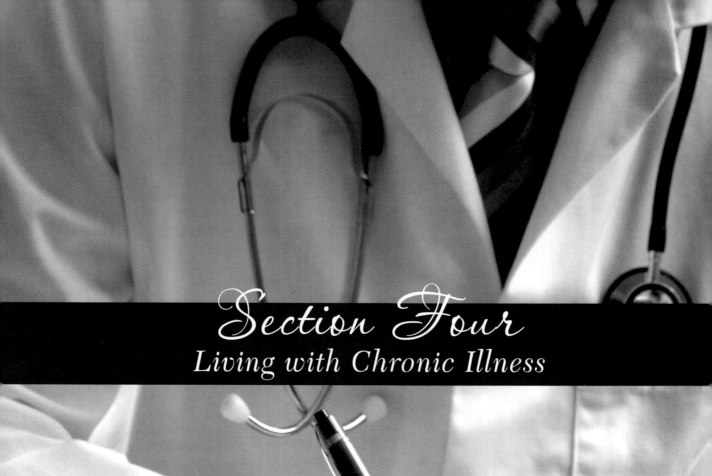

Section Four
Living with Chronic Illness

Q: What are the top ten signs that your parent needs help?

A: Many older relatives won't ask for help because they fear that they'll be a burden to their families. Or, they think that if their children see any sign of dependence, they'll jump to the conclusion that it's not safe for them to live on their own. A dear friend of mine fell in her bathroom and was unconscious for a short period of time. She kept the incident from her daughter because, as she put it, "They'll make me move in with them, but I don't want to move to another city even though they'll be wonderful to me." Yet my friend was frightened by the incident, so we explored new housing options. She's now thriving in her apartment surrounded by a new set of friends, along with assisted living support when and if she needs it. Rather than expecting loved ones to tell you they could use some help, there are things that you can look for whenever you visit. Recently, the Home Instead Senior Care Advisory Board (www.homeinstead.com) released their take on ten telltale signs that your older relative may need assistance or additional companionship. Here is their list:

1. Household bills piling up – The simple task of opening and responding to daily mail, as well as balancing a checkbook, may become overwhelming, particularly if eyesight is deteriorating. Look for overdue bills, utilities being turned off due to lack of payment and other creditor issues.

2. Reluctance to leave the house – Seniors who are having trouble walking, remembering directions, seeing, or hearing will slowly pull away from their community and isolate themselves, which can lead to loneliness, depression, and malnutrition.

3. Losing interest in preparing/eating meals – Are excessive amounts of junk and convenience food around the house, outdated food in the refrigerator or are there signs of excessive weight loss? Poor diet can increase the risk of dementia in seniors and weaken the immune system.

4. Declining personal hygiene – Take note of unkempt hair, body odor, unshaven faces and wearing clothing that is unclean, unchanged for days or inappropriate for the weather. Doing the laundry or getting in an out of the tub may be too physically challenging. Many who live alone also fear slipping and falling in a shower or bathtub so they don't bathe.

5. Decline in driving skills – Look for evidence of parking or speeding tickets, fender-benders, dents or scratches on the car as signs that driving skills may be deteriorating. The decreased ability to see, poor sense of direction, inability to merge into traffic and slow reaction times are recipes for disaster.

6. Signs of scorched pots and pans – This may be a sign of short-term memory loss or even the onset of Alzheimer's, as pots used in cooking are left on the open flame of the stove and burn. Fire is one of the greatest safety concerns that families of older relatives face.

7. Symptoms of depression – Depression causes marked changes in behavior and one's daily routine over time. Be on guard for increased listlessness, not wanting to get dressed, decreased visits with family and friends, changes in sleeping patterns (sleeping long periods or not sleeping at all) and lack of interest in usual hobbies and activities.

8. Missed doctors' appointments and social engagements – While this can be a symptom of increased forgetfulness, it is often simply a result of not having transportation and not knowing how to access transportation options.

9. Unkempt house – Changes in housekeeping may occur simply because it is too difficult or tiring. From dirty laundry to dirty dishes, these everyday tasks become too much to handle on their own.

10. Losing track of medications – Missed doses and medication mistakes (overdosing and running out of pills before the next prescription can be refilled) can lead to very serious medical complications.

 : Does seeing a geriatrician make a difference?

 : Absolutely. A RAND-UCLA study published in the *Annals of Internal Medicine* found that two out of three older patients with health problems threatening their independence do NOT receive the health care they need for geriatric or age-related conditions like malnutrition, pressure sores, dementia, incontinence, osteoarthritis, falls and mobility disorders. One out of two does not receive adequate care for ischemic heart disease and pneumonia.

Those numbers are downright alarming. Imagine any other business where two out of three customers didn't receive the services they paid for. They certainly wouldn't be in business very long. The researchers contend that the health care system must take major steps to improve primary care physicians' diagnosis and treatment of diseases of aging, such as dementia, mobility disorders, urinary incontinence and osteoarthritis.

But while they're calling for reforms within the health care system, what should your parents do? They would do well to have a geriatric assessment by a team of physicians, nurses, therapists and social workers who are all specially trained in geriatrics. This would provide them with a comprehensive work-up on their health status by a team of professionals who will view them as a whole person. All too often, older people see different kinds of physicians for each bodily system or part: A cardiologist for their heart, podiatrist for their feet, ophthalmologist for their eyes, urologist for their kidneys and the list goes on. If these doctors aren't on the same page, they won't be aware of how the treatment and prescriptions each of them prescribes interact with each other.

To find a geriatric assessment center near your parents, call your local hospitals and ask if they offer such a service or could provide you with a list of geriatric specialists. Most university-based hospitals have a geriatric specialty and perform such assessments. You can also call the American Geriatrics Society at 1-212-308-1414 or visit their website at www.americangeriatrics.org. They can send you a list of physicians certified in geriatrics or email the information to you. If you can't find a center, then look for physicians who have received certification in geriatrics by taking special courses and passing an exam. Ask the physician if he or she has a fellowship or received certification in geriatrics. The benefit of having a physician who has specialized in geriatrics is his or her ability to "piece things together." This type of doctor understands the physiological changes of aging and knows what's normal and what's not. He or she will also have a better appreciation of how medications interact with your parent's physiological changes. This is especially helpful since many drugs prescribed to the elderly were never tested on older subjects.

You can also find local internists who've received certification in geriatrics by writing to the American Board of Internal Medicine, 510 Walnut Street, Suite 1700, Philadelphia, PA 19106 and asking them for a list of local certified physicians. They only take letter requests in writing or you can send them a request by fax at 1-215-446-3590. One of the lead researchers of the RAND-UCLA study, Dr. Paul Shekelle, says "Family members and patients need to make sure that everything is being done for age-related ailments, just as they would speak up if their chest pain wasn't being attended to."

Q: What is a Geriatric Care Manager?

A: If you've been trying to juggle long-distance caregiving or you need professional advice on how to organize your parent's care, a Geriatric Care Manager can be a godsend. These are members of a relatively new field of social workers, counselors and nurses who will assess, organize, monitor and manage your parent's caregiving needs. For example, they'll meet with your parent, conduct an assessment to identify his needs, determine his eligibility for a host of services, make arrangements for those services, interview home health care and senior care workers, monitor them, arrange for transportation to and from doctors' appointments, analyze financial, legal or medical information – they'll even oversee a move from your father's home to assisted living, a nursing home or retirement community.

Fees range from $50 to $150 per hour, depending upon the care manager's credentials and experience. Some charge by the hour, while others charge set fees for a package of services. The initial assessment may cost from $150 to $350 and then, based upon your parent's needs, you and the Geriatric Care Manager agree on a monthly fee. Make sure all of this is in writing and that you have clear expectations of what services will be performed.

When you interview a Geriatric Care Manager, there are a number of questions you should ask:

▸ What services do you provide and who provides them?

▸ What are your credentials? Are you licensed in your profession?

▸ How long have you been providing care management services? How long have you been practicing in this community?

▸ Do you have any affiliations and memberships in community organizations?

▸ Are you available for emergencies? Who do you have on backup if you are not available?

▸ What can I expect to learn from your initial assessment? What does it include (e.g. physical and mental status, financial resources)? Who conducts the medical component, and what are their qualifications?

▸ How do you perform quality checks on the service providers and referrals you recommend?

- How do you communicate information to me about my parent and how often?

- How often will you have face-to-face contact with my parent?

- How many cases do you handle at one time?

- What are your fees and can you provide me with references?

It is very important for you to do your homework by checking out their references and asking them these questions because this is essentially an unregulated industry. Anyone can put up a shingle and call themselves a geriatric care manager. So ask if they have received any type of certification, where it is from and if they are a member of the National Association of Professional Geriatric Care Managers (a non-profit association, not a credentialing institution). To track down a Geriatric Care Manager, call the National Association of Professional Geriatric Care Managers at 1-520-881-8008 or visit their website at www.caremanager.org. On their site, go to *"Find a Care Manager,"* where you can search by state and zip code for a local manager with a description of what services they offer and degrees they hold. You will also find them listed in the Yellow Pages, usually under Social Workers, Eldercare and or Home Health Care.

If your parent is low or moderate income, he or she may qualify for geriatric care management through their local Area Agency on Aging. You can find it by calling the Eldercare Locator at 1-800-677-1116.

 My wife just had a stroke and the doctor wants to give her an antidepressant right away. Shouldn't we wait and see if she even gets depressed?

 Your doctor might be responding to a recent study funded by the National Institute of Mental Health that found that, in their year-long study of 176 stroke patients, only 9 percent of patients who received an antidepressant immediately following a stroke became depressed, while 22 percent of those who received a placebo (sugar pill) *did* become depressed. People who received neither pill, but attended therapy sessions, did rather well with only 12 percent becoming depressed. This is the first randomized, control study of its kind.

The lead researcher, Dr. Robert Robinson, a psychiatrist and head of the department at the University of Iowa College of Medicine, reports that more than half of stroke survivors develop depression within two years. Besides a patient's emotional struggle with losing their ability to function independently as a trigger for depression, he and others suspect that the depression is also linked to whether or not the stroke has damaged parts of the brain that affect mood. So, the cause could be biological as much as it is behavioral. Robinson's view, along with Dr. Roger Cadieux, a geriatric psychiatrist affiliated with Hershey Medical Center, is why wait? Since the risks are pretty high that people suffering from a stroke will become depressed, why not take a preemptive strike? In Dr. Cadieux's words, "If we could treat patients with antidepressants as soon as they stabilize from the stroke, it would prevent a great deal of emotional distress later on in the course of their illness and facilitate their rehabilitation."

Others caution that a larger study is needed to confirm this finding. What I found encouraging is that therapy was also very effective in preventing depression. The answer isn't always in a pill. But, prescribing therapy should be done quickly as part of the normal course of treatment rather than wait for the patient (or his or her family members) to ask for it. In most cases, that is not going to happen.

According to the American Heart Association, about 780,000 people suffer a stroke every year and more than one-third will develop depression within 24 months causing them further debilitation. Depression blocks progress towards recovery and increases the likelihood of death. Your wife's doctor is being proactive, given that the odds of becoming depressed are stacked against her. If you are uncomfortable about the antidepressant, bring it up with her physician and ask if your wife would be a good candidate for therapy. But before you even take that step, see if this is the course your wife wants to take.

 : My Dad had a stroke and now has a hard time swallowing. What kind of meals can my Mom make for him?

 : One of the potential complications of a stroke is dysphagia (dis-FAY-jee-yuh), which means experiencing difficulty in swallowing liquids, foods and/or saliva. Dysphagia has many causes and includes any condition that weakens or damages the muscles and nerves used for swallowing.

People with diseases of the nervous system, such as cerebral palsy, Parkinson's disease or advanced Alzheimer's are prime candidates for swallowing problems. And, as in your father's case, a stroke may affect the coordination of the swallowing muscles or limit sensation in the mouth and throat that signal the act to swallow. People who suffer from cancer of the head, neck, or esophagus are also at high risk of dysphagia.

About a half-million people each year in the United States are diagnosed with dysphagia due to a stroke, while about 6.2 million people over sixty years experience difficulty in swallowing unrelated to strokes and 40 million have a chewing disorder. The major dangers of dysphagia are the risk of choking or aspiration, in which a small piece of food travels to the lung and, in turn, leads to pneumonia. The condition can also lead to poor nutrition because people lapse into soft diets that are very limiting and unhealthy.

I received a review copy of the *I Can't Chew Cookbook* by Randy Wilson (Hunter House 2003). It sounds like this may be just the ticket for your Mom and Dad. It contains over 200 recipes that Randy created when his wife was diagnosed with a TMJ disorder and underwent surgery that required her to eat soft foods for six months. He became tired of preparing two different meals every night, so he got creative and started to play around with recipes that the whole family would find enjoyable, appealing and nutritious. I imagine that it was also a psychological

boost to his wife that she wasn't relegated to eating puréed foods while everyone around her ate enticing meals that were off limits to her.

The book offers recipes in five food categories: Beverages, Soups, Main Dishes, Vegetable Dishes and Desserts. Every recipe offers a Nutritional Analysis for each serving, specifying the vitamins and minerals in that meal, which is very helpful to know when someone faces a chronic illness where nutritional health is essential to their well being. Also noted with each recipe are the amount of calories, protein, carbohydrates fiber, fat, cholesterol and sodium intake per serving.

What I found especially helpful is a chapter on *Tips for Getting the Most out of Meals* by nutritionist Debra Mestas. Here are just a few of her strategies:

› You can adapt foods for a soft food diet by: serving macaroni, spaghetti or noodles and chopping them into tiny pieces; using a blender to strain beef, lamb, pork, veal, chicken and liver; making smoothies out of fruits by chopping them up and placing them in a blender with crushed ice and apple juice; steaming vegetables so they become soft and can be mashed by a fork before each bite.

› Soft foods like mashed potatoes, yogurt, scrambled eggs, poached eggs, egg custards, cottage cheese with small curds, milk shakes, puddings, gelatins and creamy cereal are trusted stand-bys.

Feel free to also try "toddler" baby foods and add adult spices.

- When you use a blender – blend foods that are warm rather than hot and blend only small amounts at one time. Add gravy prior to blending small pieces of meat. Food tastes better if it is cooked before blended.

- Arrange food nicely on a plate and vary the food selections so it is colorful. Sprinkle chopped parsley or cilantro along the side or add a slice of tomato.

The one thing that I noticed in the "Entrée" section was the good number of appealing casserole dishes presented that offer a nutritiously balanced meal easily prepared in one dish. If your mother doesn't have a small slow cooker, this might be the perfect time to get her one.

The book is available through most bookstores and www.Amazon.com, you can call Hunter books directly at 1-800-266-5592 or go to their website at www.hunterhouse.com. It sells for around $12.00 on Amazon (not including shipping and handling).

Q: Can depression really cause someone to be placed in a nursing home?

A: A major study cited some pretty strong evidence that depression left untreated can, indeed, land a loved one into a skilled nursing facility. Dr. Yael Harris at the Centers for Medicare and Medicaid Services studied 141,000 older people living in the community for nearly four years. Nearly 15 percent who reported that they "felt sad or depressed much of the time" were admitted to a nursing home. Diabetes and heart failure were the two most predictive conditions for a nursing home admission, while depression came in third.

Harris and his fellow researchers believe that depression has a negative effect on underlying diseases that the older person may have. For example, studies have shown that people with depression may have higher blood pressure and heart disease. Depression is also linked to unhealthy life styles, such as poor diet, lack of sleep and alcoholism. No matter what the link, Harris and his colleagues argue that "appropriate identification and management of depression could prevent or postpone the use of nursing home services."

That's well and good but depression is one of the most missed and under-diagnosed conditions among the elderly. This is despite the fact that the National Institute of Mental Health estimates that one in five people over sixty suffers from some level of depression that requires medical intervention, yet most receive no treatment of any kind.

Depression is an illness of intense sadness that interferes with the ability to function, feel pleasure, or maintain interest. Researchers have discovered that biochemical imbalances in the brain go hand-in-hand with depression. It might follow a recent loss or sad event, but the intensity of the feeling and its duration persist far beyond what is healthy.

The National Institute of Mental Health (NIMH) offers this checklist of symptoms of clinical depression:

› Persistent sadness, anxiety or feeling of emptiness

› Loss of interest or pleasure in ordinary activities, family or friends

› Decreased energy, listlessness, fatigue, feeling slowed down

› Changes in sleep patterns

› Eating problems and changes in appetite

› Difficulty in concentrating, remembering or making decisions

› Feelings of hopelessness, guilt, worthlessness and helplessness

› Thoughts of suicide or death

› Irritability

› Excessive crying, sometimes without reason

› Recurring aches and pains, such as headaches and backaches that don't respond to treatment.

If you think your parent exhibits these symptoms, get him to his family physician to rule out any other physical problems. Studies show that a combination of psychotherapy and carefully prescribed medications can be 80 percent successful in treating depression among the elderly. Antidepressants are powerful drugs, however, and they should be prescribed very carefully and in conjunction with other mental health services. Two websites that are valuable resources on depression are www.nimh.nih.gov and www.depression.org.

NIMH also encourages older people to ask themselves the following questions, before they tell their doctor, "I'm just fine." Ask yourself if you feel: nervous or empty, guilty or worthless, very tired and slowed down, you don't enjoy things the way you used to, restless or irritable, no one loves you or if you feel like life is not worth living. If you're answering yes to these questions, it means you should share this information with your family physician and not let it slide.

Depression is not a normal part of aging. Ignoring its symptoms can complicate other health conditions and send a loved one into a tailspin leading to premature nursing home care. It's not something your Mom or Dad is simply going to "snap out of." So, don't look the other way. Bring up how you've noticed they haven't been themselves and get them to answer the NIMH *"Before you say you're fine check-list"* cited above. They might feel relieved knowing that what they are feeling isn't normal and there is a biochemical side to what they're feeling. The good news is that their depression can be treated so they can get on with enjoying their life.

 My Mom has osteoarthritis and thinks that exercise will make it worse. I think it will help. What should I tell her?

 The one person who can best explain to your Mom about the benefits of exercise *especially if she has osteoarthritis* is her physician. He or she can prescribe a physical therapist to work with your Mom to teach her how to safely exercise, giving her muscle strength to hold off the effects of further deterioration. Her doctor can also address your Mom's fear of over-exercising and explore her possible lack of motivation caused by the pain, stiffness and swelling she may be feeling in her joints.

Osteoarthritis is a degenerative joint disease that affects cartilage within the joints that fray and become worn down. Sometimes this will lead to ulceration and, in extreme cases, the cartilage will wear away entirely causing bone to scrape against bone. At the edges of the joint, bony spurs may also form. All of this leads to joint pain, loss of function, reduced range of motion, and deformity. People are at most risk for becoming disabled in weight-bearing joints, such as knees and hips and in their spine.

Chances are the pain your mother feels is what's holding her back. She might think that the less she moves around then the less she risks kicking up joint pain. But studies show that exercise can actually reduce joint pain and stave off the stiffness she likely feels every morning or when she's been sitting for too long. In other words the, "use it or lose it" school of medicine. Treating arthritis should involve a comprehensive treatment plan that includes good nutrition, weight control, medication, relaxation exercises, pain relief and learning how to be gentle to weakened joints.

There are basically three types of exercises that are often prescribed for someone living with osteoarthritis: *Range-of-motion* exercises that focus on maintaining joint movement to relieve stiffness and foster flexibility. *Strengthening* exercises that build strong muscles to protect and support fragile joints. And, finally, *aerobic or endurance exercises* that keep your heart fit to keep your circulation flowing to nourish bones and muscle. The added benefit of endurance exercise is to keep your weight down so you're not placing added pressure on your joints. And, if all of these benefits aren't enough to convince your Mom about the advantages of exercise; research studies now show that pain-producing inflammation is also diminished.

Once your Mom meets with a physical therapist, she'll be given the key to a dynamic world of joint-friendly therapies. Mobilization therapies offer gentle traction that steadily pulls muscles and tendons, along with massage and manipulation by trained hands to restore movement to stiff joints. Hydrotherapy in the form of water aerobics and water exercises in large pools takes the weight off painful joints so it's easier to stretch. Whirlpools can provide the added benefit of heat to warm up stiff muscles. Moist heat provided by warm towels, hot packs such as microwavable "buddies" that may also include herbal remedies, or simply a hot shower or bath bring pain relief and prepare muscles for exercise. When joints are inflamed or swollen, a fifteen minute dose of ice wrapped in a towel over the area can ease the pain. A pack of frozen vegetables like peas or corn can also do the trick and easily wraps around the joint. TENS (transcutaneous electrical nerve stimulation) is an electronic device that produces electrical signals used to stimulate nerves to provide pain relief. Some people find these helpful, while others claim little or no results.

Relaxation therapy can release tension hiding away in muscles; this can be done through listening to relaxation tapes, breathing exercises, visioning, aromatherapy and self-hypnosis. The Arthritis Foundation offers self-help courses on exercises, relaxation therapies, tai chi and loads of terrific information to help your Mom take charge of her osteoarthritis. Go to www.arthritis.org or give them a call at 1-800-568-4045 for free brochures. The website also directs you to a link on how to negotiate the Medicare maze to get therapeutic relief for arthritis.

Massage therapists can also offer relaxation therapies and other forms of therapy like Reiki (pronounced ray key), a channeling of energy done with the hands of a therapist. Acupuncture also provides pain relief by placing needles in certain sites of the body to stimulate deep sensory nerves that signal the brain to release its own painkiller – endorphins. Acupressure has the same mission, but uses pressure instead of needles.

Trust your instincts and get your Mom's doctor involved to include exercise in her treatment plan and then help her reach out to a world of therapeutic resources waiting to make her life worth living.

Q: My husband was just diagnosed with cancer in addition to a heart condition and diabetes. Should cancer treatments now be his major focus for medical care?

A: Your husband, like many others who are older, often face other diseases when they are diagnosed with cancer. Experts estimate that more than half of patients diagnosed with cancer are dealing with another chronic illnesses, such as hypertension, osteoporosis, lung disease, heart conditions and diabetes. In medical lingo, these secondary illnesses to cancer are tagged as "comorbid," meaning that they can form a type of partnership, each contributing towards poorer survival rates and death. Six out of ten cancer cases are among those sixty-five years of age or older who often contend with two and more chronic conditions. As a result, this "comorbidity factor" will continue to run high among the elderly.

At first glance, it makes common sense that treating your spouse's cancer should trump everything else. You're probably thinking what else really matters, if you can't stop the cancer? But, on the other hand, if his diabetes isn't kept under control or his heart condition isn't kept in check, the cancer treatment won't matter, either. So, be sure to advise him that even though he will now be adding an oncologist (physician specializing in cancer) to his list of doctors that he will be seeing, it doesn't mean that the others now take a back seat. You'll find this easier said than done because our health care system promotes specialization of body parts – cardiologist for heart, podiatrist for feet, urologist for kidneys, pulmonologist for lungs – I'm sure you get the point. Cancer care is a world unto itself and a pretty single-minded one, at that. Your husband is about to engage a medical juggling act and, all too often, it will be up to the patient and his or her family to keep the balls from dropping. Here are a few pointers to help your husband juggle his cancer care with his other medical conditions:

›   If your spouse has a primary doctor or internist, ask what role he or she will play in coordinating his cancer care with his other specialists. Ask the oncologist how he or she will coordinate his cancer care with either the primary doctor and/or the other physicians treating his heart and diabetes. Find out how and when they will coordinate with each other.

›   He should exchange information on his medical condition with each physician every time he sees them. Say, for instance, that lately his diabetes has been difficult to control; he should also tell his cancer and heart doctor.

- Have your husband always inform each doctor as to what prescriptions he is taking and that includes over the counter drugs. He should not assume that his cardiologist knows what cancer drug he has been given or that the drugs won't affect each other. For example, taking a drug like Advil (ibuprofen) for arthritis can affect the cancer drug Alimta to treat lung cancer, as it will block the removal of Alimta from the body which could become toxic. Antacids for heartburn can make some cancer drugs that treat bone cancer less effective. If the doctors don't know what you're taking, then they can't prevent poor side-effects.

- Your husband could ask his oncologist to share with him his "comorbidity score." Doctors use this measurement to assess the impact that other illnesses will have on survival outcomes. This may be helpful in providing your husband a framework to weigh the risks and benefits of treating his cancer, given his other health conditions and vice versa. There are two types of scoring mechanisms used: the classic Charlson Index that assigns weights to 19 categories of diseases, or a more recent measure known as the Adult Comorbidity Evaluation 27 (ACE-27) that rates 27 possible illnesses by a review of the patient's medical records. This scoring is one way of assuring that his oncologist is completely aware of all of his medical conditions.

If you would like to review a very helpful chart on common drug interactions with cancer drugs go to my website at <u>www.lindarhodescaregiving.com</u> and click onto the sidebar *"Free Caregiver Tips."*

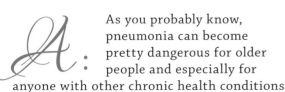 **: Can you give me a crash course on pneumonia?**

 : As you probably know, pneumonia can become pretty dangerous for older people and especially for anyone with other chronic health conditions like heart problems, diabetes or chronic lung disease. It is the second leading cause of hospitalizations among Medicare beneficiaries and the fifth leading cause of death among Americans ages 65 years and older. So, getting on top of it quickly is wise on your part.

Pneumonia infects or inflames the lungs in basically two ways: a lobe of the lung is infected or inflamed (lobes are like pie slices and there are five of them), known as *lobar pneumonia* or you may have patches affected throughout both lungs, known as *bronchial pneumonia*.

The first question you want to ask your doctor is whether or not your pneumonia is viral or bacterial? There are three major culprits linked to pneumonia: viruses, bacteria and mycoplasmas. The later is another form of bacteria known for its "stealth" quality because without cell walls it acts like a tiny jelly fish taking on different shapes. As a result, it becomes tough to identify and is able to travel throughout your body, damaging more than just your lungs. How does your physician know which type you have? Your doctor will listen to your lung sounds, and likely order a chest x-ray, sputum culture and blood tests. He or she will be checking your oxygen saturation rate which indicates the level of oxygen in your blood. If it is too low, it means your infected lungs aren't functioning as well as they should and, as a result, your organs won't be getting the oxygen levels they need to stay healthy. It's a domino effect you don't want.

About half of pneumonia cases are believed to be caused by a virus tending to be less severe an illness than if it were caused by bacteria. The symptoms are similar to the flu: fever, dry cough, headache, muscle pain, weakness and increased breathlessness.

Most viral infections will heal on their own; however, your doctor will most likely prescribe medications and care to relieve your symptoms to facilitate your recovery. He or she will also monitor you closely to prevent any other complications from taking hold, given your weakened state.

If your pneumonia is bacterial, then getting the right antibiotic in your system *quickly* is the name of the game. One major study of over 18,000 Medicare patients by the Centers for Medicare & Medicaid Services (CMS) found that three out of four patients who received antibiotics within four hours of coming to the hospital presenting symptoms of pneumonia experienced reduced risk of death and spent less time in the hospital recovering than those who did not receive antibiotics. But, antibiotics aren't fool-proof since bacteria (especially mycoplasmas) are constantly finding new ways to resist being terminated.

The most common type of bacterial pneumonia acquired outside of the hospital environment is *streptococcus* or *pneumococcal*, accounting for about one in three such pneumonias. These nasty bacteria can quickly run amok, attacking the bloodstream, brain or other parts of the body and can seriously damage otherwise healthy lungs. More severe symptoms may include shaking or chills, sweats, a cough that produces rust-colored or greenish mucus, bluish lips or nails (signs of deprived oxygen) and chest pain.

Why are elderly more susceptible? Specialized cells lining our airways have hair-like projections that sweep anything that doesn't belong in the lungs up and out. But, as we age, that cleansing system gets less effective, giving bacteria and other bad guys a free pass. Coughing also becomes less vigorous, so sputum gets to hang back and cause infection. And, then there's the standard trouble maker – a weakened immune system. Your best defense – and everyone over 65-years is to get the *pneumococcal vaccination* which will protect you from 23 types of pneumococcal bacteria. It is generally given once, but if you have heart problems and other risk factors, your doctor may recommend a revaccination within six years.

Once you know what type of pneumonia you have, here is what I'd be asking: Could you please explain the tests that were done to tell you what kind of pneumonia I have? What treatment and/or medications are you recommending? How will you know if they are or are **not** working? Are there any complications you're concerned about that are unique to me? Once you go home: What symptoms should I call you about? What are the signs that I should go to an emergency room? Is this contagious? How long should it take me to feel better? What can I do to recover? Is there something I could have done to prevent this or could do in the future?

For more information check out the American Lung Association's website at www.lungusa.org (Enter *pneumonia* in their search bar) or give them a call at 1-800-586-4872 to receive any of their free publications.

 : Could my Dad be showing signs of diabetes?

Three of the major symptoms of diabetes are extreme thirst or hunger, fatigue and itchy skin. Other common symptoms are weight loss, blurred vision, sores that don't heal and increased urination, especially at night. So if your Dad is showing any of these signs, get him to a doctor.

Most people think of diabetes as a childhood disease. But nearly one in 12 people over 65 comes down with what is known as adult-onset, or Type 2, diabetes. If your Dad is over 85, he is much more at risk of being affected by diabetes. One in four people in their mid-80s and older becomes diabetic.

If your Dad is also overweight and inactive, he's dramatically increasing his odds of becoming diabetic. Diabetes is the sixth-highest cause of death among the elderly and the leading cause of blindness for those who are middle-aged and over. And it doesn't end there. With diabetes, your Dad's body can't regulate the level of glucose in his system. Without a regulator in charge, too little glucose reaches the body's cells. This badly affects the cell's performance as they don't function or reproduce. At the same time, too much glucose hangs out in the bloodstream, running amok throughout the body, leaving in its wake hardened arteries, damage to the retina, skin disorders and a deteriorated nervous system.

Make sure your father has a blood sugar level test (prick on the finger) as part of his annual cholesterol exam. The American Diabetes Association warns that of the 16 million adults with diabetes, about 5 million aren't even aware of it, and only one in four people diagnosed with the disease is receiving proper treatment. Why? Many of the symptoms appear to be age-related, so older people think it is just part of the "aging package" and many people remain symptom-free until real damage has been done. Women actually get diabetes more often than men. African-Americans, people with high blood pressure, and those who have parents or siblings with diabetes are at greater risk of acquiring diabetes. So if your Dad is diagnosed with diabetes, you'll need to monitor your own health.

The doctor will probably recommend some lifestyle changes to your father such as losing weight, exercising and following a diabetic diet. Insulin therapy, which will stimulate insulin secretion to get fuel levels regulated, might also be in order. Medicare covers some diabetic supplies, so be sure to check with your doctor's office as to what is covered. Few patients take to this new routine like fish to water. Old habits, especially when they involve food, are hard to change. Become your Dad's trainer and help with food preparation, exercising, and medications. Your father's blood sugar will need to be monitored every day with a blood-testing meter. Also, watch out for his foot care since he is vulnerable to nerve damage and he might not notice injuries to his feet. Infections can easily set in, placing him at risk for amputation.

If you're worried he is not eating properly, hire someone (or take it upon yourself) to prepare meals for the week that are diabetic-friendly and freeze them in microwavable containers. Meals on Wheels programs also provide diabetic meals. Call your local senior center to find the program that's closest to your Dad.

An excellent website with links to plenty of other top-notch sites is by the National Institute of Diabetes & Digestive & Kidney Diseases at www.niddk.nih.gov. Be sure to check out their *Am I at Risk for Type 2 Diabetes?* online publication. The American Diabetes Association is another great resource. Call them at 1-800-342-2383 or visit them at www.diabetes.org. And if you're over 45 years old, the American Diabetes Association recommends that you add to your annual physical – or at least every three years – a blood glucose check, even if you don't have symptoms.

Q: How do I warn my diabetic mother about taking care of her feet?

 A: In response to a column I wrote on Type 2 Diabetes, a reader was inspired to send me the following letter. It is so compelling that I asked her if I could share it.

"Your column relating to diabetes was particularly noteworthy to me. My Mom is one of those older people who developed Type 2 Diabetes about 15 years ago. Her condition has been exacerbated due to her failure to fully appreciate the devastating health effects that this disease may precipitate. She continued to smoke, did not lose her excess weight, and did not fully curb her sugar intake.

Recently, the effects of the disease (along with her associated high blood pressure) have reared their ugly head, and she's been hospitalized for about 3 weeks now, having undergone an artery bypass surgery in her leg to restore better blood circulation to her foot and ankle. Unfortunately, however, due to a foot ulcer that could not heal, she has had one toe amputated. She continued to struggle with an infection in her foot, and just underwent a transmetatarsal amputation. She's become bedridden due to the need for her foot to heal properly, and must undergo extensive physical therapy to restore her mobility. I am sharing these details with you because, obviously, the subject of your column hit very close to home and I think two simple points should be further emphasized. First, people diagnosed with Type 2 Diabetes need to take the diagnosis seriously from the minute they receive it. Weight management, sugar control and exercise can go far to limit the devastating effects that this disease can cause. By reducing your weight, it's easier on all bodily systems to manage glucose intolerance. Exercising increases blood flow and mitigates small and large blood vessel disease (plaque build-up) as well as high blood pressure.

Second, proper foot care is essential. Never walk barefooted. Make sure any cuts or sores to your feet receive immediate medical attention. If you are not able to wash your feet properly, don't be proud – ask for help." – D.K.

As D.K. says, diabetes can cause <u>nerve damage</u> (peripheral neuropathy) that reduces sensation in the foot. Small injuries can occur and your parent won't even notice it, which may lead to an infection. Since diabetes often affects <u>blood flow</u> in legs and feet, cuts or sores are very difficult to heal. Life Clinic offers an excellent check list on foot care for anyone with diabetes which includes:

Daily Foot Care for Diabetics

- Look for cuts or sores

- Check for warning signs: redness, swelling, warmth, pain, slow healing, dry cracks, bleeding corns or calluses, black or blue skin, tenderness, loss of sensation

- Wash your feet daily and dry them carefully, especially between the toes

- Use talcum powder

- Put your feet up when sitting.

- Wiggle your toes and move your ankles up and down for five minutes, two or three times a day.

- Don't cross your legs for long periods of time.

- Do not cut corns or calluses - see a foot care specialist if needed

- Keep toenails trimmed and smooth

- Promptly treat dry skin or athlete's foot

- Keep blood glucose under control

- Wear shoes and socks at all times

- Keep a pair of slippers next to the bed

- Don't wear shoes or socks that are too tight

- Wear well-cushioned shoes

- Wear shoes that are roomy and "breathe"

Medicare covers annual foot exams by foot specialists (podiatrists) for anyone with diabetes. People diagnosed with neuropathy are covered twice a year. In fact, diabetics should make it a habit to take off their shoes and socks at every physician visit for a preventive foot exam. Medicare also covers therapeutic shoes if a physician certifies that your parent has diabetes and has one or more complicating conditions in one or both feet.

For an excellent booklet, *Prevent Diabetes Problems: Keep your Feet and Skin Healthy* (DM-205), call the National Diabetes Information Clearinghouse at 1-800-860-8747 and ask for a free copy or visit their website at <u>www.niddk.nih.gov</u>. Also call 1-800-DIABETES for a sample "Survival Kit" by the American Diabetes Association.

Q: Does Medicare cover foot care?

A: If you are a diabetic, yes. Medicare will cover a foot exam every six months if you have diabetic peripheral neuropathy and loss of protective sensations. Therapeutic shoes or inserts are also covered if you are diagnosed with severe diabetic foot disease. The shoes and inserts must be prescribed by a podiatrist (foot doctor) or other qualified physician and provided by a podiatrist, orthotist, prosthetist, or pedorthist. Medicare will assist you in paying for one pair of therapeutic shoes and inserts each calendar year. It is essential that the supplier from whom you buy the shoes or inserts is enrolled in Medicare and has a Medicare supplier number. If they don't have a supplier number certified by Medicare, then you'll be picking up the tab for the shoes. Routine foot exams are not covered by Medicare, but an exam by a podiatrist is certainly in your best interest whenever foot pain is in the picture.

As we age, our feet change. Those trusty soles tend to get wider, the fatty padding on the bottom erodes, the skin wears thin, giving way to dryness and cracks, and toe nails become discolored, rough and difficult to trim. It is often the result of poor circulation and years of wear and tear. If you want pain-free days with your feet, then give them special attention and here is how:

1. Wash your feet daily with mild soap and warm water. Never use hot water on aging skin.

2. Dry your feet completely especially in-between each toe. Don't use rough cloth.

3. Place lotion on your feet on the top, sides, bottom and the heel, but don't put moisturizer in-between the toes, as these should remain dry. Let the lotion become absorbed before you put your socks on.

4. Wear socks and stockings that are always clean and that absorb sweat. Cotton is a good choice.

5. Inspect your feet everyday; if you have difficulty seeing the soles of your feet, use a mirror or ask a family member or friend to check for you.

6. If you see redness, swelling, cracks, open sores that bleed, smell or exude pus or clear drainage, red streaks, pale or blue skin, changes in sensations such as tingling, numbness, burning or no feeling at all, areas that are either cold or warm to the touch, then see a doctor. These could be symptoms of infection, nerve damage and/or poor circulation. If you are diabetic, these symptoms are alarming and must be tended to at once.

7. Ingrown toe nails, corns, bunions, calluses and fungus should be treated and monitored by a physician or podiatrist.

8. Trim toenails straight across but do not cut them too short. If you have trouble cutting them, then get them done by a professional. Some primary care physician offices may do this, as will podiatrists, and pedicurists. This may also be offered at clinics, some of which are sponsored by the Veterans Administration. You can call the VA at 1-877-222-8387 to see if the service is offered in your area and if you qualify.

National surveys show that most Americans buy shoes without having their feet measured and, if you're older, chances are your foot size has changed. Wearing shoes that are too small leads to blisters, ingrown toenails, back pain and can make matters worse for pre-existing conditions. The American Podiatric Medical Association (APMA) offers these smart strategies to buying shoes:

Shop for shoes later in the day when normal swelling will be at its greatest and have your feet measured while you're standing. Buy shoes that don't pinch your toes, either at the tips, or across the toe box, as you want to give your toes wiggle room. Look for the upper part of the shoe to be soft and flexible with lining that's free of ridges and seams. The instep should cushion the arch and the heel should fit snugly so there is no slipping or pinching. Walk around the store with both shoes on and do not buy shoes that you think you need to break-in. They should feel good right from the start. Bring the same kind of socks or stockings you plan to wear with the shoes and any orthotics you wear for shoe fittings. High heels and pointy toes aren't fashionable for healthy feet.

For free brochures on foot health, contact the APMA at 1-800-FOOTCARE (1-800-366-8227) or visit www.apma.org online.

 My Mom was recently diagnosed with epilepsy. Isn't this a childhood disorder?

 Most of us are still under the misunderstanding that epilepsy only affects children and teens. Or, we think that when adults do have epilepsy, it is a condition stemming from their childhood. But, the truth of the matter is – the incidence of epilepsy in people 75 years and older is higher than in the first ten years of life. Today, about 7 percent of people 65 years and older are epileptic. The elderly are the fastest growing age group affected by the disorder numbering over 300,000 people nationwide. So, what's going on? As people are living longer, they face more chronic conditions like heart disease, high blood pressure, dementia and strokes, all of which can negatively affect brain function. In fact, strokes are the most frequent cause of seizures in later life. Epilepsy occurs when clusters of nerve cells or neurons in the brain send-off abnormal signals that can cause strange sensations, emotions and behavior. Think of it as an electrical storm taking place in your brain. It can even cause convulsions, muscle spasms, and loss of consciousness, which is what most people think of when they hear the word *epilepsy*. These types of seizures are commonly known as "grand mal" or "generalized tonic-clonic" seizures. Yet, among the elderly, the seizures themselves are more likely to be partial seizures rather than the more dramatic generalized type. A seizure's effect on an older person, however, can be more lasting and damaging. Your mother's doctor should explain to you what kind of seizure your mother had, leading him to reach this diagnosis. There are three kinds:

1. **Simple Partial Seizure** – this affects a part of the brain usually involving the frontal lobe, causing such symptoms as trembling, suddenly feeling that familiar things are unfamiliar, out of body experience, disturbed speech and sudden shifts in mood.

2. **Complex Partial Seizure** – this involves loss of memory in that the person won't recall what they did even though they remain awake during the seizure. Behaviors such as smacking lips, swallowing, picking at clothes, repeated phrases, clumsy movements, disrobing or being unaware of danger or pain are exhibited. Someone having this type of seizure appears like they are in a dreamlike state.

3. **Generalized Seizure** – affects both sides of the brain which can cause brief staring, abrupt muscle contractions, sudden falls, blackouts and convulsions that may involve biting the tongue or frothy saliva around the mouth. Breathing may be shallow or even stop for a few moments.

The best way to diagnose epilepsy is for a physician to learn from a witness to the seizure as to what happened and for how long. He or she will need to know what led up to the seizure, what kind of behaviors were exhibited, what type of body movements were made (e.g. jerking, convulsing, staring, trembling), how long the symptoms lasted, and what happened after the seizure. If you, a friend or a loved one is with your mother during an attack, it is so important to keep track of this information. Write it down immediately to give to her doctor and the paramedics should you need to call them. Once your doctor is given this information, she'll likely order a MRI or CT scan of the brain to hone in on the diagnosis. An EEG that measures brain waves may also be helpful in picking up patterns that signal epilepsy. Researchers have found that diagnosing epilepsy among the elderly is illusive and often delayed because the symptoms sometimes mimic a "mini stroke" or Alzheimer's. If your parent has episodes with any of the symptoms I described earlier, bring up the possibility of epilepsy with his or her physician. Again, write down what you see during such an episode.

Treating epilepsy is most frequently done by way of drug therapy referred to as AED medications (anti-epileptic drug). A common drug prescribed in the past has been *carbamazepine*, but now there are newer drugs available, such as *lamotrigine* and *gabapentin,* which some experts say are better tolerated among the elderly, especially if they are taking other drugs like *statins* that are used to lower cholesterol levels, like Lipitor. So, be sure to ask your Mom's physician what medication is best for her. If she is having problems with one, ask about alternatives.

For more information about epilepsy and support groups, visit the national Epilepsy Foundation's website at www. epilepsyfoundation.org. If you're a nurse or interested consumer and would like to take a free one-hour online course on "Seizure Disorders in the Elderly," by Montefiore Medical Center in New York City go to www. cme2epilepsy.com.

 : My wife broke her hip and her doctor prescribed a blood thinner. Please tell me why?

: Your wife's doctor is playing it safe and for good reason. On average, people who have had hip or knee surgery are given a 50/50 chance of developing a blood clot in veins deep in the body. You've probably heard warnings about developing DVT (deep vein throm-BO-sis) when you are on a plane or taking a long drive. That's because blood needs to be on the move. All of your organs rely on blood cells to deliver oxygen, fight infections and cleanse waste products. Muscle contractions make it possible for blood to travel throughout your body. Your heart contracts to send blood on it's merry way but, if you aren't walking, standing, flexing your ankle, or moving your hands and feet, blood has no way of returning back to the heart and ends up standing still. Blood that stagnates will thicken and eventually form a clot.

Now here's the thing: if that clot breaks off (known as an em-BO-lism) and starts making its way to your lung or heart, it can turn fatal by blocking blood to these vital organs. A blood clot in the lungs is called a pul-mo-nary embolism and it kills more Americans every year than breast cancer and AIDS combined, ending life for 300,000 people every year. Yet, with timely intervention and prevention, death can be averted following an acute episode with excellent survival rates. Your wife's doctor is preventing your wife from getting a blood clot, in the first place.

Any older person who has recently had surgery, has suffered a stroke, or is extremely overweight is at risk for DVT. Symptoms of a blood clot are any new swelling, soreness, pain or warm spot on your arm or leg. If your wife shows any of these signs, call her doctor immediately. To determine if there is a blood clot, her doctor may order tests that use ultrasound, x-ray or an oversized blood pressure cuff placed around the thigh. Not all DVT blood clots break off and travel towards the heart or lung and some never exhibit any symptoms.

Symptoms of a pulmonary embolism (PE) are much more severe and demand immediate medical attention. A blood clot may have gone to your wife's lungs if she suddenly has: difficulty breathing, chest pain, a fast heartbeat, fainting spells, a mild fever or a cough with or without blood. Anyone who experiences these symptoms – especially after surgery, stroke or being sedentary – should call 911.

Blood-thinning drugs (anticoagulants) are the most common way to both prevent and treat blood clots, as they lower the body's normal blood-clotting capacity. Heparin is frequently prescribed and given intravenously when the condition is urgent. Once a patient is stabilized, they are often prescribed blood-thinning pills in the form of Coumadin or under the generic name of warfarin. When taking these drugs, bleeding can become a troublesome side-effect, upon which your doctor will need to monitor and adjust the dosage. Besides pills, your wife may be prescribed compression stockings to wear.

Preventing DVT is really everyone's business – especially since 600,000 people a year develop a deep vein blood clot. Change your position often during long trips, get out and walk every hour or so during car rides and walk up and down the aisles when you're on a plane, don't cross your legs for any length of time, eat less salt, exercise, and if you are overweight or smoke – get it under control. If you'd like a free copy of *Your Guide to Preventing and Treating Blood Clots,* call the Agency for Healthcare Research and Quality clearinghouse at 1-800-358-9295 or download it at www.ahrq.gov/consumer/bloodclots.htm. You may also be interested in their *Guide to Coumadin/Warfarin Therapy* by calling the same number or download it at www.ahrq.gov/consumer/coumadin.htm.

Q: Why do my Mom and some of her friends get so depressed before and during the holidays?

A: Holidays can be bittersweet. Family gatherings can make it all the more noticeable that some members are absent due to divorce, death, unresolved family feuds and long distances. Despite being in a room filled with family and well wishers, your Mom can feel utterly alone. She may fear being seen as the Holiday Spirit Scrooge if she shares what she's feeling while everyone else appears to be so happy. So, while others are listening to *I'm dreaming of a White Christmas* soundtrack, your Mom is playing the blues.

The commercialization of the holidays is no help, either. We're bombarded with picture perfect images of extremely happy loved ones handing out lavish gifts amidst the dazzling display of holiday decorations, and a dinner feast laid out in Martha Stewart fashion. Expectations run high, and, in many respects, are downright unrealistic. Add to this stress-ridden pace: the quiet grieving for loved ones who have died, a fixed income, and lack of energy or physical abilities to keep up with the holidays and it is no wonder your Mom and her friends find depression stealing away the holidays. Dr. Roger Cadieux, Clinical Professor of Psychiatry, Pennsylvania State University, College of Medicine in Hershey, sheds further light on the holiday blues: "The holidays are potentially both joyous and stressful, especially for the elderly. It is a time of high expectations and anticipation. If the expectations are not realized, then the individual may feel very disappointed and even guilty. The elderly, whose physical and emotional stamina is not at a level of their children, grandchildren and other relatives, are all the more vulnerable to depression."

So, here are some tips for you and your friends to help your parents navigate the holidays:

> Encourage your Mom to acknowledge her feelings. If you also have mixed emotions about the holidays, let her know. You'll be giving her permission to not feel guilty about being downhearted. Not until you know what's making her feel sad, can you address it.

> Don't let "but we've ALWAYS done things this way" box you and your Mom into unrealistic expectations of each other and other family members. Circumstances change, and so should your responses to them. It may be time to create a new tradition or celebrate get-togethers that aren't fixated on one day that only leads to conflict over whose relatives receive top billing.

- Encourage your Mom to do something for someone else. Call your local church or synagogue and see if they are sending gifts to our troops overseas, send a gift to a resident at your local nursing home, take a resident out for the evening for a drive through neighborhoods with cheery lights, or send gifts to women and children at a local shelter. Even if this can't be done before Christmas, Chanukah or Kwanza – then do it for the New Year.

- Make gift shopping easier for your Mom by taking advantage of the wide array of gift cards that you can easily find at most grocery stores. She'll be giving something more personal than simply giving money and you're not running around trying to figure out who wants what – especially teenaged grandchildren. Also, be sure to help her keep her finances in check with her gift-giving.

- If she has always liked sending out cards, but just didn't get to it this year, offer to help her with sending out a New Year's card. Perhaps you could write and print-out a short note on news your Mom would like to share with those who sent her cards. She won't feel guilty about not getting her cards out and you can do this during the lull after the 25th.

- Get some sun. Most experts will tell you that there really is something to Seasonal Anxiety Disorder (SAD), where lack of sunlight leaves us all feeling a bit down during this time of year. So, if a sunny day appears, move a chair and sit near a window or go to the mall with an open glass ceiling to soak in some sun.

- Find a way to acknowledge and remember family members who have died. Sometimes, we think that if we bring up a loved one's name or talk about them, then we'll make those closest to them even more depressed. But, I have found that this approach often has the opposite effect, making the grieving person feel a tinge of anger as he or she quietly thinks, "How soon they forget." My youngest brother absolutely loved Christmas and cherished our family get-together every Christmas Eve. When he died at 44 years of age, leaving two young children, we were devastated. Now, we have a photo of Paul as a child with Santa centered in the living room where we exchange gifts and light a candle in his memory.

Our picture perfect Christmas has changed.

Q: After the holidays, I thought my mother would feel happier, but she's depressed. Is this normal?

A: Depression after the holidays, especially among older people, isn't all that uncommon. In fact, a good number of people report feeling "let down" after the holidays. There are plenty of reasons why a "White Christmas" can turn blue:

Unrealistic Expectations. The barrage of holiday ads on television portray happy families and couples sharing expensive gifts, giving people unrealistic expectations that they, too, are going to enjoy a magical time with the picture-perfect family. Instead, strained relationships, unresolved conflicts or frayed nerves among family members erupt before the first gift is even opened.

Credit Card Guilt. Whether you got caught up in the season or the music in the mall had you under some Santa spell, you might have spent more than what you could reasonably afford. The financial strain of paying off the debt long after the warm glow of watching loved ones open their presents can cause anyone to feel down. On the flip side, if you couldn't afford to buy gifts you wanted to give, you may also feel guilty. And it's not just spending on presents that add up: paying for food, decorations and travel all chip away at the family budget. This is especially tough for those on fixed incomes.

Physical and Emotional Exhaustion. Since Thanksgiving, most people have been on the go, making preparations for family get-togethers, travel, organizing schedules, food shopping, baking, preparing large meals, buying and wrapping gifts, fighting crowds and traffic at the malls. It's extremely exhausting and, if you're older and not in the best of health, all of these activities are all the more taxing. And, for those who can no longer keep up, they may feel disappointed in themselves that "they aren't who they used to be." Weight gain and lack of energy caused by overindulging in high-carb, high-sugar foods can also lead to feeling depressed.

Remind. Holidays are especially hard for those who have lost a loved one or have gone through a recent divorce. Not having them alongside while they watch others enjoy the companionship they used to share can call up the grief they felt when their loved one first died. Older relatives who used to host the annual family gathering, but are no longer in a position to do so, may feel relief from the responsibility, but also a sense of loss as they see their role change in the family and watch loved ones go their separate ways. Loss of good health, independence, and feeling vulnerable to harsh winter weather along with the lack of sunlight can bring on feelings of sadness. And for some, because of the loss of family and friends no longer living near them, they've spent the holidays alone.

So, it's not hard to see why your Mom might be feeling post-holiday blues. You could help her by encouraging her to go out with friends, get family members to call and reminisce as to what a good time they had with her (especially grandkids), send her a photo book of the family get together, make an extra effort to do something with her, like going to the movies or getting your nails done together, or ask if she'd like you to help her find an interesting volunteer activity or track down an old friend she's lost touch with. Staying physically active is one of the best defenses against depression. Joining a mall walking group is a great way to feel sun shining through skylights during cold winter days and meet some interesting people. Bottom line: look in on your Mom, keep her active and let her know she's your "Christmas" – all year long.

Q: How do you talk to a loved one who's depressed?

A: It's so hard to see people we love suffering and it's not uncommon for us to be at a loss for words when it comes to consoling them when they are experiencing mental pain. It seems easier to cheer someone on following a broken hip, a short illness or even a heart attack. These will mend and the older person can look forward to resuming their life pretty much as they knew it. But depression affects the very way we look at life: our mood, how we think, how we see things, how we act; it even changes our biochemistry.

Getting older requires coping with quite a few losses. Chances are your loved one has lost some of his or her independence from diminished sight, hearing, or the ability to physically get around. Driving becomes more difficult, so parents stop going anywhere at night, while many figure it's not worth fighting traffic to visit friends or go to events they used to enjoy. Death steals away old friends and beloved spouses. Many older people begin to feel like a burden to those around them, so they'd rather not ask for help. Soon they become isolated. What a ripe environment for depression to take hold!

Most of us at one time or another will feel the "blues." It's usually short-lived and in reaction to an event in our lives that has us feeling down. But depression can lead to what psychiatrists term a "mood disorder," an illness that often requires both therapy and medications to treat.

According to the Diagnostic and Statistical Manual of Mental Disorders (DSM), there are nine symptoms of major depression: **changes in mood** especially feeling consistently sad, **lack of pleasure**, **changes in eating patterns** (eats too little or too much), **changes in sleeping patterns** (can't sleep or sleeps much more), **changes in activity level** (reacts slowly as in a haze or is easily agitated and restless) **lack of energy**, **changes in perception of self** (feels worthless), **lack of focus** (can't make decisions), **lack of future** (life isn't worth living, hopeless). If your loved one has been exhibiting these behaviors, it's best for him or her to see a professional, as it is unlikely that he or she is going to just "snap out of it" on their own. Depression is an illness and should be treated as such; you'd be taking Mom or Dad to the doctor if either of them had the flu – so too, with depression.

And, what do you say to your loved one? I recommend *Talking to Depression: Simple Ways to Connect When Someone in Your Life is Depressed* by Claudia J. Strauss. This terrific book makes depression easier to understand and walks you through the day-to-day interaction of relating to a loved one who is depressed. Here are some of Strauss's do's and don'ts of approaching someone with depression:

- Don't say, "It's not that bad." Do say, "It sounds really bad. I'm sorry."

- Don't say, "Things could be worse." Do say, "I wish I knew how to help."

- Don't say, "There's light at the end of the tunnel." Do say, "We're going to get you through this. I'll help in any way I can."

- Don't say, "Buck up." Do say, "It's okay; this is going to take time – a lot of time."

- Don't say, "It's God's will." Do say, "You're right, this will never make sense."

- Don't say, "Put it behind you and move on." Do say, "I wish it didn't have to be this way."

If someone you love is depressed, reach out to him or her and quietly listen, learn about the disorder and get professional assistance.

Q: Do you have a script we can follow when we meet with my wife's doctor? She's just been diagnosed with cancer

A: Receiving a cancer diagnosis is always pretty frightening, but today there are a wide range of treatment options that can beat back this silent killer, giving many patients their lives back. On the other hand, cancer can be discovered when the only form of care is to extend a patient's life for as long as possible in as little pain as possible. Getting answers involves asking good questions. Sometimes physicians misinterpret a patient's or family's silence after a diagnosis as a sign that they understand everything and that they really don't have any questions to ask. Other times, families just don't know what to ask or they don't want to appear like they don't understand what the doctor has told them. That's why it makes great sense to bring in a list of questions with you and a family member as a "second set of ears." Most doctors appreciate patients who bring lists (okay, short ones) because they know that patients who do their "homework" are more likely to follow doctor's orders on how to get well.

Here is a script of questions I recently prepared for a dear friend of mine whose husband was just diagnosed with stomach cancer. Hopefully, it will help you, too, and the answers will bode well for your wife.

Reviewing Test Results
(Biopsy, PET Scan and CT Scans):

Ask your doctor to provide you with copies of the reports so you can review them while he or she explains them to you.

1. Could you please go over the test results and tell us what each means?

2. What type of cancer do I have? What is the stage of the cancer and has it spread? Please explain what the staging means.

3. Are you confident with these test results to form your diagnosis? Should any other tests be performed?

Reviewing Treatment Options:

1. Please tell me how you reached your decision as to what you're recommending (e.g. surgery, radiation, chemotherapy).

2. What are the pros and cons of what you are proposing?

3. What is the major goal of what you are recommending? Is it to remove the cancer, slow down the growth of the cancer or relieve me of my symptoms?

4. Would you please describe the treatment and/or surgery? How will it work?

5. If surgery is recommended, what will you do if you see that the cancer has spread to nearby organs or lymph nodes?

6. What can I expect to feel during my recovery? How will it affect my daily life?

7. If I don't do the surgery or other treatment options, what will happen?

8. From your experience in treating other patients similar to my case, what were their results?

9. How will you know that the treatment is succeeding?

10. What is my prognosis for survival if I follow this treatment? And, if I don't follow it?

11. How much time should I take to think about what I should do?

12. Will you be the one coordinating my care, and if so, how can I contact you?

Before you leave, be sure to ask the physician or nurse if they can give you some educational materials to help you better understand the kind of cancer you have and the treatment options being proposed. If you need more information, the American Cancer Society is an excellent resource at www. cancer.org or call them at 1-800-ACS-2345.

 My husband is finding all of the treatment options for prostate cancer confusing. Can you shed some light?

 Taking the time to learn about prostate cancer is definitely a smart move. It's also helpful to talk with friends who've been diagnosed with prostate cancer and ask them about their experiences with various treatments. But remember that each patient is different given their stage of cancer, age, health status and lifestyle preferences. Here is a quick run down on most of the treatment options:

First up is whether or not to treat the cancer. If your husband has a small, slow-growing, localized tumor and he's in his seventies, it may not become a life-ending cancer. So, he might be advised to carefully watch the cancer's development. This option is known as "active surveillance," upon which your husband will have blood work and exams performed every six months and an annual biopsy of the prostate.

Second on the list is surgery. A radical prostatectomy removes the entire prostate gland, including some surrounding tissue. It's a serious operation involving a hospital stay of two to three days. The most common complications are incontinence and erectile dysfunction. To deal with potential impotence, surgeons have been testing a new technique known as a "sural nerve graft." You should ask your surgeon about this option and make sure that your insurance will cover the procedure. Some companies still see this as experimental and will not cover it. Surgeons can also remove the prostate through a laparoscope which means they don't have to make a long incision in the lower abdomen and the recovery is shorter.

Third on the agenda is radiation. This is done on an outpatient basis, usually five days a week for up to about nine weeks. Radiation can be directed at the cancer either externally or internally. External radiation uses computers to map out the cancer in three dimensions, known as 3D-CRT, sending very precise beams at the tumor. Intensity-modulated radiation therapy (IMRT) goes a step further by delivering specific doses of radiation to different regions within the tumor itself. There are side-effects to radiation that may include: bowel problems such as rectal bleeding, bladder complications, such as an urgency to urinate, and fatigue. Subsequent damage to nerves and blood vessels can also cause impotence – and for some men – it will be permanent. Internal radiation is known as brachytherapy or "seed therapy." In this instance,

radioactive pellets are injected into the prostate attacking cancer cells for several weeks and the seeds will remain there permanently. Another procedure, known as "high-dose brachytherapy," places small catheters into the prostate and doctors fill them with radiation. It's a very short procedure, lasting anywhere between five and fifteen minutes. Side-effects are similar to radiation therapy.

And finally, your husband may be offered hormone therapy to supplement either radiation therapy or surgery. "Androgen Deprivation Therapy" blocks male hormones from fostering the growth of prostate cancer cells.

The Prostate Cancer Foundation suggests that your husband ask the following questions for any option his doctor recommends:

1. Given the staging of the cancer, my health and age, why is this treatment the right approach for me? If surgery is being recommended, then ask:

   a. Which surgical technique will be used and how often do you do it?

   b. Can you use a nerve-sparing technique so I won't have erectile dysfunction following surgery?

   c. What's your success rate in preserving potency and bladder control?

d. What will you do if you find cancer outside of my prostate during the surgery?

e. What can I expect following the surgery in terms of recovery time?

f. How long will it be before I can return to my normal activities?

g. What are the side effects of the surgery, both short-term and long-term?

h. What will we do to monitor my prostate cancer following the surgery?

2. If radiation therapy is being recommended, ask what type and what are the possible side-effects.

For a free copy of *Report to the Nation on Prostate Cancer: A Guide for Men and Their Families,* call 1-800-757-CURE or go to <u>www.pcf.org/guide</u>.

Q: What can my mother do about her incontinence?

 When June Lockhart of "Lassie" fame starred in an adult briefs commercial, incontinence officially came out of the closet. That's the good news. The bad news is that it gave everyone the impression that incontinence is a normal part of aging and the only thing you can do is to get yourself some adult briefs: Wrong on both counts.

Incontinence (now also termed "overactive bladder") affects at least 18 million Americans, but it is not normal. About 25 percent of men over 65 face some degree of incontinence, along with 40 percent of women in that age range. Before your Mom resigns herself to adult briefs, she needs to be seen by an internist or urologist to determine the cause of the disorder. Medications, an acute illness, a urinary tract infection or endocrine problems can all cause incontinence. It also could be the symptom of an underlying disease, and that's why she needs to see a physician.

A common sign and consequence of incontinence is isolation. All too often, people affected with the condition stop going on trips, to the movies, and on outings with their friends because they live in constant fear of having an accident. Chances are your

Mom won't be inclined to talk about her incontinence. So you might want to gently explore the topic by mentioning you read an article on overactive bladder and that you were surprised to learn that it's not a normal part of aging, that it can be the sign of something else, it may be reversible and it's something that some of her friends may be going through, too. There are three major types of incontinence:

Stress Incontinence. The muscles of the pelvic floor, which have been dutifully supporting the bladder for all these years becomes weakened – mostly due to the wear and tear of childbirth. The bladder slips down without the muscle support and now the abdominal muscles can squeeze the bladder to leak out urine, such as when she coughs.

Overflow Incontinence. Urine in the bladder builds up to a point where the muscle that controls the flow (urinary sphincter) can't hold it. Urine leaks out throughout the day. Men who have an enlarged prostate are especially vulnerable as the prostate blocks the normal flow of urine, causing it to hold up in the bladder until it overflows.

Urge Incontinence. In this case, there's hardly any time between feeling the need to void and actually urinating. This might be caused by an infection or medications, which would make it reversible. If your Mom has had a stroke, dementia or suffers from another neurological disorder, it can mean

that the brain is no longer capable of sending "hold off" signals to the bladder. Here are some basic tips to share with your mother:

› Schedule bathroom trips before the urge to urinate.

› Shut down drinking liquids three hours before going to bed.

› Eliminate drinks that irritate the bladder, such as coffee, tea, and sodas with caffeine. Alcoholic drinks also make this hit list.

› Stay clear of foods that are not bladder-friendly, such as sugar, chocolate, spicy foods and grapefruit.

› Inhaled cigarette smoke irritates the bladder. No smoking in the house.

› Take medications, especially diuretics, on a schedule that won't force you to get up in the middle of the night to urinate or wake up to soaked sheets. This also can save you from a nasty fall as you grope to find your way to the toilet.

› When out at an event, know where the rest rooms are before you need them. Try to find seating closest to the rest rooms.

› Try bladder training by scheduling bathroom trips and slowly extending the time between them to train the bladder to "hold it."

In extreme cases, surgery might be needed to remove a blockage, repair the urethra or reposition the bladder. Medications, pelvic devices, collagen injections and catheters are other possibilities, as well as wearing adult briefs.

Two great resources for more information are: Simon Foundation for Continence, 1-800- 237-4666 (<u>www.simonfoundation.org</u>). and the National Association for Continence, 1-800-252-3337 (<u>www.nafc.org</u>).

 Sometimes my husband's doctor doesn't listen to him or we leave with different opinions of what she said. How can we fix this?

 What you want to fix – creating more of a partnership with your doctor – is something that Dr. George Blackall at Hershey Medical Center and his colleagues, Drs. Simms and Green, think they have figured out in their book for physicians, *Breaking the Cycle: How to Turn Conflict into Collaboration When You and Your Patients Disagree*. You and your husband may not be in disagreement with his doctor now, but if you are leaving the visit confused or feel she hasn't heard everything you had to say about his health, then frustration and disagreement are a good bet to follow.

You and your husband aren't alone; studies show that the average time before a doctor interrupts his patient is 18 to 23 seconds. Fifty percent of the time, doctors and patients don't agree on the main health problem they discussed and doctors aren't obtaining adequate information on the patient's concerns or complaints. So, given this back-drop, what's the best way to develop a working relationship with your doctor? I had a chance to catch up with Dr. Blackall and here are some tips he offers:

1. Do your homework. Be sure to walk-in with a list of your symptoms and your concerns. Make it short and to the point. You'll send your physician the signal that you respect her busy schedule and it will make her less anxious over juggling her time. Besides, if you're going over a short list, she's less likely to interrupt you.

2. Recognize that your doctor is really trying to help. If you find yourself frustrated that you're not getting an answer as to what's wrong with you, rather than blame your doctor as being

incompetent, try saying, "Doctor, I know you're spending a lot of time trying to help me and I really appreciate it, yet there is one thing I need some help understanding...."

3. Demonstrate your knowledge as to what the physician has told you. After she has explained your condition or given you instructions, be sure to follow-up with, "Doctor, this is my understanding of what you just said (then repeat back what you've heard); is this correct?" You could also tell the doctor how you learn best such as, "I learn best from pictures, could you show me an illustration how this affects my kidney (or whatever body part you're discussing)?"

4. You're responsible, too. Your doctor is a partner and that means he or she is just one member of your health care team.

"The doctor as the expert will take you just so far," advises Dr. Blackall, "how you cope with a chronic illness and your ability to make lifestyle changes to get well is up to you."

Developing a collaborative relationship between physicians and their patients is a two-way street. Both need to listen to each other and respect each other's abilities. Blackall tells doctors that patients are experts, too. They are the ones, after all, who know best how to "define their own treatment goals and objectives in terms of their own values and preferences."
It sounds like you really respect you husband's physician. Hopefully, by following some of these simple steps, the three of you can create a doctor-patient relationship where everyone's a winner.

Is there a basic list of questions my husband can ask all his doctors?

First of all, I'm glad *you* asked. Far too often, older people feel they appear impolite if they ask their doctor questions or they worry that their question will sound foolish. So, they clam up. But, not asking could lead to medical errors caused by either the patient or the doctor.

Misunderstanding the directions on how to take a prescription or not comprehending the risks of a procedure often lead to a troubled outcome that a simple question could have avoided.

I saw an ad the other day sponsored by the Agency for Healthcare Research and Quality

(AHRQ) that features a waiter with a voice in the background saying, "You don't have trouble asking him about side dishes," and then pans out to a doctor holding a prescription bottle with the announcer asking, "So why can't you ask him about side-effects?" The goal of their new ad campaign is to illustrate how often we ask questions in everyday life but go mum in medical settings. Part of the agency's public awareness campaign is to offer consumers lists of questions to ask their doctors. You can check them out at their website at www.ahrq.gov/questionsaretheanswer and learn more on how to be an informed consumer advocate. Based on AHRQ's questions and my own experience, here are five questions your husband should ask his doctors:

1. Take a list of all his medications to every doctor who treats him and ask each doctor: Should I continue to take all of these? Are there any side-effects I should be concerned about? Do any of these medications interact negatively with another? If a new drug is prescribed, ask the same questions, but also ask how to spell the drug and what it is for.

2. If a blood test, x-ray, scan or any other diagnostic procedure is prescribed, ask: What are these tests for? When will you know the results? How will you let me know the results? If I haven't heard from you, who should I call at your office to find out the results? Don't assume that no news is good news or accept, "we'll get back to you, if there is a problem." You need to know either way.

3. If surgery is recommended, then ask: What is this surgery for? Can you explain what's done during the surgery and could you draw or show a picture of it? Is there an alternative that I should try first? What are the possible complications, given my age and health condition? How long will my recovery be and what can I expect during it? Can you give me two choices of surgeons to see?

4. If your spouse has been told he has a specific health condition, ask: Do you have any reading materials about this condition? Do you have any video or audio tapes I could review? Are there any written instructions I should follow?

5. At the end of every office visit, ask the doctor: Could you please tell me what are the two or three most important things I should remember or do as a result of today's exam? (Your husband should bring a notepad and write these down.)

None of these questions should feel off-putting. An informed patient is more likely to follow doctor's orders – and that makes physicians happy campers.

Q: Now that my wife has been diagnosed with cancer, what should be our next steps to help her get through this?

A: Besides giving her emotional comfort and support, one of the best ways you can help your wife is to give her a sense of control over the treatments she'll receive and the decisions she will need to make. Here's how:

Give her knowledge. The uncertainty of cancer and the vast array of information available today may truly overwhelm her. Yet, understanding her cancer and how various treatments can work for her are absolutely essential to her mental well-being. If she has always been a passive patient rarely asking her physician questions, then go with her to appointments and, beforehand, both of you should prepare a list of questions together. Ask her doctor for any materials that he or she shares with patients about the cancer. If your wife benefits from visual displays, ask her physician to show her illustrations or videos that describe her cancer in an easy to understand format.

Do the research. There is a great deal of information available on the internet which can be both a good thing and a bad thing. Always find out who is sponsoring the website by going to the *"About Us"* navigation bar to determine if it is sponsored by a group that has something to gain from what it recommends. For instance, a number of drug companies sponsor very good educational sites, but you need to keep in mind that they benefit from the drugs they recommend for treatment. Sites with a *.com* at the end of their name are commercial businesses, whereas those with *.edu* are academic and educational institutions. Those with *.org* are usually non-profit organizations and associations, while *.gov* are government-sponsored sites. Here are some tried and true websites to get you started:

AMERICAN CANCER SOCIETY
www.cancer.org

This website should be your first stop on your internet cancer tour. You'll find a wealth of information on cancer and a great deal of resources that you can download or link to for further assistance. They also offer a searchable database of local support services and a "Cancer Survivors Network" community.

CANCER.GOV (NATIONAL CANCER INSTITUTE)
www.cancer.gov

This site offers wide-ranging patient friendly information on cancer, including physician reviewed summaries on treatment, screening, prevention, and supportive care.

ASSOCIATION OF CANCER ONLINE RESOURCES (ACOR)
www.acor.org

This not-for-profit organization offers links to free, un-moderated discussion lists for patients, family, friends, researchers and physicians to discuss clinical and non-clinical issues of all forms of cancer.

MEDLINEPLUS
(NATIONAL LIBRARY OF MEDICINE)
www.medlineplus.gov

This consumer targeted website provides a gateway to online resources arranged by topic, covering specific cancers, drug information, medical reference, medical tests and procedures along with physician and hospital directories.

CANCER CARE
www.cancercare.org

This not-for-profit group provides support services for cancer patients and caregivers by offering useful and timely information on coping with cancer, its treatment, and effects. They also give practical advice on managing insurance and financial issues.

AMERICAN SOCIETY OF CLINICAL ONCOLOGY (ASCO)
www.plwc.org

This group offers an oncologist-approved education site for patients known as People Living with Cancer. You'll find a great deal of information, along with a medical illustrations section that graphically portrays common cancer sites by cancer stages. Look for it under the *Library* navigation bar.

Besides what's available online, read a few books and gather material from the doctor's office. Go to your local bookstore or your local library and spend some time scanning through the wealth of books on cancer, and choose one or two that speaks to your needs. You can also visit an online bookseller and conduct a search on cancer. It's a great way to find out what is available and read reviews of books. Most doctors' offices have educational videos that are really worth watching.

Cancer Support Groups. One of the best ways for your wife to feel normal and in control is to meet other people who have cancer and who are walking in her shoes. Even if she goes to the group sessions just to listen, she'll be encouraged by their stories on how they are coping. Check out the American Cancer Society website mentioned earlier for a support group near your wife or give them a call at 1-800-ACS-2345. Also, ask your local hospital, cancer center and oncologist for any support groups that they are aware of that would be helpful to you and your wife.

Q: What are the most common mistakes women make regarding insurance for breast cancer treatment?

A: Women who have breast cancer should not have to spend so much of their energy fighting for coverage or finding their way through the insurance maze. Here are a few tips that can prevent you from making the common mistakes many women unfortunately make.

1. Three insurance steps to take when you are diagnosed with breast cancer

First, if you're employed, ask your benefits manager whether the company or organization you work for is self-insured or buys its insurance from a third party. Depending on that answer, state and federal laws about breast cancer coverage apply differently. Second, before you begin any major treatment or make any significant purchase (e.g., prosthesis), always ask: "Is this covered under my policy?" Whoever prescribes your treatment should be able to answer this question. If not, check with your insurer before you proceed. This applies to Medicare beneficiaries as well as those with private insurance. Never assume that just because the doctor is prescribing it, your treatment is covered. Third, if you are forced to pay for treatment, supplies, medications or a device, ask how much this will cost and whether there are any programs that might help defray these costs.

2. Hospital Stays and Mastectomies

No health insurance plan can force a woman to receive a mastectomy on an outpatient basis. Women must receive inpatient care for a length of stay that her treating physician believes is medically necessary. Mastectomy patients may also receive home health care within 48 hours after leaving the hospital if her discharge occurs within 48 hours following admission to the hospital for a mastectomy.

3. Time Limits on Reconstructive Surgery for a Mastectomy

If an insurance carrier covers mastectomies (Medicare does cover it), then they must also cover reconstructive surgery related to a mastectomy. This also includes any surgery needed to establish symmetry with a patient's remaining breast. These provisions are covered under the federal Women's Health and Cancer Rights Act (WHCRA) of 1998.

Some states have passed legislation requiring insurance companies to place no time limit on how long after a mastectomy a woman chooses to have reconstructive surgery.

So, if you want more time to make up your mind, you can take it. Check with your state insurance commissioner's office to determine if your state mandates this provision Medicare covers prosthetic devices such as foam or silicone breast forms as a result of a mastectomy. Even mastectomy bras are covered. Always, make sure you have a prescription from your doctor before ordering.

4. Chemotherapy Options

There is a tool called *Oncotype DX* that can test your breast cancer tumor genes and predict whether you will benefit from chemotherapy. This is for women with Stage I or II breast cancer and is to be taken within six months of diagnosis. The cancer must be node-negative and the tumors are estrogen receptor-positive. Ask your oncologist whether or not this test would be appropriate for you, so you can make a more informed decision as to whether or not you should pursue chemo treatments. Researchers using the test at Loyola University Health System discovered that nearly one in four women who would have been recommended to undertake chemo could manage without it. The test is covered by Medicare.

 My mother has lymphedema following a mastectomy. What is it, how is it treated and does Medicare cover it?

 Let's first start with what it is: If your Mom's breast cancer surgery involved removal or radiation of her axillary lymph nodes located in her armpit, it is quite possible that her lymph nodes may not be draining as well as they did prior to her surgery. If this occurs, she may develop a condition known as lymphedema, which simply means the build-up of lymph fluid (edema) in the fatty tissues just under her skin. About one in five women develop this condition. Most of them report experiencing an overall sense of heaviness in their arm, swelling and/or tightness of the skin. For some, it can be quite uncomfortable and painful. Treatment for lymphedema can be offered on an outpatient basis by a certified therapist and the treatments include:

1. Light exercises of the affected arm to cause the lymph fluid to move out of the limb.

2. Wrapping the arm with bandages so that the lymph fluid flows out of the arm towards the trunk of the body.

3. Manual lymph drainage which is a type of massage used to gently move lymph fluid to healthy lymph nodes that can drain the fluid. This type of massage is not recommended if you have a skin infection, active cancer, blood clots, radiation on the affected area or suffer from congestive heart failure.

4. Pneumatic compression devices use a pump that connects to a sleeve worn over the arm. The pump inflates the sleeve, exerting pressure on the limb which, in turn, gently moves lymph fluid away to reduce the swelling.

5. Compression garments are long, tight-fitting sleeves usually made of material like support hose. These are worn over the arm and are designed to cause the lymph fluid to flow out of the affected limb. Even when the fluid is reduced, some women wear them to prevent the fluid from building up again.

When several of these treatments are combined, your mother's doctor may refer to this type of therapy as complete decongestant therapy (CDT).

Now, for what's covered by insurance and Medicare: Pennsylvania and federal law requires that those health insurance policies that provide coverage for mastectomies also provide coverage for physical complications resulting from the surgery and that includes lymphedema. Just make sure your physician writes a prescription for the treatment to assure coverage. Medicare also covers most treatments for lymphedema and it will cover lmphedema pumps/pneumatic compression devices when certified by your physician as medically necessary. Unfortunately, Medicare does not consider compression garments (a tight fitting sleeve on the arm) as a prosthetic device, so they won't cover it. This policy, however, is currently being debated at the Centers for Medicare and Medicaid, as two Administrative Law Judges disagree with Medicare's interpretation and recommend that they do cover compression garments (2010). If things change (and I hope they do), it will be posted at www.medicare.gov or ask your doctor.

 : We were told that my mother had a mini-stroke. Are there different kinds of strokes?

 : It sounds like your Mom had a TIA, which stands for a *transient ischemic attack*, a temporary deficiency in the brain's blood supply. These usually come on suddenly and last from two to thirty minutes. The symptoms are similar to a stroke, but they are temporary and reversible. So your Mom probably got dizzy, might not have been able to see, and experienced slurred speech for a few minutes before returning to normal. This is a warning sign. About one third of all strokes are preceded by a TIA and half of those will strike within a year.

I am sure her doctor has given her a list of things that she can do to prevent a stroke, such as keep her blood pressure down, maintain a healthy weight, exercise and eat a well-balanced diet. If she smokes, she should absolutely stop, and if she has diabetes or heart disease, she needs to manage these conditions so they don't contribute to a stroke.

There are two kinds of strokes – now often referred to as "brain attacks." With an *ischemic* stroke, an artery carrying blood to the brain is blocked, usually by fatty material. The lack of blood and oxygen damages the part of the brain that didn't receive them. In a *hemorrhagic* stroke, the blood and oxygen make it to the brain, but the vessel carrying them bursts and leaks blood into the brain, destroying brain cells in its wake. A stroke caused by hemorrhaging inside of the brain is considered more dangerous and is involved in about 17 percent of stroke cases. Both of these types of strokes may be referred to as a *cerebrovascular accident*.

Strokes are America's number three killer, right after heart attacks and cancer. You and your Mom should be aware of the symptoms. The American Heart Association lists the following stroke signals:

> Sudden weakness or numbness of the face, arm, and leg on one side of the body.

> Sudden confusion, trouble speaking or understanding.

> Dimness or loss of vision, particularly in one eye.

> Sudden trouble walking, dizziness, loss of balance or coordination.

> Sudden severe headache with no known cause.

These symptoms definitely warrant calling 911. You should also be aware that a study of 38,000 Medicare patients – all of whom had strokes – revealed that patients who were seen by a neurologist within 72 hours had a much better recovery and survival rate than those who did not. The researchers contended that these specialists of the nervous system were better prepared to diagnose and treat a stroke quickly.

The only FDA approved treatment for stroke is an intravenous clot-breaking drug known as TPA. Because the drug must be given within three critical short hours from the onset of stroke symptoms, there is no time to waste in making a correct diagnosis. (It is not a drug to be given to a patient suffering a hemorrhagic stroke since it may cause bleeding, which would make matters worse.) Tragically, only two to four percent of stroke patients ever receive TPA – experts believe it is because patients coming into emergency rooms are not being treated quickly enough by stroke experts.

The message for you? Call your local hospitals and ask for the Patient Advocate. Ask if their hospital has a written plan on how they treat acute stroke patients. Is there a neurologist available at all times? Do they have a special stroke program? You might want to consider using the hospital that has this expertise. If your Mom has a stroke, once you get to the emergency room, request that she be seen by a neurologist quickly. The National Institute of Neurological Disorders and Stroke has a top-notch website describing brain attacks and prevention strategies. Visit them at www.ninds.nih.gov. Also, go to the National Stroke Association website at www.stroke.org. You can also call them for information about family support groups and their services at 1-800-STROKES.

Q: What is glaucoma and does Medicare cover its treatment?

 Yes, Medicare covers screenings every twelve months for people at high risk of glaucoma. According to Medicare, nearly 3 million people have glaucoma, which is a leading cause of blindness in the United States. Although anyone can get glaucoma, some people are at higher risk. They include:

▸ African Americans over the age of 40

▸ Anyone over the age of 60

▸ People with a family history of glaucoma

▸ People with diabetes

Note that Medicare won't automatically cover everyone over sixty. An eye care professional, certified by Medicare to conduct the screening, has to state that the individual is at risk and should be tested. Be sure to ask the eye care provider if he or she is Medicare certified so that the test will be covered. Your parents will pay 20 percent of the Medicare-approved amount after they pay their yearly Part B deductible. If they have a Medi-gap insurance policy, then that policy will cover the 20 percent.

The most common form of glaucoma is open-angled glaucoma. At the front of the eye, there is a small space known as the anterior chamber in which clear fluid flows in and out of the chamber to bathe and nourish nearby tissues. In glaucoma, the fluid drains too slowly out of the eye, causing the fluid to build up. This, in turn, creates pressure inside the eye. Unless this pressure is controlled, it may cause damage to the optic nerve and other parts of the eye. The end result can be partial or total blindness. Glaucoma is downright sneaky. Chances are your parent won't complain of any symptoms. There's rarely any pain or loss of vision in early stages. But as the disease progresses, a person with glaucoma may notice a decrease in their peripheral vision – the ability to see things off to the side. If this isn't treated, the disease worsens, narrowing the field of vision and finally leading to blindness. Your parent might be given an "air puff" test or other tests used to measure eye pressure in an eye examination. But experts warn that this test alone cannot detect glaucoma. Glaucoma is found most often during an eye examination when the pupils are dilated, allowing an eye care professional to see more of the inside of the eye.

Open-angle glaucoma cannot be cured, but it usually can be controlled. The most common treatments are eye drops, pills, laser surgery or surgery to help fluid escape from the eye and thereby reduce the pressure. The goal is to stop the disease from getting worse. There are a number of organizations that can help you better understand glaucoma. Be sure to check out:

THE GLAUCOMA FOUNDATION (www.glaucomafoundation.org)

The website contains excellent information on the causes, detection, treatment and new developments in combating glaucoma. The Glaucoma Foundation can also be contacted by calling 1-800-GLAUCOMA (1-800-452-8266).

THE GLAUCOMA FOUNDATION (www.nei.nih.gov)

The NEI website contains eye health information about the most common eye disorders and their treatments. It also identifies available consumer eye care resources. There is no toll free number.

THE GLAUCOMA FOUNDATION (www.preventblindness.org)

The Prevent Blindness America website offers many programs and services to help fight blindness and save sight. You can find many consumer resources, basic eye tests and information on all eye services. You can reach them by calling 1-800-331-2020.

Q: My Mom says women rarely get heart attacks. Is she right?

A: I know mothers are hardly ever wrong (at least that is what mine has told me), but your Mom is dead wrong on this one: Heart disease is the number one killer of women in the United States today, affecting one in nine over the age of 45. But the statistic that should really get your Mom's attention is that heart disease affects one in three women by age 65. Women who are overweight, smoke or have diabetes are at even more risk. Heart disease tends to strike women ten years later than men – after menopause – when female heart vessels are more prone to develop plaque.

So, the bottom line is to get your mother a thorough physical, including a heart exam. Heart attacks in many women often go unrecognized until it is too late. This is due partly to the public's misconception that heart attacks are a "guy thing" and because women may experience less classic signs of a heart attack (such as chest pains).

The American Heart Association lists the following less obvious symptoms that women may experience as warning signs of a heart attack:

- Shortness of breath

- Pain in the abdomen, back, jaw or throat

- A general sensation of uneasiness, just feeling sick

- Unexplained anxiety

- Weakness or fatigue

- Palpitations, cold sweat or paleness

- Chest discomfort lasting more than a few minutes, or recurring chest discomfort, with lightheadedness, fainting, sweating, nausea or shortness of breath

These symptoms are definitely worth paying attention to as almost a half-million women annually die of heart disease and half of that number died from a fatal heart attack. Within six years, one-third of the women who had a heart attack will have a second attack – twice the number experienced by men. The death rate from heart disease in African-American women is 70 percent higher than that of men. Heart disease is the number one killer of African-American women over the age of 25. Heart disease can take a number of forms:

Atherosclerosis is a thickening and hardening of the inner walls of the arteries. The walls become narrower due to plaque buildup from deposits of fat, cholesterol, and other substances. This creates an environment for blood clots to form that block blood flow resulting in heart attacks and strokes.

Coronary artery disease affects the blood vessels (or coronary arteries) of the heart. It causes angina (chest pain) as a result of some part of the heart not receiving enough blood. This eventually leads to a heart attack. The most common trigger for angina is physical exertion.

High blood pressure (or hypertension) affects the force of blood being pumped from the heart against the walls of your blood vessels. More than half of all women over age 55 suffer from this potentially serious condition. It is more common and more severe in African-American women.

Heart failure essentially means that the heart is not able to pump blood through the body as well as it should. This condition usually evolves slowly over time and though the term "failure" implies that the heart literally stops, it does NOT. It simply means the heart is failing to do its job at its expected level.

Lifestyle changes such as losing weight, exercising, eating heart-healthy diets and quitting smoking are often in order. The Jewish Healthcare Foundation launched an excellent "Working Hearts" campaign focusing on women, called "Take Ten." Women are urged to take ten minutes every day to do something healthy for their hearts – such as a short walk, taking steps rather than an elevator, parking a little farther from the mall, or getting up to answer the phone instead of keeping it right beside you, and another ten minutes to relax and lower blood pressure, such as read, meditate, try Yoga, pray, pet a dog or cat, or watch the sunset. Taking ten minutes here and there every day is great medicine for both the body and soul. For more information on heart disease and other conditions affecting women visit www.womenshealth.gov or call their toll free number at 1-800-994-WOMAN (9662). And of course, check out the American Heart Association's website at www.americanheart.org.

Q: How do I stop my Dad from getting bed sores?

As you may know, your father's skin becomes more fragile with age. Lying in one position for long periods of time can irritate his sensitive skin, especially in weight-bearing, bony areas such as the heels, elbows, and tail bone where pressure decreases the blood flow. Sometimes you'll hear other terms, such as pressure sores, decubitus ulcers, ischemic ulcers or pressure ulcers. If your Dad isn't being routinely repositioned or "turned" while he is bedridden, his skin will begin to get red and tender from the constant pressure. If not treated immediately, an open wound will develop, which becomes a prime source for infections.

Here is a list of action steps recommended by a wide range of experts to prevent pressure sores:

1. Get your father to move his body regularly throughout the day – at least once every two hours. Assist him in moving his legs and arms.

2. Place pillows and foam pads under and around the "pressure points" of his body to reduce his full body weight upon them (e.g. elbows, tail bone, hips, buttocks, heels).

3. Be careful not to restrict blood flow with pillows and cushions. For example, if your father is lying on his back, place a pillow under his legs between mid-calf and ankle. Don't place the pillow under the knees or use doughnut shaped pillows.

4. Egg shell foam that you can place on top of the mattress is very helpful; so is a sheepskin pad underneath tender spots of the body.

5. Keep your father hydrated. Water is the best medicine to keep skin healthy. If he's using a bedpan, he might hesitate to drink 8 glasses of water a day, but the hassle of using a bedpan is far less than the health problems he'll induce by refusing fluids.

6. Change his clothes whenever they are wet. Be sure to change adult briefs and pads frequently.

7. Keep a disposable, absorbent pad underneath him to soak up any bowel or bladder "accidents" and then be sure to wash and dry his skin immediately.

8. When helping your Dad move in and out of bed, be careful not to pull or drag him so that the friction between his skin and the sheets causes an abrasion.

9. Be very careful using soaps, as they can break down the skin. Use emollient or superfatted soaps as opposed to alkaline bars.

10. Provide your father with very gentle massages (don't rub the reddened skin) using lotions with vitamin E and/or aloe.

If a pressure sore isn't healing, ask a home health nurse or your father's physician to take a look at it and see if more aggressive measures need to be taken. Don't wait for it to become worse.

: My Mom is ignoring signs of breast cancer. What can I do?

: Your mother, like a good number in her generation, may have views of cancer and cancer treatment that are locked in the 1950's when their parents may have been diagnosed with cancer. When I visit senior centers, I am often surprised at the number of older women who will tell me that they don't get mammograms because as they put it, "what you don't know, won't hurt you." I usually respond, "I guess you're right, you don't hurt when you're dead." Kind of harsh, but with Medicare covering the cost of the test, and the high incidence of breast cancer among older women, there's really no excuse to walk away from life.

Your Mom is from a generation when cancer wasn't discussed. Families felt ashamed if their parents had it so they didn't tell their friends. It was common back then not to even tell the person who had cancer! In addition, your Mom might have seen or known friends who became very ill from chemotherapy or radiation, but nowadays some people go for treatment in the morning and return to work the same day. So, how do you approach your Mom?

› Acknowledge her possible fear. Let her tell you what she's thinking, explore what she's afraid of and then try to address each fear separately. For example, did she have a friend die of cancer? What was the friend's treatment like? Does she think the cancer is throughout her whole body? Not until you know what she fears can you change her behavior to go see a doctor.

› Provide her with matter-of-fact information on cancer testing and treatment; show her how far treatment therapies have advanced.

› Share with her how an early diagnosis highly increases survival rates.

› Make cancer screening a family affair; perhaps both of you can go get a mammogram and your Dad should be screened for prostate and colon cancer.

› Enlist the support of her family physician and close friends to encourage her to be examined.

› Let her know how much she's needed. If there are grandchildren in the picture, encourage her to take care of herself for them. (Don't start with the "Grandma card." Deal with her fears first, but if all else fails then use it.)

Hopefully, this will get your Mom to her doctor. She should also know that chances are that the lump could merely be a cyst or benign. Why live under a dark cloud when you don't have to? Two great resources dedicated to cancer education and treatment are: the American Cancer Society at 1-800-ACS-2345 or www.cancer.org and the National Cancer Institute at 1-800-4-CANCER, www.cancer.gov.

Q: What are the signs of dementia and Alzheimer's disease?

 Dementia is an umbrella term (literally meaning *without mind*) for the progressive loss of thinking, judgment, and ability to focus and learn. More than half of dementia cases are caused by Alzheimer's, a disease named after the physician who discovered it back in 1906. No one is exactly sure what causes Alzheimer's, but genetic factors are definitely in the mix. The second leading cause of dementia is the death of brain cells due to mini-strokes that block blood supply. These small, successive strokes oftentimes go unnoticed as they chip away at the brain. People with high blood pressure and diabetes are at considerable risk for this type of dementia.

We all become distracted, forget names and misplace our keys. So, how do you know when forgetfulness slides into the world of dementia? The Alzheimer's Association has developed a list of warning signs of Alzheimer's. If your parent experiences any of these symptoms, it's time to get him to a doctor.

1. Memory loss affecting job skills. Frequently forgetting assignments, colleague's names, appears confused for no reason.

2. Difficulty performing familiar tasks. Easily distracted, forgets what they were doing or why. Might prepare a meal, forget to serve it or that they even made it.

3. Problems with language. Forgets simple words or substitutes inappropriate words, doesn't make sense.

4. Disorientation to time and place. May become lost on their own street, doesn't know where they are, how they got there or how to get back home.

5. Poor or decreased judgment. Usually exhibited through inappropriate clothing, poor grooming. Forgets to wear

a coat when it's cold, or wears a bathrobe to the store.

6. Problems with abstract thinking. Exhibits trouble with numbers, can no longer make simple calculations.

7. Misplaces things. Not only loses things, but places things in inappropriate places, like placing a purse in the freezer, a wristwatch in a sugar bowl. Has no idea how they got there.

8. Mood and behavior changes. Exhibits more rapid mood swings for no apparent reason.

9. Changes in personality. Dramatic change in personality, someone who was easy going now appears extremely uptight. Becoming suspicious and fearful is commonly reported.

10. Loss of initiative. Becomes extremely disinterested and uninvolved in things that they used to enjoy.

Your parent's primary physician ought to be able to rule out any reversible causes, such as a drug reaction. After that, he or she needs to be seen by a geriatrician or a neurologist (an MD who specializes in the nervous system). A full work-up takes about two to three hours. The physician should listen to you and other family members describe changes in your parent.

Use the Top Ten Warning Signs list and note the behaviors you've seen under each one of them. We're looking for changes here, so do **not** count typical, life-long habits of absentmindedness. (My kids, for instance, certainly won't be using losing keys as a sign for me!)

Since there is no definite, proof-positive test to diagnose Alzheimer's, doctors rely on a battery of tests to rule everything else out. Between five and ten percent of cases of apparent dementia are caused by a condition that can be reversed. This might be a good point to use to convince your Mom or Dad to be evaluated. They may be trying to hide their symptoms for fear of Alzheimer's and refuse to see a doctor. Letting them know that there are a number of possible causes might alleviate their fears and encourage them to find out what's really wrong. Either way it turns out, your parent and you will be better off knowing the truth.

Q: Are adult day services a good option for my husband, who has dementia?

A: He's the perfect candidate. Adult day services provide a safe and nurturing environment for older adults who suffer from cognitive (thinking) and/or physical disabilities that require them to receive assistance and not be left alone at home. Many families will tell you that taking their loved one to an adult day center turned out to be one of the best decisions they ever made. Here's why: A good center will provide activities that can help people with their memory through activities, music therapy, speech therapy, and discussion groups. Participants usually engage in some type of physical exercise during the day and many centers offer places where people can safely wander. The mental stimulation and physical activity often improves their sleep, which many a caregiver knows is a wonderful thing.

There are three types of adult day centers: social models that cater to higher functioning participants, health-focused models that offer nursing care and Alzheimer/Dementia care centers. The later two models are often combined.

Adult day centers usually operate from about 7:00 am to 6:00 pm to meet the needs of working caregivers and can be used up to five days a week, while some also offer weekend respite care. You can expect to pay the national average (2010) of $67 per day; less if it is purely a social model, or more if nursing care is also provided. Medicare does not cover adult day services; however, Medicaid (state funded long term care) may pay for these services if you qualify and if it prevents a nursing home placement. To see if you qualify, call 1-800-677-1116 to find your local Area Agency on Aging. Many long term care insurance policies cover the service. You can track down a local adult day center by calling your local senior center, or look in the Yellow pages under Adult Day Care, Aging Services, and Senior Citizen Services. When you call a center, here is what the National Adult Day Services Association suggests you ask:

1. Who owns or sponsors the agency?

2. How long has it been operating? (the longer, the better)

3. What is your licensure and survey status? (They are licensed by the state Department of Aging).

4. What are the days and hours of operation?

5. Is transportation to and from the center provided?

6. Which conditions are accepted (e.g., memory loss, limited mobility, incontinence)?

7. What are the staff's credentials, and what is the ratio of staff to participants?

8. What type of ongoing training do you offer to your staff?

9. What type of programming do you offer for dementia clients?

10. What safety features do you provide so that clients don't wander off the premises?

11. What activities are offered? Are there a variety of individual and group programs?

12. Are meals and snacks included? Are special diets accommodated?

13. How do you let the caregivers know how well their loved one is doing at the center?

14. Do you perform a health care assessment or require one before my loved one attends?

Spend a day at the center that most appeals to you to get a sense of the people and environment of the center. Visit a few to decide which is the best fit for you and your spouse. You may need to convince your husband that he's going to a "meeting" or some type of function that he relates to for the first time. Be creative, it's worth the effort.

 : My Dad has Alzheimer's disease and is very resistant to taking a bath. What do we do?

 : Many people who care for someone with Alzheimer's know exactly what you're going through. I know that when I took care of my children's great-grandmother, a bath was always an ordeal. Searching for answers, I read an excellent book on caring for someone with Alzheimer's titled *The 36-hour Day* by Nancy Mace and Peter Rabins. You'll find it an extremely helpful resource. Your Dad's behavior is, in the most part, due to the disease. He may find taking a bath too confusing or complicated. It may cause him great anxiety and make him feel very vulnerable. The thought of having someone remind him to take a bath or shower may feel like a direct attack on his independence. Whatever his perception, you are still faced with the reality of him not taking a bath. Here are some tips from Mace and Rabins, along with other experts, that I found helpful and hopefully you will too:

- Make sure you follow your Dad's past routines. Did he usually shower or bathe? How often? What time of day? Certain days of the week? He does not need a bath every day.

- Showers, for most Alzheimer's patients, seem to cause more anxiety than baths, but if getting in and out of a tub is also difficult, try getting a shower chair and use a hand held shower hose. I actually think this is the best option. This way you are able to control the flow of water and just do one body part at a time. You can even place a towel around your Dad's shoulder, or private parts so he feels less vulnerable.

- Avoid getting into a debate about taking a shower or bath. For example, don't announce, "After breakfast, you'll need to take your bath," or give an ultimatum.

- Tell your Dad – one step at a time – what to do in preparation for bathing and act as if it's just a normal part of his routine or that he's already agreed to it. For example, "Dad, your bath water is ready." If he responds with "I don't need a bath," just hand him a towel and calmly state, "Now, unbutton your shirt." Hopefully, he'll focus on the buttons. Continue with, "It's time to stand up. Undo your trousers, Dad," and so forth. Just stay focused on the steps in taking a bath.

- Some families have found that their loved one responds better to a home health aide. Perhaps your Dad might cooperate better with a male home health aide presenting the bath as part of an exercise routine.

- Focus on a possible skin rash or spot that might look like a sore and use that as an opportunity to slowly move into a sponge bath.

- Invest in strong grab rails and non-skid bathmats – you don't want him grabbing onto shower curtains that could come down with him. You can find all kinds of bathing devices at www.abledata.com or at durable medical goods supply stores. Liquid soap with a large sponge might be easier for you to handle than a bar of soap that can easily slip out of your hands. And remember, full baths or showers are not necessary every day for an older person. In fact, they could break down your parent's fragile skin. Simple towel baths or a "bath in a bag" will work just fine between full shower days.

Whatever you do, please don't interpret his behavior as an act of defiance against you and other family members. Otherwise, you'll be caught up in a no-win, angry spiral of emotions.

For an excellent video on how to approach a person with Alzheimer's to take a bath or shower, go to my website at www. lindarhodescaregiving.com and look under *Free Caregiver Tips*.

How can I help my mother accept the fact that my Dad is not the same man he used to be as a result of his dementia?

Letting go of the most significant relationship of a lifetime is ever so hard. But, what makes it even tougher is letting go when the person you are "losing" isn't really lost. Your Mom is caught up in a world filled with what Pauline Boss calls "ambiguous loss." She's lost your Dad in some ways, but in others he is very much present. Your Dad will have moments where he is very aware and acts perfectly "normal," luring your Mom into believing that he'll emerge from the fog.

But sadly, the man she's known and loved won't appear. The hard work for your mother is to begin redefining her reality and her relationship with your father. She'll need some time while you and close friends help her come to what experts call "a new normal." As Boss explains, in her book, *Ambiguous Loss*, (Harvard University Press, 2000), "We don't cut ourselves off from a loved one, even after death, but we have to learn the most exquisite of balancing acts: how to remember what was and honor it, and at the same time, commit to going on." Your mother's task is the same: cherish what was, accept what is and continue on with her life. The Family Caregiver Alliance and Pauline Boss offer a number of suggestions that may help your Mom move towards a new kind of "normal." Here's what they suggest:

1. Spend time with friends and family in the "real" world. Connect with people who are healthy and are in the present to give you a break from the roller coaster "ins and outs" of reality when living with someone with dementia.

2. Identify your problem. Understand that "ambiguous loss" is at the center of much of your stress, guilt and anger. What you're losing is often vague, changing and confusing. If you know that this is what's going on then you can better understand what you are reacting to and thus, coping with it.

3. Understand that you no longer live in a world of either/or choices. Making a choice that either you'll be your loved one's caregiver or not or that there will be perfect solutions – either this or either that – just isn't realistic. Your life is really about balancing two different ideas at the same time. It's about "both," instead of either/or. For example, you can be both sad that your loved one doesn't understand that the baby she's holding is her grandchild and yet, feel happy while you soak up the joys of being a grandparent.

4. Revise family holidays and traditions. This doesn't mean canceling family gatherings, nor does it mean isolating the individual with dementia and their caregiver. But, it does mean to find ways to simplify them, for example, creating a quieter space for the family member with dementia, so they won't be overwhelmed by children running around or loud chatter among adults. Family members can come and sit with him or her while the caregiver can visit and be part of the celebration.

5. Find something new to hope for. Caring for someone with dementia, in addition to the physical incapacities that come with the disease, is wearing both physically and mentally. Psychologists have found that hoping for something in the midst of adversity is a surefire antidepressant. Just the act of thinking about spending a little time on a hobby or developing a new one, meeting people in a support group and developing a new relationship with one of the members, looking forward to going out with friends or thinking about doing something you've placed on hold provides the hope to go on and the reassurance that life, despite all of it's hardships, is worth living and good.

Whatever you do, help your Mom take care of herself and let her know that your job is to look out for her while she looks out for Dad.

 My Mom has Alzheimer's and my Dad thinks that she really means the hurtful things she says. Is he right?

 No. Alzheimer's is a disease that causes regions of the brain to shrink and lose their function. As the disease progresses, different areas of the brain are affected. It often starts near the hippocampus, which plays a major role in forming our memories, along with storing and processing spatial information that helps us navigate. This is why during early stages of the disease, a person may end up at a neighbor's house and not know why or how they got there. The disease spreads its tangles and plaques in parts of the brain that help form and express personality, behavior and language. Before long, a loved one's impulse control is severely damaged. All of those learned behaviors of being polite, not swearing, lashing out or undressing in public are essentially erased.

That's the biological answer. On the personal side, your mother is slowly losing her sense of "self" rather than unveiling some unruly person kept under control all of these years. One of the hardest things for some family members to understand is that someone suffering from dementia is not deliberately acting difficult. But because people with dementia can sometimes appear to be perfectly normal, it may be hard for your father to distinguish between when she is being "herself" and when her behavior is caused by the dementia. As a result, your father may think that your Mom knows exactly what she is doing, which will only make him angry. People with dementia can become easily agitated and, in a matter of minutes, she and your Dad will be in the midst of a firestorm fueled by his anger.

Ask your mother's physician to speak with your father about the disease and its stages. It would be very helpful if her doctor showed actual brain scans so your Dad can see the physical changes that are caused by Alzheimer's. You can view PET scans and take a fascinating tour of the brain and how Alzheimer's disease affects it by going to the National Alzheimer's Association website at www.alz.org and clicking on "Brain Tour." A medical explanation will help, but it should be accompanied by a description of how the behavior of people with dementia changes and the best way to react.

Staying calm, reacting in a soothing and reassuring voice and learning how to distract an agitated loved one, are skills your Dad is going to need. If you cannot get a physician to tell him, then try another professional whom he would trust. Your local adult day center would be an excellent resource along with providing respite for your father. It might also be helpful to use analogies to explain the course of the disease that would resonate with your Dad (for example, explaining the workings of the brain in car terms if he's an auto buff).

I'd also suggest that you and your Dad join a local Alzheimer's support group, so he can learn from experts and other family members how to interpret and respond to your Mom's behaviors. To find a support group anywhere in the country, go to www.alz.org or give their 24-hour Helpline a call at 1-800-272-3900 for assistance. You can also ask for a free copy of their newly released, 100 page, *Caregiver Notebook*, chock full of tips and resources in caring for a loved one. Two excellent books that can help are, *The 36-Hour Day* by Nancy Mace and Peter Rabbins (Johns Hopkins University Press, 2006), and *Learning to Speak Alzheimer's* by Joanne Koenig Coste and Robert N. Butler (Houghton Mifflin, 2003).

Q: Does Medicare cover any treatment for Alzheimer's disease?

A: Yes, there is some coverage, fortunately. Nearly 4 million Americans have Alzheimer's disease and the number is expected to explode with the aging of the population. In the past, many claims for physical or mental therapy were automatically denied based on the premise that Alzheimer's patients could not benefit or improve. But, recent studies contradicted this assumption and proved that people with Alzheimer's can, indeed, make improvements resulting from psychotherapy, physical therapy and/or occupational therapy, among other treatments. In addition, doctors and psychologists are now able to diagnose Alzheimer's disease in earlier stages when timely interventions can slow the progression of the disease.

These services will keep people out of nursing homes. Why? Because if Medicare pays for physical and occupational therapy, medications, and mental health services, families will be able to care for them at home longer. For example, occupational therapists have found that training patients with certain behavioral cues enables them to remember how to put on a coat or dress, groom themselves or go to the bathroom. Beneficiaries, however, go through restrictive eligibility requirements to receive home health care. Long-term custodial care still isn't covered, nor is assisted living or nursing home care past the usual (but not guaranteed) first 100 days (see p. 70 for more on nursing home coverage). Your parent cannot be discriminated from receiving Medicare-reimbursed services because he or she has Alzheimer's. If your parent is diagnosed with this disease and has been turned down for various therapies or can't afford a prescription to treat the disease, go back to his or her physician. Make sure he or she gets a green light from the Medicare carrier that Medicare will, in fact, cover the treatment or service being prescribed.

For more information on what Medicare provides, go to www.medicare.gov or call the Medicare toll-free information line at 1-800-633-4277. If you want to dispute nonpayment, you'll find the name and phone number of the carrier on the back of the "Explanation of Benefits" statement that your parent receives after a provider has billed Medicare for payment. Your local Alzheimer's chapter is also a good source of information and they are listed in the blue pages of your phone book or go to www.alz. org to find a chapter near you.

: How do we cope with my Dad's constant need to wander?

: Wandering is a common behavior among people with dementia. In fact, it is so common that many nursing homes have created "wandering tracks" in their facilities, so that their roaming residents can safely wander in a secure area to fulfill their need to keep moving. There are two things you do not want to do: the first is locking your Dad in a room or restraining him to a chair or bed. The second is giving him over-the-counter sleeping aids, thinking that this will calm him down and induce him to sleep through the night. Some people have taken these actions because they think there is no other way to "protect" their parent from themselves. Sleeping aids, however, can have the opposite effect with a brain-injured person, so check with his doctor first. And, despite the dementia, he'll realize that he is being tied down and/or locked in a room, making him extremely agitated and fearful. It's a strategy that will prove to be psychologically and physically abusive. So, what can you do? Here are a few tips that should prove helpful:

In case he becomes lost:

› Get an ID bracelet with his name, your phone number, and "memory impaired" engraved on it. You can purchase these through MedicAlert. Visit their website at www.medicalalert.org.

› Give your Dad a card with your phone number on it, so he can call you if he is lost.

› Alert the local police and give them a photo of your Dad, and contact any local store that he would likely go to if he found a way out of your home.

› Install sensors that will trigger an alarm if he is leaving the house, or use childproof devices to prevent him from opening the outside door.

Addressing the need to wander:

› While you are with him, constantly reassure him where he is and that everything is fine.

› Find ways to get him to exercise; go for walks together or enlist a schedule of friends for walks. If the weather is bad, there's always the mall. He can even exercise while sitting in a chair, so put on some of his favorite music and exercise with him.

› Give your Dad simple tasks to do during the day. If he likes sorting through his tool box, or folding grocery bags or clothes, ask him to "help you out" by doing these tasks.

- Reduce his water intake several hours before bedtime, so he won't need to get up to urinate in the middle of the night, risking a fall or inducing wandering.

- Get him involved in adult day services to keep him active during the day. Many families report a great improvement in their loved ones once they've started attending an adult day services program; they are less agitated during the day and are more likely to sleep at night, reducing the need to wander.

- Observe what he does just before he begins to wander and see if you can identify a pattern. Look for the cause or behavior that triggers his wandering and try to avoid it.

To find an adult day living center near you go to the National Adult Day Services Association's website at www.nadsa.org or give them a call at 1-877-745-1440.

 Is there an "Amber Alert" for people with Alzheimer's? I'm afraid my mother may wander off.

Legislation was reintroduced in the U.S. Senate in 2009 to create a nationwide network for locating missing elderly who suffer from dementia and other cognitive disorders. It's known as the "Silver Alert Act" and it would be modeled after the Amber Alert program for missing children. The law would provide resources for federal coordination and offer assistance to local and state law enforcement agencies to create search and rescue programs that address the unique needs of people with dementia.

It couldn't pass too soon: Each year about 60 percent of the 4 million Americans with Alzheimer's will wander away from their home or from their caregiver and become lost. Given their fragile health, wandering can prove fatal. In fact, experts warn that if a person isn't located within 24 hours, the likelihood of them dying from exposure and/ or injuries can be as high as 50 percent. Most will be found within 1.5 miles from home. But, because of the paranoia associated with the disease, many will hide from search and rescue teams and not respond to their calls to assist them. But, let's not wait for legislation to keep your Mom safe. Here's what you can do right now:

1. Sign her up with the Alzheimer's Association Safe Return Program. By wearing a medic-alert bracelet that says "Memory Impaired," anyone who finds your Mom would call the toll free number shown on her bracelet and read off the ID number which feeds into a national database. They'll contact local law enforcement and fax her photograph. Someone from the local Alzheimer's Association will provide you with emotional support and assistance while police conduct the search and rescue. There is a $40 registration fee. Give them a call at 1-888-572-8566 or go to their website at www.alz.org/SafeReturn.

2. Let neighbors know about your mother's condition and inform them that, if they see her out alone and wandering, to please call you or the police immediately. Meet with the local police and give them a recent photo of her and any information that would help them approach her so she won't be frightened of them.

3. Place locks on doors high or very low where they are out of her sight. Consider placing a poster, painting or mural on the door so it doesn't give her the behavioral cue to exit. You could also place an alarm on all exit doors to alert you that she is leaving the house.

4. Write her name in her garments and take an article of clothing she's worn and place it in a plastic bag to aid in search and rescue operations using dogs.

And of course, never leave her unattended. For those of you who are members of organizations that are looking for a service project, you may want to consider urging local law enforcement to adopt the Project Lifesaver® program. This program uses radio technology and specially trained search and rescue teams to recover persons with Alzheimer's or autism who wear a wristband that emits a tracking signal. There are 33 programs in Pennsylvania and they show that recovery times average less than 30 minutes. To learn more call 1-877-580-LIFE (1-877-580-5433) or visit their website at www.projectlifesaver.org. It costs about $3,000 to get the program up and running and individuals pay about $30 per month to enroll for the service.

Q: How can we keep my Dad's bedroom from looking like a gloomy sick room?

A: When someone is chronically ill, it's very easy for the bedroom to become a victim of "sickroom" décor. Chances are there are pill bottles on the nightstand, lots of medical supplies lying around, the drapes are usually closed, and the chronically ill person stays in bed much more than he should because getting in and out of bed is too much of a hassle.

More than getting the place to look like the cover of *Better Homes and Gardens*, however, your father needs to get out of bed. It can be dangerous for his health if he spends too much time in bed because the systems of the body become lazy and start to shut down. Muscles waste away, kidneys malfunction, blood pressure goes up, insulin production stops, fluid starts collecting in the lungs (leading to pneumonia), and blood clots start forming, increasing the possibility of an attack on the heart and brain. So, even before we add a designer touch to the bedroom, whenever possible get your Dad out of bed and walking around. If he is bedroom-bound, here are some tips for making it a *living* room:

› If your Dad does not take medicines on his own, then place the medicine bottles out of view. Create a shelf in a closet or perhaps keep them in a drawer. The pill bottles are a constant reminder that he's sick. Of course, if he needs to reach the pills, then they must be next to him. Even so, use daily pill dispensers, so he doesn't confuse when to take what.

› If it's difficult for your Dad to get in and out of bed, then get a hospital bed. Medicare usually covers this cost, but check first. Most companies will let you know and will deliver it to your home.

› Get rid of all clutter and supplies that remind your Dad he's sick, such as adult briefs, bed pads, gauze and bandages. Put them in the closet.

› Set up a table next to the bed where he has easy access to fresh water, the telephone, the remote control for television, his glasses and anything else he needs to use frequently. But try not to clutter it.

› If there's enough room, set up a little visiting area with a table and chairs so people can visit with him and get him out of bed.

› Purchase an egg-crate or memory foam mattress. Make sure he repositions himself every two hours to prevent bedsores.

- Give your Dad the security of being able to contact household members by purchasing a room monitor (such as a baby monitor) so he can call without yelling or ringing a bell, which plays on everyone's nerves.

- Hopefully, your Dad's bedroom is next to a bathroom. If not, you can get portable commodes through a healthcare equipment company. Medicare usually covers this expense. You can even purchase a decorative screen, so that it's not in full view.

- Place a few plants throughout the room, and if he likes the sound, get him one of those small fountains or waterfalls. You could be more adventurous and get a goldfish or aquarium.

- Place a large clock and calendar in the room because it's very easy to become disoriented when you spend so much time in one room. If your Dad has dementia, it's helpful to have a magic

marker board where you can write down things like what he just had for lunch or dinner, or what time you're coming back.

And of course, there's nothing like fresh bedding, soothing curtains and pillows to give a room a warm feeling. Make sure the designs are quiet and subtle rather than loud and dramatic. Large, bold patterns may confuse or aggravate him if he has dementia. I've seen some families re-design the downstairs dining room to make it into a bedroom for their parent for two reasons: It's less isolated from the hub of family life, and there are no steps. Most families today aren't using the formal dining room and find it an easy space to convert.

There is a national Family Caregiver Support Program that helps qualifying families with a one-time grant for home modifications when they care for an elderly relative. Call your local Area Agency on Aging 1-800-677-1116 to see if you qualify.

: How can I help my Mom recuperate from her hip fracture?

: I'm sure that your Mom can't wait to get home. Be thankful: One in four older people who suffer a hip fracture remain institutionalized for an entire year. People who've had a hip fracture are more likely to have another, so she needs to be very careful. Your mother is

already counted among the almost 400,000 hip fractures every year. Let's not make her a repeat statistic. Research has shown that the most common hazards include tripping over rugs or something lying on the floor, absence of stair railings or grab bars, slippery surfaces, unstable furniture and poor lighting. One-half to two-thirds of all falls occur in or around the home and usually from a standing position.

So, given that "home sweet home" is where Mom will most likely fall, you need to go throughout the house and remove all throw rugs, de-clutter walkways, add non-slip mats in the bathtub and on shower floors, install handrails on both sides of stairways and increase the lighting throughout the home. There are also a number of devices you can purchase. Before you buy any, check with a local medical equipment company and ask if it is covered by Medicare. Here is a list of things to consider:

1. Purchase a bathing chair designed for showers. Make sure it has rubber, non-skid tips on the legs and is adjustable.

2. Install a hand-held showerhead to easily control the flow of water so your Mom can bathe in the chair.

3. Buy a "reacher" that can help her "grab" things that are either too high or too low for her to reach.

4. Make sure that her shoes are easy to put on and are sturdy.

5. She might need a walker to steady her. There are several types available, some of which offer a folding seat so that she can take a rest whenever needed.

6. Get her a long shoehorn so she won't have to lean forward and lose her balance when she puts on her shoes.

7. Install a sensor light on the bed stand, or buy a lamp that lights up simply when it's touched so her pathway will be lit if she gets up in the middle of the night.

8. Purchase a toilet seat with sidebars so that it will be easier for her to get up.

Besides making changes in her environment, make sure that she follows the exercise routine recommended by her physical therapist or prescribed by her physician. I'd also ask her physician if Medicare will cover having an occupational therapist make a home visit to help your mother identify risks in the home and advise her on assistive devices to help her with her daily living. If she's taking a diuretic (water pill) she should take it in the morning rather than before bedtime, which will cause her to get up in the middle of the night, increasing her risk of a fall. It's also a good idea to ask her doctor to review her medications to identify any that can cause dizziness, which could induce her to fall. The most important thing is to keep her spirits up and keep her exercising. For an excellent website with all kinds of aids for daily living go to www.abledata.com.

Q: My Mom really needs to see a therapist, but I know she won't go if she has to pay for it. Is it covered by Medicare?

A: If paying for it is the only roadblock you face in getting your mother to a mental health professional, then she's well on her way. All too often, the older generation is embarrassed about needing to see a psychologist or psychiatrist, so they suffer in silence. Yet, depression is often mistaken for "normal" sadness due to the losses of aging and mental illness can go undetected or misdiagnosed for several years.

Generally, if your mother sees a mental health professional who accepts Medicare assignment, then Medicare will cover about half of the costs of her mental health care. Chances are she has a Medi-gap supplemental policy, which will pick up the other half. Two important points – she needs to see someone who accepts Medicare assignment, and she needs a referral from a physician. Medicare assignment simply means that the provider seeing your mother has agreed to accept whatever Medicare "assigns" for reimbursement as payment in full. Now let's get down to the specifics:

If your mother needs inpatient care, then:

> Part A of Medicare will cover inpatient hospital, skilled nursing facility, and some home health care. Everyone pays a deductible during each benefit period before Medicare kicks in. For example, in 2010 your Mom's deductible is $1,100., after which Medicare covers 80 percent of the bill. Hopefully, she has a Medi-gap policy to pick up the other 20 percent and the deductible.

> What's a "benefit period"? A benefit period starts when your Mom enters the hospital and ends when she has been out of the facility for 60 consecutive days. Don't be confused in thinking that this is an annual deductible.

> Medicare has a lifetime limit of 190 days a patient can spend in an inpatient **psychiatric** hospital. After that, you're on your own! However, there is no lifetime limit on inpatient mental health services received in a general hospital.

If your mother needs outpatient services from a psychiatrist, clinical psychologist, clinical social worker, nurse specialist or physician assistant, then:

> Part B of Medicare will cover individual and group therapy, family counseling,

psychological tests, diagnostic services and evaluations, occupational therapy, laboratory tests, and drugs that can only be given by injection.

‣ These services can be provided in an office setting, clinic or hospital outpatient department.

‣ Part B may also cover partial-hospitalizations, however, this must be prescribed by a physician.

‣ Medicare will cover half of these costs while your Medi-gap policy will cover the other half. Usually, Medi-gap policies pick up your 20 percent co-payment, but when it comes to mental health services, they are required by law to pick up the remaining 50 percent of the bill.

To keep your mother's costs at a minimum, make sure that whoever provides care to her accepts Medicare Assignment. Medical professionals who accept assignments are called "participating providers" and you can get a list of them by calling 1-800-633-4227. If you'd like to learn more about mental health coverage and Medicare, go to www.medicare.gov or www.MedicareEd.org and enter the keywords "mental health services."

Your Mom is far from alone – nearly one in five people over 55 years of age experience a mental disorder not associated with aging. Regretfully, only one in two people who acknowledge their condition ever seek treatment. And fewer numbers still receive the specialized psychiatric help they need. Let's help your Mom beat the odds.

 : My Dad is going to need surgery and chemotherapy and I really want to care for him, but I work full time and don't want to lose my job. Any suggestions?

 The first thing you need to do is find out from your father's doctor what your Dad's recovery time will be from the surgery and what he can expect from his chemotherapy treatments. Ask his doctor to give you an idea as to what your father's caregiving needs will be in each instance. Will he need nursing care at home following the surgery, physical therapy, how many follow-up appointments and tests will he need? When it comes to his chemotherapy, are there side-effects that require someone to be with him, how often will he receive them and for what duration of time? Once you know this, you'll have a better sense of the amount of time involved in his recovery and treatment.

The next step will be to sit down with other family members and friends to determine who can do what. Who can take him to which appointments? Who can make sure he has meals everyday and receives his medications? Who can coordinate his care? Who is the point person in the family to talk to the doctors and nurses and report any symptoms that should be quickly addressed?

By this point, you'll have a good idea as to the amount of time you will need to care for your father and how this will affect your job. You might decide that it would make sense to take every Friday and Monday off for a three week period, or if you have no other family, then you may need to take off of work for four full weeks.

But, before you make those decisions, schedule a meeting with your employer's Human Resources Department (and your supervisor) and share with them what your situation is and ask if they could assist you in developing a schedule to meet both of your needs. Be honest with them and yourself on what you realistically can do for your Dad and your boss. Don't make your life so stressful that you can't fully commit to being a caregiver and an employee without damaging your own health. Remain open to accepting help and hiring it when you need to.

There is a law, known as the Family Medical Leave Act (FMLA), that will protect you from losing your job when you need time to care for a seriously ill family member (spouse, parent, child or self). Employers with 50 or more employees must allow their workers at least 12 weeks of unpaid leave to care for a family member. To qualify, you must have worked for the company at least 1,250 hours over the previous 12 months. Your company must give you full health benefits during your leave and you are entitled to get your old job back or another position with equivalent duties and the same salary and benefits when you return.

You can break up the 12 weeks worth of time as needed. For more information on the FMLA go to the U.S. Department of Labor website at www.dol.gov (enter *FMLA* in the search bar) or call them at 1-866-487-9243. If your employer is not covered by FMLA because it has too few employees and you feel you are being discriminated against and not given accommodations to perform your job, then contact your state's Human Relations Commission, as they may be able to assist you.

Q: What's the best way to research cancer, so we know what to ask and do?

A: Most physicians will welcome the opportunity to fully explain the diagnosis and the options that your parent should consider. I find that it helps, however, if you have a basic understanding of the disease beforehand, so that what you're being told will make more sense. It also means that you'll be better able to ask educated questions. How you share information with the doctor and ask questions can help set the tone for your relationship.

Share information with the physician in a spirit of respect. Explain that you and your parent want to better understand the disease and treatment. You're not there to second-guess him with your newfound "medical degree" – you want to establish a partnership.

Here are three basic steps to a crash course on cancer:

1. Tried & True Websites: It's important to know who is sponsoring the website. Go to the "About Us" navigation bar and determine if it is sponsored by a group that has something to gain from what it recommends. For instance, a number of drug companies sponsor very good educational sites, but you need to keep in mind that they benefit from the drugs they recommend for treatment. Sites with a

.com at the end of their name are commercial businesses, whereas those with .edu are academic and educational institutions. Those with .org are usually non-profit organizations and .gov are government-sponsored sites.

The Oncologist, a journal on cancer, hosts an excellent website at www.theoncologist.org and their editor, Karen Parles, M.L.S., has compiled the following list of cancer-related websites, along with a description of what each offers:

> **CANCER.GOV**
> (NATIONAL CANCER INSTITUTE)
> www.cancer.gov

Extensive patient-oriented information on cancer, including peer-reviewed summaries on treatment, screening, prevention, and supportive care. Features a searchable database of clinical trials, with in-depth information on finding and understanding clinical trials.

> **ASSOCIATION OF CANCER ONLINE RESOURCES** (ACOR)
> www.acor.org

Not-for-profit organization offering over 130 online support groups for specific cancers and cancer-related conditions.

> **MEDSCAPE**
> www.medscape.com

Commercial website aimed at health care professionals. Highlights include conference summaries of major oncology meetings and a weekly e-mail service providing updates of developments in cancer research.

> **STEVE DUNN'S CANCERGUIDE**
> www.cancerguide.org

Provides guidance and insight from a patient's perspective on how to find answers to questions about cancer, and most importantly, how to learn which questions to ask.

> **AMERICAN CANCER SOCIETY**
> www.cancer.org

Comprehensive information on cancer. Particular areas of interest include a searchable database of local support services and a "Cancer Survivors Network" community.

> **MEDLINEPLUS**
> (U.S. NATIONAL LIBRARY OF MEDICINE)
> www.medlineplus.gov

Consumer website provides a gateway to internet resources, arranged by topic. Covers specific cancers, drug information, medical reference, medical tests and procedures, and directories to doctors and hospitals.

> **CANCER CARE**
> www.cancercare.org

Not-for-profit organization providing support services for cancer patients and caregivers. Offers useful information on coping with cancer, its treatment, and effects. Provides practical advice on managing insurance and financial issues.

> **AMERICAN SOCIETY OF CLINICAL ONCOLOGY**
> (ASCO) www.asco.org
> (ASCO Online) www.cancer.net

ASCO Online maintains two excellent cancer websites, one for its membership and one aimed at patients.

2. Read a few books and gather material from the doctor's office. Go to your local bookstore or your local library and spend some time scanning through the wealth of books on cancer, and choose one or two that speak to your needs. You can also visit an online bookseller and conduct a search on cancer. It's a great way to find out what's available and read reviews of books. Most physician offices have educational videos that are really worth watching. Also, take the free booklets on the type of cancer your parent has.

3. Talk with the doctor. Your physician is your primary source of information, and he or she will be interpreting all of the test results and making an educated recommendation on the best treatment for your parent, given his or her unique set of circumstances. After you've had a chance to do your homework, then set up a consult visit where you can review all of your parent's options. It's always smart to prepare a list of questions ahead of time and to take notes during the visit.

 Q: My Dad needs to be screened for colon cancer. What kinds of tests are there and what does Medicare cover?

A: Colorectal cancer occurs in the colon and the rectum and is often referred to simply as "colon cancer." The colon is the large intestine and the rectum is the passageway that connects the colon to the anus. Your Dad shouldn't fool around by ignoring the opportunity to have a colonoscopy. Colorectal cancer is now the second leading cause of cancer death in the United States, but many experts believe that one in three of these deaths could be avoided if people were properly screened to catch the cancer in its early stages. The cancer usually starts from polyps in the colon or rectum. Polyps are little growths that are foreign; in other words, they shouldn't be there. Screening tests can find the polyps and remove them before they even become cancerous.

You can have colorectal cancer without experiencing any symptoms. That is why screenings are so important. By the time you do exhibit symptoms, the cancer may well be too far advanced to cure. Symptoms include blood in the stool, aches or cramps in the stomach that are frequent and unexplainable, a change in bowel movements such as stools that are narrower than usual, and loss of weight without dieting.

There are a number of tests to screen for colorectal cancer beyond the colonoscopy. The most basic and primary is the "Fecal Occult Stool Test," which you should have on a yearly basis. You receive a test kit from your doctor and smear small pieces of stool on a test card and send it to a lab. In a flexible sigmoidoscopy, the doctor places a short, thin, lighted tube into the rectum to check for polyps. This type of test is recommended every five years. A colonoscopy is the same as a sigmoidoscopy, except that it examines the entire colon. Physicians can find and remove most polyps and some cancers with this procedure. This test is recommended every ten years, unless you fall into the high-risk category.

Medicare does cover a colonoscopy every ten years if you are not at high risk for colorectal cancer. It sounds like this would be your Dad's first, so Medicare would cover 80 percent, while his Medi-gap policy would cover the remaining 20 percent. If he is at high risk for colorectal cancer (for example, another family member has been diagnosed with the disease), then his doctor can order the procedure every two years and Medicare will cover it. There are a number of "fine print" loop holes that you should be aware of; if you have flexible sigmoidoscopy, then Medicare will make you wait 4 years before a colonoscopy will be covered. And, if you have either of these tests done at an ambulatory center or hospital outpatient department, then your Medi-gap policy will have to pick up 25 percent of the cost rather than the usual 20 percent deductible. If you have any questions about your Dad's coverage for this procedure, call Medicare at 1-800-633-4227 or visit www.medicare.gov. And by the way, if you're over fifty years of age – male or female – you should sign up for your first colonoscopy!

 : My Dad's vision is getting worse. What eye diseases should he be concerned about?

 : As we age, the lens of the eye becomes more rigid, which leads to a form of farsightedness called presbyopia, in which the eye cannot focus easily on close objects. One of the first signs is holding your menu an arm's length away. By the time your parents are in their 60s and 70s, this condition becomes more pronounced, and they might notice other changes, such as finding glare from headlights blinding, difficulty seeing in dimly lit rooms and hallways, trouble refocusing from light to dark rooms, and finding it harder to distinguish between colors, contrasts and shadows.

These vision problems are common in older people and many can be managed with minor lifestyle changes and glasses. There are four major eye diseases that affect the elderly:

1. **Cataracts:** Most people with this condition will tell you that they feel like they are looking through a cloud. That's because the transparent lens of the eye becomes filmy. All light that enters the eye passes through the lens. So, if

any part of the lens blocks, distorts or diffuses the incoming light, then vision will be impaired. Cataracts can also block bright light from being diffused. The result? The trapped light touches off a fireworks display of halos around lights, scattering light and glare. If your Dad is diagnosed with cataracts, his physician will probably recommend implanting a plastic or silicon lens. The surgery is usually an outpatient procedure and you'll need to make sure that your Dad dutifully takes his eye drops at the prescribed times.

2. **Glaucoma:** This is a sneaky disease caused by pressure in the eyeball that increases to such a point that it damages the optic nerve. All too often, you won't hear any complaint from your parent until there has been damage. The pressure is caused by fluid inside the eyeball that fails to drain, leading to a loss of peripheral vision. Treatment can range from medications to laser therapy to surgery.

3. **Macular degeneration:** The macula is the central, most vital area of the retina. Its main job is to focus on the fine details in the center of your field of vision. If your father's macula degenerates, he might start complaining that straight lines appear wavy. He also might have blind spots that appear directly in front of what he is looking at. My mother has this condition and says it's like seeing around a small black hole. Macular degeneration is categorized as wet or dry. Dry means that a pigment is deposited in the macula with no scarring, blood or other fluid leakage. If it is wet, then there may be small hemorrhages surrounding the macula. Both eyes are usually affected, though each might be at different rates of progression. Little treatment to reverse the condition is available. If new blood vessels grow in or around the macula, laser surgery can sometimes destroy them from doing further harm. There are a number of products such as telescopic glasses and goggles that can greatly help people with macular degeneration.

4. **Diabetic retinopathy:** High blood sugar levels make the walls of small blood vessels in the retina thicker and weaker, so they are more prone to deformity and leaks. This leads to blurred vision and, if left untreated, blindness. The major lesson here is to keep those glucose levels controlled and blood pressure levels in normal range.

An annual visit to an ophthalmologist is your Dad's best defense against these diseases. Many physicians also recommend wearing sunglasses on sunny days to protect the eyes and taking a daily dose of Lutein dietary supplement.

My mother has cancer and we're concerned about pain management. What do we need to know?

Your Mom will undoubtedly be meeting with a team of doctors. She'll now have an oncologist, a cancer specialist, who will coordinate her care with other specialists who may treat her. If she is given chemotherapy or radiation therapy, she will be seeing a different physician for each. If she has other health problems, such as a heart condition, then she'll continue to see her cardiologist. Thus, it's very important to make sure that either her oncologist or her primary care physician (if she has one) acts as the "air traffic controller" of her care. She should ask them to decide who will be her central point of command. Who does she call when she's in trouble? Who receives all of the results of any tests, lab work and treatments and interprets them for her? Make sure this decision is nailed down.

Now, let's deal with her fear of pain. Her oncologist should schedule her to meet with a pain management team, which usually includes physicians, pharmacists and nurses; they may also be referred to as "palliative care." Their goal is to get your mother through her cancer as comfortably as possible. They are experts in pain management and know how to respond to the various kinds of pain she may experience, including the side effects of various treatments like chemotherapy. But, in order for them to be effective, your Mom has to be an active team member. These experts must rely on *her* assessment and description of *her* pain. Not until they understand the nature and degree of your mother's pain can they diagnose and prescribe the best treatment regimen for her. It will be very helpful to the pain management team and oncologist if she keeps a diary of her pain. Here are some of the things she should keep track of:

> ➤ The time of day the pain hit (does it change during the day or night?)

> ➤ Did she experience any symptoms prior to the pain (e.g. flushing, dizziness, nausea)?

> ➤ Was she doing anything prior to the pain (e.g. eating, getting out of a chair)?

> ➤ The location of the pain.

> ➤ Ranking of the pain on a scale of 1 to 10, with 10 being the worst. She should ask her doctor for a pain rating scale so they are on the same page.

> ➤ How quickly the pain came and how long it lasted.

> Did anything reduce the pain (e.g. ice, heat, massage, medication) and how much did it reduce her pain (using the rating scale)?

> How long did it give her relief?

> What did the pain feel like (e.g. stabbing, burning, electric, throbbing, dull, or aching)?

With this type of diary, the pain team is in a better position to pick up patterns and determine the causes of her pain. The diary is also a way for your Mom to take some control of her disease and her care rather than feel helpless.

Palliative care teams frequently tell their cancer patients to be sure to report their pain *early* and not wait until they can't bear it any longer. If you wait that long, it is more difficult to get ahead of the pain and reach a plateau of comfort.

One thing your Mom will be cautioned about is "breakthrough pain." This is pain that can break through the pain medication and/or treatment she is receiving. It usually comes on suddenly and lasts for a short period of time, however, it can happen repeatedly during the day. This type of pain can be triggered by an incident, like getting out of a chair; "spontaneous," coming out of nowhere and for no identifiable reason; or caused by an "end-of-dose failure" when a long-acting drug wears off before it's expected.

It will be important for your Mom to tell the doctor which type of breakthrough pain she thinks she is experiencing (incident, spontaneous or end-of dose failure). This will help her physician know what type of drug to prescribe. There is a wide range of short-acting opiates, and one is available as a lozenge that takes effect within 15 minutes.

If your Mom's pain is continuous and can't be controlled any other way, her doctor may prescribe a "PCA" or "patient controlled analgesia" pump. This pump continuously dispenses small doses of pain medication intravenously, 24/7. If your Mom feels breakthrough pain, she can simply push a button to give her an extra boost of the painkiller. If her pain is severe, the pain team might recommend that the pain medication be delivered directly into her spine (intra spinal) through a pump that can either be placed under her skin or within her body.

The bottom line is that your Mom's oncologist has a wide range of devices, medications and resources to keep her as comfortable as possible. If she is under hospice care, these medication expenses should be covered – so costs need not deter her. Help her help herself by making sure she knows how to report her pain and that she shouldn't be shy about doing so.

Q: How do those electronic pill dispensers work?

A: One of the most common reasons older people end up in emergency rooms – some estimates are as high as 100,000 people a year – is because of harmful reactions to medications. Drugs that don't work together, negative side-effects, or patients who don't follow prescription directions are the leading causes. The higher the number of medications you take, the greater your chances will be to experience what experts call an "adverse drug event." In response to this growing problem, the National Institute on Aging funded a study to see if electronic pillboxes help people keep up with their meds and avoid harmful mistakes. The electronic pillbox used in the study set off a beep when the person was to take their medication and a voice recording told them how many of the pills to take and gave instructions on how to take them (for example, "take with food"). Patients between 65 and 84 years of age participated and were taking at least four medications a day. Here is what they found: The number of days that people forgot to keep up their drug regimen dropped in half and patients were much better at taking the second or third dose of a medicine rather than just taking one for the whole day.

There is a wide range of electronic pill dispensing and reminder products on the market. The trick is to find something that works best for you. Two credible sources on assistive devices of daily living are Abledata (www.abledata.com or 1-800-227-0216), and CAST, the Center for Aging Services Technologies at (www.agingtech.org). Each organization describes available products and directs you to the company's website and contact information. Also, visit your local pharmacy to see what products they offer. Make sure that whatever electronic dispenser you buy, the seller allows a thirty day or at least two week return policy so you can test it out. Here is a quick re-cap of the kinds of electronic pill management products you'll find on the market:

Reminders: These devices come in the form of watches, wristbands or pendants that you wear or clocks and timers that are programmed to beep when you need to take a medication. Many offer voice recordings with pill-taking instructions.

"Talking" pill bottles: These products have a recording device on the bottle and you push a button to listen to a message (e.g. how many pills to take and how). Your pharmacist may have this type of recording unit or a family member can record the relevant information.

There are also "smart bottle caps" with recordings or digital screens that display pill-taking instructions, or bottle holders that do the same when you place the prescription bottle in it.

Electronic pill dispensers: Dispensers organize all of your pills ranging from a week to a month supply. An alarm beeps when to take a medication and automatically dispenses the pills. They often include voice-recorded instructions and some can be phone-activated so that caregivers far away and doctor's offices can monitor whether or not you've taken your medications.

Q: Do you have any safety tips for my parents, who take a lot of prescriptions?

 The more drugs your parents take, the higher their risk for some sort of mistake being made by a health care provider – a doctor, nurse, pharmacist or pharmacist technician – or by themselves. A study published in the *Journal of the American Medical Association* reports that almost one-third of all older Americans take more than five prescription drugs. Not only does this increase the likelihood of a mistake, it also raises the probability of a drug-drug interaction that can cause some pretty nasty side effects. At least 1.5 million people a year are harmed by medication errors, according to the Institute of Medicine. Here are some tips to help your parents get their prescriptions safely and mistake-free:

1. Look for pharmacies that use bar codes. This safety feature reduces human error so pharmacy technicians are less likely to take the wrong drug off the shelf or pharmacists from giving the wrong dose.

2. When you buy a drug, herb or dietary supplement over the counter, stop by and ask the pharmacist his or her opinion as to whether or not it will interact with any of your current prescription medications. It's smart to keep a list of these medications with you. Just because you can buy a drug without a prescription doesn't mean it is safe.

3. If you have been taking a generic, a pharmacist can substitute your refill with another generic that's different from the first. If you have been satisfied with the generic drug you have been taking, tell the pharmacist.

4. Two out of three patients walk out of their doctor's office with a prescription in hand. When you read the prescription,

ask for the spelling of the drug, what it is for and the dose. Double check this with the pharmacist and the label on the medicine bottle. Also, don't be afraid to ask your doctor if there is another solution to your health problem other than taking a pill. It reduces your risks of adverse drug reactions.

5. Talk to your pharmacist: Half of us, according to the Institute for Safe Medication Practices, are taking medications improperly. So, ask your pharmacist about any special directions you should follow. And, always check with the pharmacist before you crush medicines or cut them in half, as they may be a slow release drug that should be taken whole.

6. If you are the type of person who will do better taking a pill once a day versus three or four times a day, ask the pharmacist (or your physician) if the medication you've been prescribed can be given in a way that will be easier for you.

7. Most pharmacies will enter your health history, allergies and list of medications into a database. That way, they can cross check any new medications you are prescribed for possible adverse reactions or drug-drug interactions. It's your job to give them this information and keep it up to date.

8. If you're home and discover that the labels or directions are confusing to you, call the pharmacy and ask to speak to the pharmacist to explain it to you rather than guess at what you should do.

9. Don't wait until a prescription has run out before getting a refill, especially if it is a drug that requires you to stay on schedule. The same goes for calling your doctor's office at the last minute for a refill that has expired. Because of busy schedules and large volumes of prescriptions being filled, you might end up missing a dose.

10. If you notice on a refill that the pill is a different color or shape from what you had before, or if the dose has changed (e.g. 10 mg to 100 mg), ask the pharmacist to explain. It could be a mistake.

Patient safety is everyone's responsibility and that includes consumers. An excellent website on medication safety is www.consumermedsafety.org, sponsored by the Institute for Safe Medication Practices, a nonprofit organization dedicated solely to medication error prevention and safe medication use.

Q: My husband is 73 years old with a heart condition and insists he can shovel snow. Should he?

A: Shoveling snow is risky business, even for guys in their forties who are overweight and out of shape without a heart problem. Heart attacks triple among men 35 to 49 years during a typical winter. The National Registry of Myocardial Infarction reports that winter is the peak season for heart attacks with January topping the charts. Winter heart attacks are more deadly, as one in ten proves fatal. Shoveling snow is a leading culprit.

Your husband probably thinks that it's just a matter of being able to lift snow. And, that he can do. But there's a lot more going on: The combination of cold air and strenuous lifting boosts his blood pressure and with his heart beating faster, the shape of his blood vessels change and that increases the risk of plaque breaking off or rupturing, which can lead to a heart attack. And there's more: The blood vessels in his arms are smaller, so while he's lifting and throwing snow from his shovel, his heart is working two and half times harder than normal. The cold air just makes matters worse because it causes blood vessels to constrict to help conserve body heat, making an overtaxed heart work even harder. One study found that a ten degree drop in temperatures yields a 38 percent increase in risk of heart attack.

So, come on, husband, is shoveling snow really worth the risk? You're starting off with a compromised heart. It's just common sense to hand over the chore to an enterprising neighborhood kid. Now, for those of you who think you are healthy enough to tackle snow shoveling, here are ten tips to keep you danger-free from heart attacks:

1. Before you do anything, warm up your muscles for five to ten minutes by stretching and walking in place.

2. Shovel early and often during a snowfall before it piles up and becomes heavy to lift.

3. Use a shovel that's lightweight (plastic) and is curved like an S to prevent fatigue and back pain. Spray the blade with a silicone-based lubricant like WD-40 so the snow won't stick and easily slides off.

4. Take breaks; shovel for 5 to 7 minutes then rest for 3 minutes. I read where one older gent brings out a plastic lawn chair to sit it out between breaks.

5. Wait at least an hour after eating to start shoveling and ditch the caffeine and nicotine, as they cause your blood vessels to constrict.

6. Drink water, as you'll become dehydrated from the exercise.

7. Push the snow out of the way rather than lifting and throwing it.

8. Layer your clothing so you can take the top layer off if you become overheated.

9. If you need to lift the snow, hold the shovel close to your body, and use your legs to lift, keeping your back straight and feet apart.

10. Listen to your body! If you feel any pressure, discomfort or pain in your chest and/or shoulders, neck, jaw, arms or back, or if you feel dizzy, nauseous, faint or experience shortness of breath, stop immediately and call 911. Grab an aspirin and lie down while you wait for an ambulance.

I recently found an excellent product that I bought for my father (and myself) to use when the ice is too thick to melt with salt. These are called "Ice/Snow Carpets" that have rubber backing that grip the ice.

They are reusable and come in a set of two runners of 10 feet in length each. You can find them at www.skymall.com or call them at 1-800-SKY-MALL.

 Is it true that walkers can cause people to fall? My wife uses one and she seems to have trouble handling it.

 Walkers, canes and other assistive devices are a tremendous help in staving off falls and for good reason: Every year about a million and a half older people are injured from a falling accident. But now, even walking aids can play a part in causing a fall. The National Center for Injury Prevention has found that about 47,300 people aged 65 and over suffer injuries from falls every year using walking aids that land them in Emergency Departments. Walkers are seven times more likely to be involved in a fall than a cane.

Women in their late seventies and eighties are at the highest risk of tripping while using a walker, resulting in fractures, bruises, sprains and abrasions. More women than men use the device and people who rely on walkers suffer from overall weakness, poor balance control and less ability to bear weight. The majority of accidents occur in the home while one out of five takes place in nursing homes. At least one-third of those using the device at the time of the fall were walking.

Researchers claim patients should be better trained on how to use a walker and have it fitted to their body frame. They also call on manufacturers to consider making improvements on the design of walkers. Okay, so now what do we tell your wife? First, call the place where she bought the walker and ask if she can come in and have someone show her how to use it and properly adjust it, or ask her primary care physician to prescribe a physical therapy or occupational therapy evaluation to do the same.

The Mayo Clinic offers six safety tips on using a walker. Here they are:

1. **Types of walkers:** If stability is a significant concern, a walker without wheels is a good choice. But if you need help walking, a two-wheel walker allows you to place weight on the walker as you move. If you don't need to lean on the walker for balance, you'll walk faster with a four-wheel walker.

2. **Selecting a grip:** Most walkers come with plastic grips, but you can add foam or soft grip covers. If you have trouble grasping with your fingers from arthritis or other joint pains, a larger grip may relieve stress on joints.

3. **Fitting your walker:** Adjust it so that it fits your arms comfortably to reduce stress on your shoulders and back. First, place your hands on the grips. Your elbows should bend at a comfortable angle. Second, relax your arms at your sides. The top of your walker should line up with the crease on the inside of your wrist.

4. **Taking your first step:** If you need to place weight on the walker as you move, start by pushing the walker forward and keep your back upright.

5. **Don't lean over the walker:** Stay upright as you move. Always step into the walker, rather than walking behind it. Be careful not to push the walker too far in front of you or set the handles too high.

6. **Walker accessories:** Many people trip with their walker while they are carrying something. You can add trays to carry food and other items, a pouch or basket. Some walkers also have seats, so you can take a rest.

If you'd like to see the Mayo Clinic slide show on how to use a walker, go to my website (www.lindarhodescaregiving.com) and click onto *Caregiver Tip for the Week.*

Q: My husband has recently fallen three times and laughs it off, but I'm worried that something is wrong. What should I do?

A: Plenty of comedians have been falling or tripping for years to get a quick laugh from their audience. But, it sure isn't a laughing matter when you're older: Every year nearly 20,000 people die from a fall, over a half-million will be hospitalized, and well over 1.3 million will land in the emergency room. Every day over one thousand people break their hip, hurling them down a path toward medical complications, loss of independence and even death. And if you've fallen and stumbled before, you're three times more likely to do it again. So, you have every right to be worried about your husband. Most of us think that the best way to reduce someone's chance of falling is to simply remove obstacles around the house. It's a start, but there's so much more to consider.

Here is what you want to look for:

Medications. Review whatever medications he is taking and see if dizziness is listed as a side-effect. Ask him when he takes them and if he notices feeling drowsy or dizzy within the hour. Maybe he could take this medicine at bedtime or ask his doctor if there is an alternative drug. If he's taking a diuretic (water pill) and needs to urinate frequently, it would be good not to take that medication at bedtime, as it will cause him to get up during the night and increase his risk of falling. Stay clear of alcohol, as it often contributes to dizziness when taken with medications. If he has blood pressure problems, monitor it closely, as high or low pressure can cause him to lose his balance and fall.

Vision and Hearing. If your husband suffers from age-related eye diseases, such as macular degeneration, glaucoma or cataracts, he won't be able to negotiate steps or see obstacles in his path. It may also affect his sense of balance. He should be seeing an ophthalmologist to treat these conditions and visit the local Blind Center, where he can get all kinds of lifestyle tips and assistive devices for people living with low vision. When was the last time he saw his optometrist to make sure his prescription is up to date? Changes in hearing can also trigger loss of balance, so he should have his ears and hearing examined.

Walking, Muscles and Bones. Be sure to take a look at what kind of shoes he wears. Are they the right size? Are they rubber-soled and low-heeled? Is he wearing long pants that are easy to trip over? Does he wear

slippers around the house that give him no
support, flip-flop or glide across the floor?
If he has a strength or balance problem,
then he should try using a cane or walker to
steady his gait. He must keep his bones and
muscles in good shape. Older people who
exercise, lift weights and stretch survive falls
(and are less likely to fall in the first place)
than their couch potato counterparts.
It would also be helpful, if you went over
with him how he fell each of these three
times and the events that led up to each.
Did he take a pill beforehand? What was he
wearing? What did he feel before the fall?
What time of day? See if you can find any
pattern to share with his doctor.
For information on how to create a fall-free
home, see p. 314

PART II

Navigating Life

Section One
Staying Well

Q: Can you explain to my Dad how he can prevent a heart attack?

A: It's not surprising that your father may need an explanation. All too often, older people feel that heart attacks are due to an aging heart that stops "ticking." Just 15 years ago, even the medical community thought that the hearts of older people just gave out from the wear and tear of normal aging. But, along came this 25-year study by the National Institute of Health. It was quite a shock when they discovered that the hearts of the older guys were pumping blood practically the same as their younger counterparts. Yet, eighty percent of the 1,300 people who have heart attacks every day in this country are over 65. Why? Unhealthy lifestyles and age-related conditions pose undue pressure and stress for our hearts to function properly. Who's at greatest risk?

➤ Parents who are smokers

➤ Overweight people

➤ People with high blood pressure

➤ People with high cholesterol

➤ Diabetics

➤ Stressed-out people
(You better not be the cause!)

➤ Couch potatoes

➤ Anyone with heart disease in the family tree

Nearly everything on this list is something your Dad can do something about to stave off a heart attack. Here are two major culprits he can take on:

High blood pressure
Of all the risk factors for heart attack, high blood pressure is the "big one." Imagine your garden hose hooked up to a fire truck. The pressure shooting through the hose would wear it thin in no time. Now imagine a small pump at the end of that hose trying to redirect the high-pressured water through other small hoses. Any bets on how long the pump can handle the pressure?

In a less dramatic way, this is what high blood pressure does to your parent's heart. It's the continuous, high-pressured rush of blood flowing through blood vessel walls (hose-like arteries and veins) that wear them down to a point where they can tear or leak. Your Dad needs to monitor his blood pressure, which is a measure of the force of blood coursing through his arteries. Blood pressure is expressed in two numbers. Mine usually comes in at 110/80 (unless I've just read my teen-age son's report card). The first number is the systolic blood pressure, the force of blood as the heart is pumping. The second, diastolic number represents the pressure that remains in the arteries when the heart is relaxed.

High numbers aren't good; hitting 160 on the systolic is a sure sign to get to the doctor. You should check with your Dad's doctor as to what's considered high for his age and weight.

Decreasing salt intake can reduce high blood pressure, so be sure to check out the sodium content of packaged and processed food – you'll be shocked at the high numbers. Weight control, managing stress and medications also can bring blood pressure down. The most commonly prescribed medication is a diuretic, which pulls salt and water from the circulatory system and sends them off to the urinary system. Any medication has to be closely monitored by a physician so that other conditions aren't adversely affected. No matter what, a salty diet has to go and blood pressure checks should become routine. African-Americans should be on high alert for high blood pressure as they are more likely than anyone else to have the condition.

Cholesterol

Back to our garden hose analogy: Imagine fatty, sticky stuff stuck to the inside of your hose; the result would be a dribbling stream of water. Cholesterol is the fatty sticky stuff stuck to your Dad's blood vessels. When this stuff reaches a level that actually clogs the vessels, it's given a name: atherosclerosis. Cholesterol readings can tell your Dad how much of this stuff is in his system. He is at more risk if he smokes, has high blood pressure, is diabetic or is obese. If that's the case, he should have an annual blood test to check his cholesterol.

To reduce his risk, a low-cholesterol diet is the way to go. Get him to cut down on fats one step at a time. Cholesterol is found only in animal products: meat, poultry, seafood, organ meats, eggs and dairy products such as butter and cheese. One egg yolk will just about consume one day's healthy limit of cholesterol. Check out the American Heart Association's website at www.americanheart.org for all kinds of cholesterol information, diets and treatment, or call them at 1-800-242-8721 to request copies of their publications.

 What are some simple ways that I can tell my husband about heart-health?

 The American Heart Association (AHA) has come up with seven simple steps to show your heart how much you love its every beat. The steps are straightforward and anyone can do them. If you follow them, you'll enjoy good health and can steer clear of hospitals and expensive drugs.

"Life's Simple Seven" is featured at a special website set up by the AHA titled, "My Life Check" (www.mylifecheck.heart.org). On the site you can take a quiz to see how you're doing on the seven key indicators of good heart health. You'll get a score with information on how you can improve your numbers (and your life) and an explanation as to how each affects your heart and health.

The seven keys to taking care of your heart are:

1. **Get Active:** Moderate exercise of 30 minutes a day or vigorous exercise of 75 minutes a week lowers blood pressure, controls blood sugar, reduces stress and keeps you slimmer. So go climb stairs, take walks, swim, lift weights, and don't fight for the closest parking space.

2. **Control Cholesterol:** Most of us know that there's good cholesterol that helps our cells do their work and there's bad cholesterol that can clog your arteries which, in turn, can cause a heart attack or stroke. Most of your cholesterol comes from your body (75%) while the rest comes from food. The AHA recommends a total blood cholesterol level of 200 mg/dL.

3. **Eat Better:** You may be eating plenty of food, but the contents may be delivering too few vitamins, minerals and fiber that your body needs. Eat oily fish twice a week, select fat-free or lowfat dairy products, go for whole-grain foods with fiber, keep your salt intake down to 1500 milligrams of sodium each day, and consume at least 4 cups of fruit and vegetables per day.

4. **Manage Blood Pressure:** high blood pressure causes the blood running through your arteries to flow with too much force stretching them past their limit and causing tears in the artery walls. When your body repairs the tear, it causes scars which leads to blocked, hardened and weakened arteries. Control your blood pressure with screenings, diet, exercise, no smoking and, if necessary, medications. Maintain a blood pressure of 120 over 80.

5. **Lose Weight:** Too much body fat increases your blood pressure, and raises your risk of diabetes and high blood cholesterol. Keep a healthy Body Mass Index (BMI) of less than 25. This is measured by assessing your body weight relative to your height.

6. **Reduce Blood Sugar:** Most of the food we eat is turned into sugar (glucose), giving our bodies energy and providing the basic fuel for all the cells in your body. Your pancreas produces insulin to help the glucose get into your bodies' cells. If you develop diabetes, your body is either not producing enough insulin or your cells are ignoring it. People with diabetes are almost four times more likely to suffer from heart disease. AHA recommends a fasting blood glucose level less than 100.

7. **Stop Smoking:** This one we've heard a zillion times, yet it remains the number one cause of premature death in the U.S. Smoking leads to the buildup of fatty substances in the arteries, increasing the

chance of blood clots. It also raises the odds for an aortic aneurysm and peripheral artery disease (PAD). Good news: it's never too late to stop.

So there you have it, seven ways to send both you and your hubbie a Valentine to your heart.

Q: My parents have been getting MRIs, CT scans and sonograms and I'd like to know what's the difference?

A: Long gone are the days of just a simple x-ray in a doctor's back pocket of diagnostic tools. In fact, I'm glad you only asked me about just three! Each of them is used to help diagnose different conditions, providing physicians a wide range of images within the body. Here is a quick scan of your parent's tests:

MRI

What it is: MRI stands for "magnetic resonance imaging" and magnetic is the operative word. Powerful magnet and radio waves produce two and three dimensional images illustrated by computer photography. These images are extremely good at picking up differences between normal versus diseased tissue. It is more sensitive than CT scans when it comes to distinguishing soft tissues, and that's why doctor's like to order them for examination of the brain, spine, inside of bones and soft tissues of joints. Because an MRI uses a magnet, it is not used for people with any type of metal implant, like a pacemaker or aneurysm clips, as they could become dislodged or rendered useless.

What to expect: In a closed MRI you'll be placed in what looks like a long tunnel that encases your body. From personal experience, my best tip is to keep your eyes closed throughout the test, especially when you enter the "tube." That way you never realize how close it wraps around you. Often, you'll be given headsets to listen to music while the scanner does its thing, which also drowns out the rather loud clanging sound while images are being taken. Open MRIs have a larger opening so people don't feel so closed in and some have mirrors so when you look up you can see the opening. The open type is often used for exams of shoulders, ankles, wrists and knees. It's painless and takes about a half-hour or more, depending what is being explored.

CT SCAN

What it is: Also known as a "CAT scan," this type of scan combines the use of X-rays and computer technology known as "computerized axial tomography." The scanning machine takes rapid images of your body, illustrating them in cross-sectional views generated by computer-controlled X-rays that rotate around the body. These images show up as slices taken from a wide range of angles that give the radiologist the ability to detect tumors and other abnormalities, along with their characteristics. The CT scan offers detailed pictures of bones, organs, tissues and blood vessels.

What to expect: Depending on the kind of CT images your physician wants, you may need to receive a contrast that will travel through your bloodstream, given by way of an intravenous injection and/or you may need to drink a chalky-like substance that helps "light up" abnormalities and provide a clearer definition. The machine is very open and you'll lie upon a table that will slide in and out of the scanner. These scans are usually pretty fast and pain-free.

SONOGRAM

What it is: Also known as ultrasound, a sonogram uses high frequency sound waves and their echoes to capture images inside the body by using a wand (transducer). The device sends and receives sound waves that are sent to a monitor depicting images of whatever is being examined. Because there is no radiation, it's a valuable diagnosis tool for women who are pregnant and their fetus. Physicians also use it to diagnose

blood circulation and heart problems using a "Doppler" ultrasound. And it is used to detect cancerous and benign tumors, masses in the colon, rectum and prostate gland and breast lesions for possible biopsies.

What you can expect: A technician will place a gel over the surface of the body area to be examined, which enhances the contact between the wand and your skin, so it can send the sound waves to a computer. Images are displayed on a monitor once the computer calculates the sound waves and echoes being transmitted from the transducer. The images can be two or three dimensional. And, like the other scans, it is painless.

But if you think ultrasound is extremely high tech – bats, whales and dolphins have been using this technique for, let's say … a million years.

Q: My Mom's doctor wants her to have another kind of cardiac stress test because the treadmill test wasn't good enough. What's going on?

A: Sounds like your Mom's doctor is being vigilant about her heart. Far too many women remain undiagnosed for heart disease and they miss the signs of an oncoming heart attack. Women often have different symptoms than men when they're having a Myocardial Infarction (MI). In a study of 515 women who had heart attacks, researchers found that 43 percent did not experience acute chest pains – a classic symptom among men. If they did feel chest pain, it came in the form of aching, tightness, pressure, sharpness, fullness, burning or tingling. The most common symptoms of heart attacks among women are: shortness of breath, weakness, unusual fatigue, cold sweats, dizziness, pain or pressure in the back or upper chest, pain or discomfort in one or both arms, a burning sensation in the chest or upper abdomen, irregular heart beat or nausea.

According to the National Heart, Lung, and Blood Institute, women account for half of all heart attack deaths and it remains America's number one killer. So, taking heart attack symptoms seriously is a lesson for all of us. Overall, cardiac stress tests evaluate how the heart responds to the stress of physical activity for the purpose of determining if there is any abnormality. Here's a run down on various forms of the test:

Exercise Electrocardiogram (ECG) Stress Test: By asking patients to walk on a treadmill or ride a stationary bike at various levels of exertion, the heart is monitored by way of an electrocardiogram while your heart rate and blood pressure are also being measured. A cardiologist examines the ECG readings to assess changes in heart rhythm and potential decreased blood flow that can signal a blockage along with other possible heart conditions.

Exercise Echocardiogram: This test (often referred to as an "echo") uses ultrasound that produces images of the heart at rest and during peak exercise by use of the treadmill. By accurately visualizing the motion of the heart's walls and pumping activity under exertion, doctors are better able to see those areas of your heart that may not be getting an adequate blood supply. This also allows them to see if the heart is beating irregularly.

Nuclear Stress Test: In this instance, a small amount of radioactive substance (thalium or cardiolyte) is injected into a vein. A special camera is used to see how the thalium is being absorbed. Parts of the heart that have good blood flow will collect the radioactive material and the camera will pick this up. On the contrary, if the heart muscle shows up as a "cold spot" without any of the radioactive material, it means there is a decreased blood supply often caused by a blockage. Pictures are taken during a resting state and following exercise so the cardiologist can compare the difference.

Physiologic Stress Test: Some people are not physically able to get on a treadmill or stationary bike to perform the exertion necessary to stress the heart. So they are given drugs (dobutamine and adenosine) which will cause the heart to respond just as if they were exercising. While these drugs are being administered, either an echocardiogram or nuclear imaging will be performed to measure how the heart is responding.

Chances are your mother started off with the standard ECG "treadmill test" and her physician may have learned something that warrants further study for a second type of cardiac stress test. Your Mom should ask her doctor why this second test has been ordered and what it is he or she is looking for. If your Mom agrees, it would be good to accompany her when her physician reviews the test results. Everyone benefits from a second set of "eyes and ears" when you're getting pretty significant news about your health.

 My wife is thinking of having one of those CT body scans that you can pay for yourself, but I heard CT scans use a lot of radiation. Is this a good idea?

 The Food and Drug Administration, along with the American College of Radiology, the American Heart Association, the American Medical Association and other professional societies, do not recommend "full-body CT scans" for screenings. They don't believe that the benefit outweighs the risk when it comes to using CT scans for testing healthy people who have no symptoms that anything is wrong. So what are the benefits and the risks?

CT (computed tomography), also known as CAT scans (computerized axial tomography), use x-rays to capture images of cross-sections of the body. It's a remarkable medical tool that can pick up diseases like cancer, damage caused by trauma or other abnormalities so doctors get a detailed picture of what's going on to help them better decide what treatment to offer.

It's been invaluable in emergency departments where quick and accurate diagnoses are vital. According to Dr. Fred Mettler, Chief of Radiology and Nuclear Medicine at New Mexico's Veteran's Health Care System, before the use of CT scans, around 20 percent of the time a normal appendix was removed, but now it's less than one or two percent. On the flip side, this high-tech diagnostic device can save your life by getting you the surgery or treatment you *do* need.

So what could be the down-side? Getting these super-charged images requires a good dose of radiation. The three-dimensional images produced by a typical CT scan of your chest will give you around a 175 times greater dose of radiation than a simple chest x-ray, and a heart CT scan can deliver doses equivalent to 600 chest x-rays, according to a study cited in the *Journal of the American Medical Association*. As the CT x-ray tube rotates around your body, the radiation can possibly ionize your DNA, causing mutations which could lead to cancer growth later.

No large-scale studies have tracked patient exposure to CT scans and its link to causing cancer, though a few have begun. However, the Center for Radiologic Research at Columbia University estimates that one to two percent of cancer deaths in the United States, "may be attributable to the radiation of CT studies." To put this in perspective, the average person's lifetime risk of dying from cancer is around 20 percent. Radiologists and other experts agree that children and young people are at greater risk from CT radiation exposure and that they should be given lower pediatric doses.

So, where does all this leave your wife and the rest of us? Keep track of your CT scans (dates and what kind) and share the list with any physician who wants to prescribe a CT scan. Ask him or her whether or not a sonogram, MRI or x-ray would be acceptable? Many times it will not, but if you've had quite a few CT scans, let your physician know so he or she can help you weigh the benefits versus the risks. You could also ask if they know of a CT provider that offers low dose scanning, which is becoming more common.

Full body scans are being marketed to the "worried well" and the FDA is advising people to think twice before they spend anywhere from $600 to $2,000 dollars on a full body CT scan that poses risks of radiation, often leads to incidental findings that lead to more tests, can render a wrong diagnoses or gives people a false sense of security.

Q: My Dad sees three different specialists and I can tell he doesn't really understand what they are telling him. How can I help him?

A: It's really important that we find a way to help your Dad. An alarming study was recently released showing deadly results for those who don't comprehend the medical information they are given. David Baker, M.D., M.P.H. of Northwestern University Feinberg School of Medicine, found that among the 3,260 Medicare patients he interviewed and followed over time who were not able to read items like prescription labels, appointment slips and instructions on how to prepare for an X-ray, were 50 percent more likely to die than those who were able to understand basic health information.

Dr. Baker and his colleagues believe that the inability to read and understand simple health care information places the elderly at grave risk because they are more likely to suffer multiple chronic medical conditions like heart disease, asthma and diabetes. So, for them, the stakes are higher whenever they don't know understand how each condition affects the other or don't know how to follow directions. Add to this our "body part" medical system forcing older people to see separate specialists for each and every condition and it's no wonder that what the experts dub as "health illiteracy"

is so prevalent and dangerous. One out of four people over the age of sixty five years is health illiterate, according to Baker. Complicating this even further are hearing and vision losses among the elderly that make communicating so difficult. To help your Dad become health literate and reduce his risk of medical errors, here's what you and he can do:

1. Write down every medication he takes, along with over the counter drugs, the dose and what he takes it for. List alongside the medication, the doctor who prescribed it. Keep this list up to date and your father should take the list to EVERY doctor's appointment so that all physicians who are treating him know what he is taking.

2. If you or another family member can accompany him on his non-routine physician visits, do so. It's always helpful to have another set of ears to hear what the doctor is saying. Be sure to write down what the physician recommends and explain it to your Dad. After you have done that, ask your father to explain back to you what you just said.

3. Encourage your father to ask questions. Help your Dad make a list of questions

before his appointment. When he meets with the doctor, he should take out the list and ask if he could please go over them. If your Dad is uncomfortable or shy about asking him a particular question, he could precede it with, "My daughter helps me with my medical care, and she asked me to ask you this ...." And, then ask the question – that way your father is off the hook because the question is really yours, not his.

4. Prior to a doctor's appointment for a particular condition, get your Dad to write down and describe his symptoms and to also rate his pain level from a scale of one to ten with ten being the worst pain he has ever known. He should share this list with his doctor and you.

5. If he sees multiple doctors, find out if your father's internist will coordinate his care. Make a list of each of your Dad's conditions and the contact information of the doctor treating the respective condition and share this information with each doctor, along with his medication list.

6. Before your father leaves the doctor's office, he should ask the nurse who he should call if he has any questions later. Get the name and number.

7. If your father is in the hospital, it is always wise to have a family member at his bedside when physicians examine him to learn first hand of any directions he should follow. If you have further questions, ask his nurse or the physician in charge of his care during his hospital stay, often referred to as a "hospitalist."

8. If you cannot make it to your Dad's physician appointment, ask your father to bring a cell phone and hand it to the doctor so he or she can explain what your Dad is to do regarding his healthcare. If he doesn't have a cell phone, ask him to request that the doctor call you directly.

9. Research your father's conditions so that you can interpret, translate and explain his medical condition and care to him. This will also better prepare you to ask informed questions of his physicians.

If you'd like the equivalent of a textbook on medical terms, then pick up the *Webster's New World Medical Dictionary* or go online to explore terms and their meaning at www.medicinenet.com. Both will also offer explanations of medical tests and procedures. You can also go to my website at www.lindarhodescaregiving.com and click onto *Caregiver Tips*. Check out "*Getting Through Medicalese*" for an easy to use chart that will help you understand medical terms.

Q: I worry about my Mom during heat waves. What should I do?

A: Your Mom might not realize how much her brain's thermostat has started to lose its sensitivity to pick up temperature changes, especially if she is in her eighties. Complicating this are circulatory problems and medications that can throw an older person's "thermostat" out of whack. Your mother is also losing her ability to sweat, which means she's left without nature's protective cooling system. And to make matters worse, older people also lose their sense of thirst, so your Mom may not crave a glass of water to cool her down.

So, while it is normal for your Mom not to feel the heat like she used to, it doesn't mean she can take the heat. We really need to view heat waves just like we do warnings about cold spells. Most older people respect warnings about not going out in extreme cold yet seem to happily garden, mow their lawns or walk in ninety-degree heat. It's almost seen as a badge of honor to be able to "take the heat" since their generation grew up without air conditioning. Just as you'd check in on your aging relatives during an ice storm, it's good to do the same when the temperature stays in the nineties for more than two days. Here are some things you can do to make sure your Mom doesn't suffer from a heat stroke or hyperthermia:

➤ Make sure she's drinking plenty of fluids. Get her bottles of water to help keep track of her intake.

➤ Make sure she uses air conditioning, but is not sitting directly in front of it, as her body could cool off too much and suffer hypothermia. On the other hand, don't assume she has it on. Many older people keep it off so their electric bills won't go up.

➤ If she's using a fan, make sure a window is open to create a draft rather than simply circulating hot air in a closed room. You'd be surprised at the number of people who keep the windows closed because they are afraid someone will break-in.

➤ Call or visit twice a day. If your Mom starts acting confused, has a headache, is dizzy or nauseous, then she's showing signs of a heat stroke. Call for immediate medical help.

➤ If she doesn't have air conditioning, suggest she spend the day at the mall. If necessary, take her there along with a few of her friends.

➤ One of the most effective ways to cool down is to take a lukewarm bath.

> ▸ Suggest that your Mom keep a cool cloth around the back of her neck.

Whatever you do, check in with your parents and reach out to elderly neighbors when the National Weather Service and your local weather station warn of heat waves. They can be every bit as devastating to human life as a tornado. In Philadelphia in 1994 over 100 people, most of them elderly, died from the heat. In response to that crisis, the governor of Pennsylvania asked me to head up a task force to prevent that from ever happening again. As a result, many Area Agencies on Aging throughout the nation now give out fans, take people to air-conditioned senior centers or malls and have identified at-risk elders through their home delivered meals programs to reduce the incidence of heat related deaths. You can call 1-800-677-1116 to find the nearest Area Agency on Aging to find out what they can do for your parent during a heat wave.

: With the cold weather, I don't get out to take my regular walks and I don't want to join a gym. Do you have any suggestions?

: Sure do. How about going to the local mall and walk? It's safe, warm, parking isn't a hassle and you get to meet interesting people. If you are more of a loner, you don't have to mingle…just walk. "Mall Walkers" usually begin their trek in the morning when the mall doors open, which can be as early as 7:00 a.m. to 10:00 a.m. Most malls offer informal programs: there is no club to join or membership fees and they are very happy to accommodate walkers. On most mornings at any local mall, you'll see between thirty to fifty walkers, most of whom are either older or mothers with babies in strollers lending a nice intergenerational touch. If you're looking for reasons to convince yourself that "mall walking" is your ticket to year-round good health, here is my top ten list:

1. Walking is an excellent form of exercise that benefits your entire cardiovascular system, which in turn keeps your heart and brain healthy. It also strengthens muscles and bones.

2. A morning walk sets your metabolism in good stead for the rest of the day, which will help you keep your weight in check. It is also an effective way to reduce weight.

3. The mall offers a "no excuse" environment to keep up with a regular exercise program. Consistency of exercise of at least four to six times a week is a key ingredient to staying fit. If the weather is too cold, if it's raining or if it's roasting outside – the climate inside of the mall is just fine.

4. Staying socially active prevents all kinds of health problems and even Alzheimer's. After walking, most mall walkers enjoy a cup of coffee and a light breakfast in the Food Court, while they read the paper and talk with fellow walkers. Friendships evolve and there's nothing like a baby's smile or touch offered by "stroller walking" mothers.

5. Malls often offer free health screenings and healthy lifestyle seminars in partnership with local hospitals. Some offer volunteer opportunities in staging community events. The only gear you need is good walking shoes, which are definitely worth the investment, especially if you'll be walking on concrete. Other than the shoes and a water bottle, you're set to go.

6. Mall scenery can ward off exercise boredom. Every month there will be a new theme for decorating the mall and store window displays. Sunlight shines through skylights while plants, flowers and water falls are located all along your walk. And, there's nothing like the age-old past time of "people watching" at the mall.

7. If you'd like to make your walk more competitive, get a pedometer that tracks your steps so you can add up the miles, or get a watch that does the same and also allows you to time yourself between stores or certain landmarks in the mall. You can pick up the pace by going up stairs, ramps and escalators.

8. Mall walking can be fun. Create your own mental games, like playing the Alphabet Game used to keep kids active in long car rides (look for words that begin with each letter of the alphabet), or play "I Spy" with a walking buddy. Use your time to think creatively or positively like how you might want to re-decorate a room in your home, plan a vacation, design your summer garden, start a new hobby, track down and talk to an old friend, do something fun with the grandkids or recall your favorite vacation. Don't use your time to make a *Things To Do List* that will quickly zap all the mental energy you're building up from your walk.

9. Okay, there are a couple of downsides: getting past the irresistible "who-cares-about-calories" aroma of fresh baked Cinnabons, and the sales. Pack light on the cash and credit cards to prevent impulse buying and get your new found friends to hold you back from those sweet attacks and buy a nutritious power bar instead.

: What kind of screening tests does Medicare cover?

: If you're old enough to receive Medicare, then routine physicals and screening tests should become a very important part of your life. You can start off with a "Welcome to Medicare" physical exam that will cover a full review of your health, certain screenings, shots, education, counseling and, if needed, referrals for specialty care. The catch is beneficiaries must have this physical within the first six months of enrolling in Medicare Part B.

What can you expect from a physical exam? Most annual physicals will include routine tests like:

> Taking a blood pressure (to monitor high blood pressure)

> Body Mass Index (BMI) test, measuring your total weight that comes from fat, as opposed to muscle, bone or organ. The higher a person's BMI, the higher the percentage of fat in their body, which places them at a greater risk for heart attacks, strokes, diabetes, joint problems and a whole host of other chronic conditions.

> Men also receive a testicular exam to check for changes in size or shape of their testicles – this ranks as the most common form of malignant cancers in men.

> The doctor will also perform a prostate exam to determine if it is abnormally enlarged, which could be indicative of cancer.

> Most annual exams will also include a panel of blood work to analyze what's going on internally, such your cholesterol count (If it is high, it means that the fatty sticky substance of cholesterol could likely be clogging your arteries, placing you in serious danger of high blood pressure and heart attack.)

Beyond the physical, here is a list of screenings covered by Medicare:

> **Glaucoma Tests.** You should also see an ophthalmologist (eye physician) to check for age-related eye diseases of cataracts, glaucoma, and macular degeneration. If you need corrective lenses, you'll be referred to an optometrist. Medicare covers screening tests for glaucoma once every twelve months if your physician determines you are at high risk for the disease.

> **Shots.** Medicare covers a "pneumonia shot" that helps prevent people from acquiring pneumococcal infections, which usually lasts a life time. Hepatitis B shots are covered for people considered

at medium or high risk and flu shots are covered each year during flu season.

> **Cardiovascular Screenings.** Blood tests for cholesterol, lipid and triglyceride levels are covered every five years.

> **Colorectal Cancer.** Medicare will cover the following kinds of tests: Fecal Occult Blood Test (once every 12 months), Flexible Sigmoidoscopy (once every 48 months), Screening Colonoscopy (once every 10 years, but if you are at high-risk, it is covered once every 24 months), Barium Enema (once every 48 months, but if you are at high-risk, then once every 24 months).

> **Prostate Cancer.** Digital Rectal Examinations and Prostate Specific Antigen (PSA) Tests are each covered once every 12 months. If you belong to the Original Medicare Plan then you will generally pay 20% of the Medicare-approved amount for the digital rectal exam after the yearly Part B deductible. There is no coinsurance and no Part B deductible for the PSA Test.

> **Diabetes.** Medicare covers a screening blood sugar test to check for diabetes – if you are considered at risk – which includes the following indicators: high blood pressure, history of abnormal cholesterol and triglyceride levels, obesity or a history of high blood sugar. Other risk factors may qualify you for

this test and would be determined by your physician. Based on the results of the tests, people may be eligible for up to two screenings each year. Recently, Medicare added coverage for Fasting Plasma Glucose Tests.

> **Breast Cancer Screening:** Every year, if you are over 40 years of age, Medicare will cover a mammogram. A co-payment or co-insurance will apply, but it will not be subject to the deductible.

> **Cervical Cancer Screening:** Every two years, Medicare will cover a pap smear and a pelvic exam. If a woman is at high risk for cervical cancer, it will be covered every year. There is no co-pay or co-insurance for the lab test of the Pap smear, nor is it subject to the deductible. But you may be asked to pay a co-pay or co-insurance for the pap exam.

If you would like to keep track of your coverage of preventive services in traditional Medicare, go to www.mymedicare.gov to use a personalized "Medicare Manager" tool, or give them a call at 1-800-633-4227. Regretfully, Medicare doesn't cover screenings for oral health, but it is an essential part of staying well and detecting oral cancer. I'd add an annual visit to the dentist as part of your routine, too.

Q: How do you find free or low cost health screenings when your parents aren't on Medicare?

A: Health screenings are a great way to stay healthy and get ahead of lurking health problems. You'd be surprised at the number of groups that offer free health screenings, but it may take a little bit of homework to track them down. Here are six sources to make your search easier:

Awareness Months. Just about every disease or health condition has a national association that dedicates one month, a week or day to a public awareness campaign. For example, January is Glaucoma Awareness month, February is American Heart Month, March is National Kidney Month, September is Prostate Cancer Month and October is Breast Cancer Awareness Month. Most often, their local affiliates sponsor free screenings in collaboration with local hospitals, clinics, volunteer physicians and nurses. Check out your local newspaper for their listing of community events to stay on top of free health screenings.

American Cancer Society. If you want to know what free or low cost cancer screenings are available in your community, then simply call the American Cancer Society at 1-800-227-2345 and choose the option for "events." Ask the representative what cancer screenings are available in or near your zip

code and they'll tell you dates, time and contact information.

Hospitals. Most local hospitals offer support programs, educational events and free or low cost health screenings. You can ask to get on their mailing list by contacting their public affairs department. Chances are you already receive their newsletters if you've been a patient at their facility. Be sure to read their events section.

Pharmacies. Many pharmacies offer screenings in association with local health care providers. So, while you're waiting in line, be sure to look at their print materials announcing special events or ask your pharmacist if he or she knows of any screenings that will be scheduled at the pharmacy.

Senior Centers. Your local senior center is a terrific resource to find out about and receive screenings. Some have clinics right on site or they have health care providers regularly scheduled to provide screenings. Find your local senior center by calling 1-800-677-1116.

HealthyWoman Program. Uninsured, low income or underinsured women can receive free or low cost mammograms and pap tests (cervical cancer screening) provided by the Pennsylvania Department of Health, 1-800-215-7494. Look for free or low cost mammograms provided by hospitals and clinics on National Mammography Day, celebrated the third Friday in October nationwide. Call the American Cancer Society at 1-800-227-2345 to find out where these will be held nearer the date or check your newspaper.

It's definitely worth a few phone calls and some clicks on the internet to screen out poor health from your future.

Q: Is a bone density test the best way to screen for osteoporosis?

A: Several years ago, the U.S. Preventive Services Task Force wasn't sure whether or not bone density tests were warranted. But, after a few more years of research, they concluded that getting a bone density test is a smart and effective prevention tool for every woman 65 years and older.

Osteoporosis is the abnormal thinning of the bone causing decreased bone mass and density. It's related to aging and the depletion of bone calcium and protein. Women are especially prone to osteoporosis after menopause and the effects can be debilitating: easily broken bones, spine fractures and hip fractures are common results of osteoporosis. Hip fractures are one of the leading causes of premature loss of home and independence, landing many women in nursing homes. Your mother is at higher risk if she smokes, is white or Asian, is small-framed, has already had a fracture that wasn't related to major trauma, gets little exercise, drinks heavily, has a poor diet low in calcium or takes corticosteroids, certain anticonvulsants or excess doses of thyroid hormones for long periods.

So, what about the test? There are several ways to measure bone density, but the most reliable test is called dual energy X-ray absorptiometry (DEXA) of the spine and hip. It is the most expensive test, at about $250, according to the task force report. Similar X-ray tests can be used for the wrist, finger, and heel at a lower cost. An ultrasound test of your Mom's heel may also be helpful, especially if she is considered low risk. All of these are good screening tests, although the DEXA of the spine and hip is considered the gold standard for diagnosis and Medicare does pay for it. Usually the referring physician will decide which kind of test your mother needs. None of the bone density tests are invasive or uncomfortable, and they take a mere 5 to 15 minutes. Many people are surprised to learn that you don't even have to undress or wear those lovely hospital gowns.

The major benefit of the test is to determine whether or not your mother's condition warrants taking a bone-preserving drug. The options include bisphos-phonates (such as Fosamax or Actonel), the hormone-like raloxifene (Evista), or hormones (hormone replacement therapy or calcitonin). It can also indicate a strong warning to your Mom to take steps to prevent the further weakening of her bones, such as changing her diet. You may need to urge your Mom's doctor to prescribe a bone density test. According to a recent survey in the American Journal of Public Health, one-third of all postmenopausal women have the condition, yet only two percent are ever diagnosed and treated. Medicare has been covering bone density tests under Part B since 1998. Of course, there are guidelines and restrictions. According to Medicare:

> Bone mass measurement is covered for certain people at risk for losing bone mass.

> Bone mass measurement tests are covered by all Medicare health plans, including managed care plans.

> Deductible and co-payments apply.

> Medicare will pay for this test only if ordered by a physician or qualified practitioner.

> Medicare will cover tests every two years or more frequently if medically necessary.

> Doctors consider a patient medical history and risk factors in deciding who should have a bone density test and the type of test.

Given the results of this new study and Medicare's coverage of the test, it makes perfect sense to have your Mom ask her doctor to prescribe it. If she's smoking, try getting her to stop; encourage weight-bearing exercise and a healthy diet with plenty of calcium and vitamin D. With more than 1.5 million fractures a year caused by osteoporosis, the odds are if she does nothing, she'll become one of these statistics.

Q: My Mom's been smoking for years and I'd do anything to get her to stop. Any suggestions?

A: I imagine you've tried telling your Mom about all of the health risks with smoking. Most smokers make the direct connection between smoking and lung cancer. But, there's always some Aunt Sallie or Uncle Joe they'll tell you about who smoked up a storm and lasted until their nineties. Okay, maybe your Mom escapes lung cancer, but what about all the cancer-related diseases and chronic illnesses that come tagging along with every puff?

Here are some questions for her: Like to keep control of your bladder? Don't smoke. Like to see your grandkids without a blind spot in the middle? Don't smoke. Like to have a hip that won't break? Don't smoke. Like to steer clear of a stroke so you can speak? Don't smoke. It's not about avoiding cancer – it's about being able to just plain *live*. Incontinence, macular degeneration, osteoporosis and strokes have all found common ground in smoking and the list goes on.

But, for some people, health reasons aren't enough to let go. Relationships, however, do matter: maybe if your Mom knew how much you enjoy her company and how it pains you to see her decline in health, it may nudge her closer to quitting. Or, maybe if she knew that her grandchild may be quietly thinking that "Nana doesn't really love me enough to make sure she'll be here when I get bigger." You'd be surprised how young children make this kind of *quid pro quo* link when they are told that smoking can kill you. Even adult children may think this way– I did. I'm not saying you should "guilt-trip" your Mom; just let her know how much she matters to her family.

The *American Cancer Society* advises that a successful "quit plan" must tackle both the physical and psychological aspects of smoking. The physical side can be addressed by medications, patches and nicotine replacement, but the emotional side is what often undermines the best intentioned person. Smokers often link the act of smoking with something else – driving, talking on the phone, with a cup of coffee, after a meal or watching television. It will be key for your Mom to be aware of the connections so she can break the link. She should also silence the voice in her head that comes up with all kinds of rationalizations: *"I'll just smoke to get me through this tough spot. I'll stop after I finish this pack. It's my only vice. You've got to die from something. By the time I get sick from this, there'll be a cure. But, I'll feel lousy if I quit."*

To ensure your Mom's chance for success, the *American Cancer Society* would tell your Mom to:

▸ Avoid people and places where you are tempted to smoke. Later on you will be able to handle these with more confidence.

▸ Alter your habits. Switch to juices or water instead of alcohol or coffee. Take a different route to work. Take a brisk walk instead of a coffee break.

▸ Alternatives. Use oral substitutes such as sugarless gum or hard candy, raw vegetables such as carrot sticks, or sunflower seeds.

▸ Activities. Do something to decrease your stress. Exercise or do hobbies that keep your hands busy that can help distract you from the urge to use tobacco. Take a hot bath, exercise, or read a book.

▸ Deep breathing. When you were smoking, you breathed deeply as you inhaled the smoke. When the urge strikes now, breathe deeply and picture your lungs filling with fresh, clean air.

▸ Delay. If you feel that you are about to light up or chew, delay. Tell yourself you must wait at least 10 minutes. Often this simple trick will allow you to move beyond the strong urge to use tobacco.

The Pennsylvania Department of Health with the American Cancer Society, offers a free *Quitline* staffed by clinically trained counselors. If your Mom wants to make a serious quit attempt she can talk to a counselor and she'll be mailed a "Break Away From the Pack" kit. Call the Pennsylvania Quitline at 1-877-724-1090. They are available 24-hours a day, seven days a week. For excellent materials on how quit, go to the *American Cancer Society* website at www.cancer.org and go to the *"Kick the Habit"* section, or give them a call at 1-800-ACS-2345 and ask them if they can send you a packet of matierials.

Q: Why did the American Cancer Society decide that most men do not need to get tested for prostate cancer?

A: In 2010, the American Cancer Society did issue new guidelines for patients and doctors to consider when deciding whether or not to be screened for prostate cancer. They felt that an update was needed, mostly in response to the findings of a large study involving 76,600 men in the United States who received annual PSA blood tests and digital rectal exams compared to those who had "usual care." Researchers found little difference in prostate cancer death rates between the two groups. A European study involving 182,000 men is finding similar results.

You would think that wide-spread screenings would make sense given the fact that prostate cancer is the most common cancer among men. It is an age-related type of cancer in that two-thirds of all men with prostate cancer are 65 years and older. Seventeen percent of men fifty years and older will develop prostate cancer during their lifetime and three percent will die.

So, why not get tested? Most forms of prostate cancer are very slow moving, so slow that a man in his seventies and eighties detected with prostate cancer is more likely to die from another type of life-ending illness, such as heart attack or stroke. The experts have found that aggressively treating a cancer that may never cause real problems for the rest of a man's natural life span can cause more harm than good. Treatment for prostate cancer has some pretty tough side-effects for many men: incontinence, bowel problems and impotence. And that's why the American Cancer Society thinks doctors and male patients should step back and talk about the benefits and risks of prostate screening tests and subsequent treatment when it's discovered in its early stages.

The American Cancer Society (ACS) also wants men to be aware of the uncertainty of tests results before making irreversible, life-altering decisions. According to ACS, "No screening test is perfect, but the degree of over-diagnosis and associated over-treatment appears to be greater for prostate screening than for any other of the cancers for which routine screening currently occurs."

These updated guidelines are directed at the general population of men who have no symptoms of prostate cancer. The over-riding message is quite simple: men should discuss the benefits and risks of prostate cancer screening with their physicians more rigorously than they have in the past and weigh their options, even if they get a positive result of cancer.

What the revised guidelines recommend:

➤ Men who are in good health should start talking with their doctor about the uncertainties, risks and benefits of prostate cancer screening at the age of fifty.

➤ Men with no symptoms who are not expected to live more than ten years due to age or poor health should not pursue prostate cancer screening as the "risks outweigh the benefits."

➤ Men who are at high risk of prostate cancer: African-Americans and men who have a father, brother or son diagnosed with the cancer before age 65 years should have a conversation with their doctor at age 45 years.

➤ Men who have multiple family members with prostate cancer before age 65 years, should seek advice at age 40.

The American Cancer Society wants men to know that it is not against prostate cancer screening, nor do they believe it should be withheld from someone who really believes they need it. What they are saying is that both physicians and patients need to have a more serious and robust discussion than they've had in the past on the risks and benefits of screenings, the uncertainty of test results and the pros and cons of treatment options, so men can truly make an informed decision.

If you'd like a copy of a guide to help you decide what to do and better understand the new guidelines, you can download a copy of *Testing for Prostate Cancer: Is it the right choice for me?* at www.cancer.org or call ACS at 1-800-277-2345.

 : Both of my parents are so worried about coming down with Alzheimer's. Is there anything they can do to prevent it?

 : Tell them to keep up with their friends and family, make new friends and get out and about. Sound kind of folksy? Expecting advice that's more medical? Well, two prestigious institutions are making the case through research that staying socially active can help keep Alzheimer's at bay. The *Harvard School of Public Health* studied 2,800 people over the age of 65 years.

Those who had monthly **visual** contact with three or more relatives or friends and yearly non-visual contact with 10 or more relatives or friends staved off mental decline much better than those who had little contact. People who had at least five social relationships and kept regular contact reduced their risk of Alzheimer's disease by almost 40 percent.

It turns out that the mental decline we associate with aging isn't so much due to the death of nerve cells, but rather the connections among them. Social interaction causes people to remain involved in the affairs of daily life and to continue to grow emotionally. It also requires making decisions. All of this interacting calls on your senses to process information and respond which, in turn, nurtures these neural connections in your brain.

Researchers at *Rush University Medical Center's Alzheimer's Disease Center* in Chicago found further evidence that socially active older people are less likely to exhibit Alzheimer's symptoms. It's the first study of its kind that examined the relationship between social networks and Alzheimer's disease pathology. The Rush researchers studied their elderly participant's social activities up until their death and were given permission to perform autopsies of their brains.

What did they find? Seniors with larger social networks exhibited fewer effects from the markers of Alzheimer's disease – tangles and plaques – than those with smaller social networks. So, even if participants had symptoms of Alzheimer's disease indicated by their brain autopsies, you wouldn't know it while they were alive. In other words, healthy and frequent interactions with friends and family build your brain's protective reserve against Alzheimer's.

They also might be interested in knowing that, according to Dr. Lawrence Katz, co-author of *Keep Your Brain Alive*, the mental decline that we associate with aging isn't due to the death of nerve cells, but rather the connections among them. And using the senses in new ways is how to maintain these connections. The bottom line is that engaging in activities such as meeting new people, taking up a new hobby, learning how to use email, mentoring young people or taking classes will actually nurture a healthy mind. Just as your body needs to be toned with exercise, so does your brain. Some of the best brain exercises are old standbys, such as reading a good book or a challenging magazine article, playing Scrabble and doing crosswords. Though TV is a form of connecting, it in no way replicates the benefit of actually getting out and about and interacting with people. If your parent is no longer driving or is finding it too much of a hassle to drive (be aware that he or she might not admit it), it's a good idea to create a schedule where you, a friend or family member make it part of your routine to come over at least once a week with the understanding that you're there to take Mom or Dad wherever they want to go.

If your parents live out of town and you are worried about them being alone and isolated, consider hiring a non-medical senior care service to drop by once or twice a week to prepare and have lunch with your parent, take them out and even play their favorite games with them like card games or checkers. Get families and friends to call every week and do something we all know is the greatest gift of all – visit!

Q: I'd like to see my Dad get more mentally active. He doesn't have many friends and he's bored with television. Any suggestions?

A: Lucky for your Dad, "brain health" is fast becoming the new exercise program among the senior set. Thought Nintendo was just for grandkids? Think again, Nintendo has released "Brain Age" to be played on their dual screen (DS) system. Designed to be a "treadmill for the mind," the game *Brain Age: Train Your Brain in Minutes a Day* is inspired by the research of Professor Ryuta Kawashima, a prominent Japanese neuroscientist whose studies reveal the positive impact of performing certain reading and mathematic exercises to help stimulate the brain.

The hand held DS system opens up like a small book. On the right hand side you can draw and write answers on the screen with a stylus (pen) and also respond by voice. You can also touch the screen for answers. Your Dad can play a wide range of games from speed counting, picture drawing, syllable counting, calculating and even reading classical literature out loud. The DS system can be bought at stores selling videos and software. Expect to pay around $129.00 for the DS system and about $18.00 for the Brain Age game software. There are also other games such as "Brain Boost" and "Big Brain." What's fun about the system is that you'll take a few tests in the beginning to get your "Brain age" and the program keeps track of your progress as you play to show you how your brain age is advancing.

Erikson Retirement Communities have become so impressed with Nintendo games for brain health that they are installing Nintendo Wii (pronounced as "we") consoles at all of their locations across the country so residents can play games like Brain Age. Even Alzheimer patients are playing games on touch screens designed to help them maintain their cognitive abilities for as long as possible.

If your father doesn't like the idea of a hand-held game, but does have a computer, there are free games online offered at www.aarp.org (just enter *brain health* in the search bar), or go to a game site featuring 50 free games at www.pogo.com. This site boasts that one-third of their visitors are fifty years and older. They feature quite a few word games that might interest your Dad. He can also enter contests with others who play online or compete with the computer. If he does not want to use the internet, there are plenty of computer games he can purchase and play.

If he'd like to skip the electronic age, there are always crossword puzzles, the number game, Sodoku, and plenty of other game books that you can buy at bookstores and newsstands. Learning a new language is an excellent way to exercise his mind, as is taking up a new hobby or taking a class at the local community college or senior center.

Besides games to exercise your Dad's mind, here are other steps he can take to keep his mental muscles toned up:

> Eat well – vegetables, foods rich in antioxidants and omega-3 fatty acids, whole grains and lots of water feed a vibrant brain. Sugar and fats aren't brain friendly foods, so reduce their intake. Multivitamins with antioxidants and folate are a good choice.

> Staying socially active with friends and attending events that encourage interacting with others is essential. Human beings are social creatures who thrive on connecting with others. If getting out and about is difficult, then call and talk to your Dad about current events. Get the grandkids to call, too!

> Exercise regularly – your brain needs fresh oxygen and a healthy blood supply.

> Keep your blood pressure and cholesterol under control.

> Learn to handle stress and get enough sleep.

> Always monitor any medications that you are taking to see if they cause side-effects of confusion, loss of memory and/or depression.

The last thing you want to see happen is for your father to become a prisoner in his own home, relegated to solitary confinement. It won't be long before he becomes depressed and won't care to think or connect with others. Even though it might look like just fun and games, getting brain fit is about winning a life worth living.

Q: Is there a link between Alzheimer's and high blood pressure?

A: Yes, and it's a lot more than just by "chance." It's been known for quite some time that there is a link between Alzheimer's and people suffering from mini-strokes that block blood supply to the brain and cause the death of brain cells. This is sometimes referred to as "vascular dementia." These small, successive strokes oftentimes go unnoticed as they chip away at the brain. People with high blood pressure and diabetes are at considerable risk for this type of dementia.

But, recent studies are showing that people with consistent hypertension weaken their arteries with the constant high pressured flow of blood which, in turn, damages the tiny blood vessels that nourish white matter in the brain. Since white matter allows the brain cells to communicate with each other, its function is hijacked when lesions block the way of transmitting vital messages. And, that's where Alzheimer's and other forms of dementia enter the picture.

MRI scans of the brains of 1,403 women 65 years and older with high blood pressure enrolled in the national Women's Health Initiative study showed a direct connection between high blood pressure and greater white matter damage. A Johns Hopkins Hospital study of nearly 1,000 people over a fifteen year period confirmed the same finding. Those with untreated high blood pressure had more white matter damage than those with lower blood pressure. In fact, for every 20 point jump in the systolic blood pressure reading, there was a corresponding incidence of white matter damage. Blood pressure is expressed in two numbers. The first number is the systolic blood pressure, the force of blood as the heart is pumping. The second known as the diastolic number represents the pressure that remains in the arteries when the heart is relaxed.

So, there you have it. There is a link between hypertension and increasing the likelihood of suffering from dementia. People with high blood pressure are also at greatest risk of heart and kidney disease.

Diet and, if necessary, medications are the best defense against high blood pressure. Consider the DASH food plan which stands for the "Dietary Approaches to Stop Hypertension," based on a clinical study by the National Institutes of Health. Eating fruits, vegetables, and lowfat dairy foods and reducing saturated fat, total fat, and cholesterol are found to be very effective in lowering blood pressure. The DASH eating plan also promotes the benefits of whole grains, poultry, fish, and nuts and advises people to significantly reduce their intake of sodium, fats, red meats, sweets and sugared beverages.

It's also smart to monitor your blood pressure so you can see the results of eating well and consistently taking medications, if you've been prescribed them. Automated blood pressure cuffs that you can find at most pharmacies (between fifty and eighty dollars) are very easy to use without any assistance.

Q: Why does my father, who has Alzheimer's, become agitated and restless late in the afternoon?

 What you are describing is known as "sundowning," and about one in five people with Alzheimer's disease exhibit behaviors of fear, frustration, agitation, tension and/or anxiety beginning around dusk – or sun down. For some, this phenomenon may even last throughout the night, which places a great deal of stress upon caregivers. It typically peaks in the middle stages of Alzheimer's and lessens as the disease progresses.

Experts aren't exactly certain why sundowning occurs, but they do believe that a number of factors are involved: mental and physical exhaustion at the end of the day, a re-wiring of the body's "internal clock," changes in sleep patterns, reduced daylight, signaling nighttime fears, or an increase in shadows that cause confusion. In the past, most experts thought that shorter days and less light led to sundowning behavior, but recent studies suggest that being overly tired contributes more to the disorder than light conditions.

Here are a number of tips that the Alzheimer's Association, experts and caregivers offer to help you reduce the negative affects of sundowning on your Dad:

Keep his days active. A person who rests most of the day will likely be up at night. Taking walks, doing chair exercises, helping with chores, such as folding clothes or doing something that is meaningful to your father would be helpful. Getting him to an adult day living center a few times a week would be an excellent choice to keep him active.

Avoid over-exhaustion. On one hand, you want to keep your Dad active; on the other, don't pack too much activity into any one day. Schedule doctor appointments, visits from family members and friends or other outings during the morning, when he's more equipped to handle higher levels of stimulation. Taking a bath or shower might be better suited as a morning activity.

Watch for triggers and over-stimulation. Keep commotion to a minimum. Vacuuming around the house or turning on some other noisy appliance, a loud radio, television, or a fast movement on your part can trigger a sundowning episode. Keep his environment calm and predictable.

Watch what he eats. Offer sweets and caffeine only in the morning. Monitor sugar content in food when serving it later in the day. You might want to keep a food diary to see if certain foods trigger anxiety or agitation within an hour of consuming it. Maintain a routine for dinner and serve it early. Offer only light foods before bedtime. He may find that a warm cup of milk or chamomile tea calms him before calling it a day. This routine may also send his body a signal that it is time to sleep.

Create a quiet time before sundowning. If your father seems to be affected the same time every day, it would be helpful to create a calming activity about thirty minutes before he usually becomes agitated. You might play very soothing music while he relaxes in his favorite chair or wherever he finds it most peaceful.

Seek medical advice. Don't just assume this "is just the way it's going to be." There may be a physical condition fueling his agitation

or making it difficult for him to sleep. Your doctor may be able to prescribe medication to help take the "edge off" and enable him to sleep through the night. Don't settle, however, for a medication that will make him groggy all day.

Keep his surroundings simple. You might want to go through the house and remove knickknacks, items on tables, clutter, and obstacles in pathways such as small tables or rugs that either mentally overload him or make it difficult for him to negotiate his way around the house. A large mirror or a portrait hanging on the wall might have him feeling fearful that someone else is in the room. Keep rooms partially lit so his surroundings don't become dark and unfamiliar.

When your Dad does become upset or agitated be sure to approach him calmly. Find out if there is something he needs – don't assume it is just due to sundowning. He may be experiencing some sort of discomfort from feeling hungry, too hot or cold, or maybe he is in pain, has an upset stomach or has soiled himself. Words escape him, so he becomes agitated or frustrated. If he's confused about the time of day, gently remind him of the time and make a connection to it such as, "Dad, it's 12:30 p.m. in the afternoon, we just ate lunch." Do this throughout the entire day, so your father is given a sense of time and order. It's best to avoid arguing or asking for explanations as it will simply upset him more. Keep reassuring him that everything is all right.

Q: Every New Year's Day my parents vow to "go on a diet." It lasts for all of two weeks. How can they really make a change?

A: Most of our parents were raised on calorie-rich "comfort" foods and this creates quite a challenge to get them interested in foods good for an older body. But, it's a challenge they better tackle: Most adults over sixty-five have chronic illnesses that are made worse by a poor diet; one in five feels depressed, causing a loss of appetite, and most take medications that require good nutrition to be effective. Your Mom and Dad may not realize that their sense of smell, taste and thirst decrease as they age, and so does their metabolism. Their physiology changes, and for the most part, they don't need as much food as they did when they were younger.

To accommodate the aging body, Tuft's University Center on Nutrition created a "Food Guide Pyramid for Older Adults," aged 70-plus. You can download a copy at my website: www.lindarhodescaregiving. com. The base shows eight glasses of water highlighting the risk of dehydration among the elderly, leading to kidney problems and constipation. The pyramid showcases foods rich in fiber for intestinal health and the top has a flag suggesting supplements in calcium, vitamins D and B-12. The bottom features illustrations of physical activities emphasizing the need for daily exercise. Want your parents to stay well with good nutrition? Here is how:

> Bring them cases of small water bottles or get them to sign up for a water delivery service. Their generation isn't one to waste, so they will be more inclined to drink it.

> Get them in the habit of asking their pharmacist to identify if their medication causes dehydration, interacts adversely to specific foods or should be taken on a full stomach.

> Research your parent's medical conditions (www.mayoclinic.com) and let them know if certain foods make matters worse. Most chronic illnesses benefit from a special diet.

> Give them "Care Packages" of high fiber snacks, frozen vegetables and fruits and a good multi-vitamin.

> Eating alone is a leading reason why older people become undernourished. So organize family and friends to dine with them or call the Elder Care Locator to find a "Home Delivered Meal" program at 1-800-677-1116. Also, ask them to locate

a senior center near them, so they can attend luncheons and make friends.

▸ Go for the Color! Tuft University's nutritional biochemist, Dr. Alice Lichenstein, urges older people to opt for dark green, red, orange, yellow or other brightly-colored vegetables and deeply-colored fruits, "Choose romaine over iceberg lettuce and pick peaches and apricots rather than apples."

▸ Arthritic hands and low vision can make it hard to eat or prepare foods. Call Able

Data at 1-800-227-0216 and ask for a catalog of eating utensils and cooking devices, or visit their website at www.abledata.com.

▸ People are living longer today, not because of a surgeon's skilled hands, but because they're taking matters into their hands. Eating well and exercise isn't brain surgery. If you'd like to see the Food Pyramid for Older Adults, visit my website at www.lindarhodescaregiving.com.

Q: My parents' doctor told them they should cut down on *trans* and *saturated* fats, but it's confusing. Can you help explain this to them?

A: Rest assured it's not only your parents who find it confusing. To stay clear of these troublesome fats requires joining the ranks of "food detective" and it's a force we all should join. To make life easier for New Yorkers and tourists, the city just banned all restaurants from using trans fats in preparing their foods. If they feel it's a pretty big deal; then, so should your Mom and Dad. So, let's get them up to speed on which fats are okay, those they should limit and fats they should absolutely avoid.

The three types of fats, also known as *fatty acids*, your parents should know about are saturated, unsaturated (poly and mono) and trans fats. There is a chemical explanation for each having to do with carbon and hydrogen atoms but I'm going to skip it, guessing they probably don't care. But, here is what they need to know: fats are not all bad, as they help the body store and use energy. The goal is to have the right mix of fats in your diet. Trans and saturated fats, however, are known to increase the level of bad cholesterol (LDL) in your blood stream – that sticky stuff that can clog your arteries, which then leads to heart problems. Trans fats are manufactured when hydrogen is added to liquid oils that turn into solid fats like shortening and hard margarine. On the other hand, unsaturated fats promote good cholesterol (HDL) that won't be sticking on artery walls. Higher use of unsaturated fats is linked to reducing strokes and heart attacks.

Here are my "Skinny on Fats" tips to help your parents navigate the world of fats:

1. Read the food labels on the back of packages and be sure to have your glasses or magnifying glass handy to read them. The food label will identify how many grams of fat are contained in each serving. The first line will show the total grams of fat and then the fats will be broken down into saturated, unsaturated (polyunsaturated and monounsaturated) and trans fat. **Go for products that have no trans fat and those with the least amount of saturated fats.** To the far right of the food label, you'll see "% of Daily Value" for each ingredient. Anything that meets 20% or more of the Daily Value is considered high. So, if you see percentages near this number next to fats for just one serving; it's a red flag to stay clear. And, that's the other thing: look at how limited one serving actually is (often just a cup); it doesn't take much to double your fat intake. You won't see a Daily Value for trans fats because there is no value.

2. If you see the term "non-hydrogenated" on a product, that's a good thing. If it has the term "partially non-hydrogenated," it means that there will be a small amount of trans fat (less than 0.5 grams). The term comes from the process of adding hydrogen to vegetable oil which increases the shelf life of products and preserves the flavor.

3. You'll find trans fat in vegetable shortenings, some margarines, crackers, cookies, snack foods (e.g. potato chips, tortillas, and popcorn), baked goods and foods made with or fried in partially hydrogenated oils commonly used among fast food restaurants. Remember that trans fats are NOT beneficial to your health.

4. Saturated fats also spell trouble and should be limited. You'll find them in animal products like beef, pork, chicken skin, butter, whole milk and cheese. Fish is a good substitute for meat and so are plant-based foods. You can get enough protein in your diet without eating meat every day. Also, look for products that offer reduced saturated fats like 1% and 2% milk or soy milk rather than whole milk.

5. If you're going to use oils to cook your food, use unsaturated natural oils like olive oil or canola oils, sunflower oils, corn or soybean.

6. Butter or margarine? The FDA recommends that soft-tub margarine is better than butter or hard-stick margarine. "Smart Balance" is a good example of an alternative for butter as it is

non-hydrogenated, no trans fat and a good balance of saturated to unsaturated fats.

Ever since we introduced the use of trans fats into the American diet, heart disease, strokes and obesity have been on the rise. It's going to take some time for all of us to wean ourselves away from large portions and processed foods high in saturated and trans fats. And, it would sure be a lot easier if food producers weren't using these ingredients in the first place. But, they are. Now that we know what's harmful and what isn't – it's really up to each of us to take control of our own health and what we choose to eat is the first step.

Q: Do you think good nutrition really can prevent cancer?

A: Opinion polls reveal that most Americans think there isn't much they can do to stop cancer other than stop smoking. People think that it's either genetics or something in the environment that causes most cancers – both of which they have little control over. As a result, we feel helpless and no wonder: Cancer will affect one person in three before the age of 75 years.

I recently reviewed a book, *Foods to Fight Cancer*, by Richard Béliveau, PhD, a leading authority in cancer research at the University of Quebec in Montréal and Denis Gingras, PhD, who is an oncology researcher in the Molecular Medicine Laboratory and Charles-Bruneau Cancer Center.

They describe the science, chemistry and molecular activity of foods and how certain properties become active cancer-fighting agents. They show how cancer evolves and how foods can effectively engage cancer at every stage. It's a no-nonsense book based on science, yet easy to follow. By the time you're done reading it, you'll "get" the connection between food, cells, and cancer. They contend that 30 percent of all cancers are diet related – something we can control. Here's a "bottom-line" list from the research in their book on how food can be your best friend to keep cancer out of your life:

1. Eat at least 5 servings of fresh fruits and vegetables every day. Include them at every meal and make them a snack throughout the day.

2. Reduce your intake of everything white, like rice, bread, and products using refined sugars and white flour. They have a high Glycemic Index (GI), dramatically

increasing blood glucose levels that trigger cancer-promoting effects.

3. Powerful vegetables to fight cancer are: broccoli, cauliflower, cabbage, Brussels sprouts, tomatoes (including tomato paste) and spinach. Plenty of vegetables are good for you; these are just their top six that many people ignore.

4. Highly effective cancer prevention seasonings are onions, garlic, and turmeric, an anti-inflammatory when combined with black pepper.

5. Green tea contains "catechins" that inhibit the growth of cancer cells. The Japanese green teas are richer in anti-cancer compounds. Let the tea brew for 8 to 10 minutes to release the molecules. Drink three cups a day.

6. Soy products have "isoflavones" that block enzymes that feed the uncontrolled growth of tumor cells. Edamame (soy beans) are a great source, as is tofu, dry roasted soybeans, soy milk and chickpeas (though less so). Breast and prostate cancer is low-occurring among populations who use soy in their diet.

7. Blueberries, strawberries, raspberries and cranberries contain large amounts of phytochemicals to ward off cancer. Buy them fresh while in season or buy frozen during winter months. Hazelnuts and apples are also a good choice. Add citrus fruits to your diet, since they are rich in anti-inflammatory molecules that also prevent cancer.

8. Substitute fish for meats once or twice a week. They are rich in omega-3 fatty acids that help prevent plaque build-up in heart disease and they are linked to a reduction in breast, prostate and colon cancers. Salmon, herring, mackerel, rainbow trout and sardines are a good choice. You can also add omega-3 to your diet by simply using a spoonful of freshly milled flax seeds with cereals or grab some fresh walnuts.

9. A glass of wine with dinner contains resveratrol, which increases cell longevity and activates the cell's repair mechanism.

10. Chocolate? Yes, a small piece of good-quality dark chocolate contains powerful antioxidants, but it must be real chocolate, not milk chocolate in candy filled with sugar and fillers.

Another book you may want to consider is *Anticancer: A New Way of Life*, by David Servan-Schrieber, co-founder of the Center for Integrative Medicine at the University of Pittsburgh and a brain cancer survivor. Bon Appétit!

Q: My husband's driving hasn't been so great since he started a new medication. Could there be a connection?

A: Actually, your hunch that his driving skills and prescriptions are making for a hazardous mix is right on target. A study released by the American Automobile Association (AAA) Foundation made just that connection: older adults aren't aware as to how their prescriptions may impede their driving. Nor do they realize that, as their body ages, they process medications differently than when they were younger.

After extensive interviews of 630 older drivers, the AAA researchers found that seven in ten were taking one or more prescriptions that are known to potentially impair driving (e.g. ACE inhibitors, sedatives and beta blockers). What's more troubling is only 18 percent were warned by their prescribing doctor that the medications they were about to take could impair their driving. As a result, less than a third of those interviewed were aware that their medications could be classified as a Potentially Driver Impaired (PDI) drug.

Even though older drivers are involved in a small proportion of all crashes, they have the highest crash rate per mile driven and their injuries are often far more extensive than other adults. The Insurance Institute for Highway Safety recently projected that as the older population grows, drivers aged 65 and older are expected to account for one in four of all fatal crashes. The study also found that people in their seventies, who were more likely to take more drugs than the rest of the population, were the least aware of their effects. Interestingly enough, older drivers who were married seemed more likely to heed the warning about taking a break from driving while on a PDI medication. Here are some steps to consider:

1. Encourage your husband to give his doctor a call (or maybe you'll need to place the call yourself) and ask him or her to review his medications and identify if any of the drugs are known to cause cloudy or foggy thinking, dizziness, or confusion. If so, ask if there might be another drug that could be substituted that may not cause this side-effect.

2. Ask your pharmacist to look over his medications and advise both of you as to any side-effects that could impair his driving.

3. Read those drug information fact sheets with every new prescription and take

their advice when you're told "do not operate machinery or drive until you know how this medication affects you."

4. Go online to www.medlineplus.com and look up the drugs your husband is taking to learn what the drug is for, what conditions it treats and potential side-effects. Print it out and share it with him.

The most alarming finding of the study is that, even when people read about the risks of how a drug could impair their ability to drive, they just don't believe they will be a safety threat. The one person, however, who could convince them to take a break from driving while they were on the medication, was the doctor prescribing it. No matter what age, we all need to respect the effect medications can have on our ability to drive.

Q: I'm worried about my Mom being a "fire risk." What can I do?

A: According to the U.S. Fire Administration, older adults represent one of the highest fire risk groups in the nation. People 75 years and older are three times more likely than the national average to die in a fire. Many elderly fire victims come into physical contact with the source of the fire, such as a faulty space heater, the stove or a cigarette. Falling asleep while smoking is the leading cause of fires among the elderly. Older adults account for nearly one-third of all fire deaths at home.

Why are the elderly so vulnerable to fire deaths and injuries? Limited sight and mobility may make it difficult for an older person to exit quickly. Impaired vision can lead to accidents while cooking. Memory lapses and mild forms of dementia can cause someone to forget to turn off the iron, oven, toaster-oven or stove top. Medications that cause drowsiness or confusion may make her less aware of her surroundings so she won't pick up smells or sounds that alert her to a fire. So, yes, you should be worried. Here are a number of fire safety steps you can take to reduce your mother's risk of fire:

> If your Mom insists on using a space heater for added heat, look for one that will automatically turn off should it become overloaded or too hot.

> Don't overload electrical outlets or extension cords.

> If your Mom cooks, tell her not to wear loose clothing (especially long sleeves) around the stove. If she has impairments

225

that pose a risk near the stove, encourage her to use the microwave.

> Buy a simple, loud timer to remind her to take food off of the stove or out of the oven.

> If she doesn't have an iron that automatically shuts off, buy her one.

> Check all of the fire alarms whenever you come to visit her. Make sure there is one on every floor. Chances of surviving a home fire doubles with the initial warning from a smoke alarm.

> Identify exit routes for every room of the house and make sure the path is well lit and cleared. Install sensor lights in the hallway.

> If your Mom lives alone and has difficulty negotiating steps, consider re-locating the bedroom to the ground floor. She'll have a much greater chance of escaping a fire if she does not have to negotiate stairs to exit.

If your Mom is using space heaters to reduce her high utility or oil bills, see if she qualifies for financial assistance for her energy bills through the nationwide Low Income Home Energy Assistance Program (LIHEAP). Home owners and renters are eligible to receive energy grants from their state's Department of Welfare if they are on a low or fixed income. If she is eligible, LIHEAP will make a payment directly to her utility/fuel company and credit the bill. For information and applications call the National Energy Assistance Referral (NEAR) office toll free at 1-866-674-6327 or go to www.Govbenefits.gov and enter the keyword "LIHEAP."

 : How can I get my Mom to exercise?

 : I'm going to offer you four tactics to help get your Mom into shape. Here we go:

1. **Scare Tactic.** Plenty of research has shown that people who do not exercise:

> Are much more likely to acquire Type 2 diabetes.

> Lose roughly 15 percent of muscle mass in their sixties and another 15 percent in their seventies.

- Land much more quickly in nursing homes since leg strength is the best predictor of whether someone will require institutionalization.

- Have twice the risk of severe intestinal bleeding associated with colon cancer.

- Are much more likely to have heart attacks, high blood pressure, strokes, osteoporosis, and arthritis and suffer from depression and dementia.

2. Feel Good Tactic. Exercise is the closest thing we have to the Fountain of Youth, despite what the Botox crowd will tell you. Consider this:

- In a landmark study of eighty and ninety-year-olds, Tufts and Harvard Universities found that, after a 6 week program of exercise, a number of subjects were able to retire their canes and they all increased their muscle strength by 180 percent!

- Another study found that after five months of light exercise training, seventy-five percent of participants said that the exercise was just as effective at relieving their depression as medication.

- Your Mom will feel better about herself, as she'll also lose weight and feel like she's in charge of her body rather than the other way around. Every ten years your body loses 7 percent of its metabolism. No wonder those pounds add up.

3. Life's an Adventure Tactic. Every decade offers new phases in life and now your Mom can finally focus on *herself*. Chances are she's spent a lifetime caring for kids, a husband, parents, grandkids, co-workers and a boss. Now, it's her turn. You might need to help her redirect those energies to nurture her body and spirit. Here's how:

- **Ease into exercise.** Start a daily routine of just stretching: neck stretches (slowly tilt head from side-to-side and front to back), arm circles, and trunk twists (slowly turn upper body to one side, then the other). This can even be done sitting in a chair.

- **Walk.** How about going to the mall? Go in the early morning or around 2:00 p.m. after the lunch crowd leaves and before teens descend after school. The mall, with its air conditioning, is particularly nice during the summer.

- **Tai chi.** A study at Northwestern University found that elderly who practiced this slow-moving Chinese martial art significantly reduced falls and balance problems in just 12 weeks. Many senior centers offer classes in Tai chi and Yoga. If she won't go, buy a video and do it with her and get one of her girlfriends to join in, too.

- **Get an exercise video.** There are exercise videos tailored to just about everyone's fitness ability. For example, Armchair Fitness is a 1-hour, gentle session that is set to big-band music (call 1-800-453-

6280). If your Mom uses a walker or is in a wheelchair, order the *Exercising with Dorothy* video by calling 1-800-779-8491. You can also visit Collage Video, which specializes in all levels of exercise videos, at www.collagevideo.com. Go to their "specialty workouts" and click on "Seniors" or give them a call at 1-800-433-6769. There's also a nice "Exercise Guide for Older People" from the National Institute on Aging. Call for a copy at 1-800-222-2225.

▸ **Check out a senior center.** Many senior centers today offer excellent programs on healthy lifestyles and exercise programs. Just call your local Area Agency on Aging (1-800-677-1116) and ask for the senior center coordinator to find out what programs are available in your area.

4. Just Do It Tactic. Enough with "I'm too old, too tired, it won't make a difference" excuses – get off the couch, turn off the television and start flexing! It could very well save your parent's life or, at the very least, make it worth living.

: Do couples have a hard time adjusting to retirement?

: If couples haven't taken the time to talk about their expectations of what they'd like to do when they retire as a couple and as individuals, then they'll likely encounter a rocky start. Couples hear plenty about financial planning for their retirement, but very little on lifestyle planning. But, even if they did talk about what they see as the good life in retirement, nearly one out of three will likely disagree as to what age they'd retire, the lifestyle they want and if they'll take up working after they retire. At least, that's what a new survey of 503 married couples by Fidelity Investments would predict, based on their results. Plenty of research before this study has found that couples who openly discuss how they want to live when they retire have a much easier time adjusting.

Many people underestimate how much retirement will affect them. If you had a strong attachment to your job and all of your friends were the folks you worked with, then it may explain why you need to fill the void by spending all of your time with your spouse and his or her network of friends. People whose entire identity was caught up in their work will be at risk for feeling depressed if they don't find another way to feel needed or purposeful. The transition to retirement seems to be particularly stressful if one spouse retires earlier than the other, especially if the husband retires while the wife remains working. Couples find that retirement brings a shift in roles; if wives did more of the housework in the past, they'll now look to their husband to pitch in. On the other hand, some women find it intrusive when their stay-at-home spouse starts taking too much of an interest in rearranging her domain.

The other day I heard someone refer to retirement as "rewirement." I think that term better defines how people are redefining how they'll experience this later life stage. Some will re-wire themselves with new careers, new hobbies, volunteer work, take up a cause, go back to school, travel, work part-time, spend more time with family and many will face the challenges of managing their health. Those couples, who view retirement as a dynamic process to engage both as a couple and individually, are the ones who will fare best.

So, couples can stay on track with three suggestions:

Envision the future. Each of you should make a list of what you'd like to do with your new-found time. Break it down by a week: would you like to go out for dinner twice a week, go to a movie, join a club, go to a senior center, play golf, or volunteer? Also, each of you should make a list of what special things you'd like to do each month and throughout the year. Once each of you has made your lists, explore with each other how you can meet your expectations separately as well as find ways to do things as a couple.

Communicate. You've gone through many of life's transitions together and you may have found that you placed your own relationship on the back burner while you raised children and maintained jobs to support your family. Some couples go through a honeymoon stage if they've retired at the same time, while others don't know what to talk about or what to do together when jobs and kids no longer take center stage.

Talk through your feelings about retirement to each other. Holding in your differences and frustrations during retirement will only lead to resentment. For example, if you need some separate space once in a while, let your spouse know upfront. If one of you is very active and the other one isn't, compromise on activities together and look for opportunities to join in community groups in which you share a mutual interest. Life is filled with compromises and if a vacation is really important to you and visiting the grandkids is important to her, then how about visiting the family on the way to a week-long vacation at a destination you'll both enjoy? Just as you've talked through issues raising a family from the stages of birth to the empty nest, you will need to do the same in your retirement. It, too, will be filled with change. It's not a one-time conversation.

 I'm going back home for the holidays to visit my parents and want to make sure everything is okay. What should I look for?

Going home for the holidays offers you a perfect opportunity to quietly assess how things are going for your parents. It also offers you the chance to help them out and prevent problems in the future. Here is my "Home for the Holidays Checklist."

FIVE THINGS TO LOOK FOR:

1. **Look around the house.** Are household bills piling up and is mail left un-opened? This could be a sign that the simple tasks of writing bills, balancing a checkbook and keeping track of due dates is becoming overwhelming. Do you see scorched pots and pans? Is the house more unkempt than usual? All of these signs could flag a decrease in thinking skills, decreased vision, and/or the inability to be physically active.

2. **Check out the refrigerator.** Is it well-stocked with fresh produce and meats or do you see signs of a very poor diet and moldy, expired food products? When you take them out to eat, are they eating a lot less and showing little interest in food? Do they appear to have lost weight? These could be signs that they are becoming malnourished. Poor diet can exacerbate chronic diseases, lead to a weakened immune system and increase the risk of dementia.

3. **Ask them about their social life.** When was the last time they went out with friends? Went out to eat? Went to church? Did the things they loved doing? If you find them reluctant to leave the house, this could be a sign that they're having a hard time driving, moving about, seeing, or hearing so they'd rather stay home. This could lead to loneliness and depression. Find out what's causing them to disengage.

4. **Let them take you for a drive.** If your parents are still driving, you might do well to let them drive so that you can assess their driving skills. You should especially do this if you see dents or scratches on the car, or if your parent has received recent speeding or traffic tickets.

5. Check out their medications. Are expired pill bottles mixed in with current ones? Are the pills organized to prevent taking the wrong dose or too many? Are they taking more than 5 medications? Can you hold a coherent conversation? Do they keep repeating the same story? Confusion, dizziness and signs of dementia can be caused by medications or taking the wrong combination of drugs.

FIVE THINGS TO DO:

1. Organize their medications. Get them pill tracker containers that separate their pills by the day, week and time of day. Color code and label the lids of their pill bottles so they know which one is a water pill, heart pill and so forth. Create a list of all their current medications and who prescribed them, then make copies for their doctors and yourself. You can download a free MedMinder form on my website at <u>www.lindarhodescaregiving. com</u>.

2. Get to know their support system. Introduce yourself to neighbors, exchange phone numbers and tell them to feel free to call you if they think your parents might need you. Sign up for the Carrier Alert program at the local post office (postal carriers will alert you if they think something is amiss). Get the phone numbers of their doctors, pharmacist, local home health agencies, the Area Agency on Aging, non-medical senior care companies and transportation services, so if your parents can't make the calls, you can.

3. Have that conversation. You need to know where all of their important papers are, such as living will, durable healthcare power of attorney, power of attorney, will and insurance policies.

4. Look into a geriatric assessment. If they haven't had a physician trained in geriatrics along with an interdisciplinary team do an overall work-up, now might be the time to set it up. Many local hospitals offer this type of service. Take the time to check it out for them.

5. Tackle the annual Medicare or Managed Care paperwork. Between now and the beginning of next year, your parents need to decide whether or not to stay in traditional Medicare or opt for a Medicare managed care plan. It can be very confusing. You can also help them choose a Medicare Part D prescription plan. Go to <u>www.medicare.gov</u> for answers on Medicare Part D and a comparison of plans.

Happy Holidays!

Q: My wife fell getting out of the car and broke her wrist. How can we prevent this from happening again?

A: Actually, getting in and out of your car is fast becoming a growing safety hazard, landing people in their sixties and older into emergency rooms. According to the National Center for Injury Prevention and Control, 37,000 people 65 years and older are injured every year when entering or exiting a vehicle. People in their sixties are ten times more likely to be hospitalized as a result of injuring themselves getting in and out of cars than younger people. Women, long known to be susceptible to osteoporosis, suffer more serious injuries and require a hospital admission for treatment and recovery. Getting out of a vehicle poses twice the risk for injury as getting into it.

Car manufacturers are finally catching onto the needs of older drivers. Ford Motors came up with what they call a "Third Age" suit that mimics limitations among the elderly and made their engineers wear it while they designed a senior-friendly car. The GM mobility engineering team recently created what they call a "Sit-N-Lift" power bucket seat that rotates, extending out of the vehicle and then lowers for a trouble-free entry and exit for passengers and drivers with limited mobility. So far, they are the only auto manufacturer in the U.S. to offer a power seat as a dealer-installed option and it can also be retrofitted on some current models. Let's keep your wife out of the emergency room by having her follow any of the following steps:

> ‣ First, check her medications to make sure she isn't taking something that could be causing her to feel dizzy when she gets up from a sitting position.

> ‣ She should get her vision checked to make sure she has good depth perception and is able to see clearly when grabbing door handles for support.

> ‣ Purchase a swivel seat cushion to make that difficult twist off the seat much easier. I got one for my mother and she loves it.

> ‣ Get a "Transfer Bar" with soft handles to grab when she's getting out of the car.

> ‣ If you need to drop her off while you park the car, take the time to assist her out of the car and escort her to a place to sit and wait for you to park.

> ‣ If she ever needs a wheelchair, you can purchase a flip-down transfer seat that acts as a bridge between a wheelchair or scooter and the vehicle.

- And finally, one of the best ways to prevent falls in general is to do weight bearing exercises that build muscles and practice Yoga-like movements that promote your ability to steady yourself when you lose your balance.

You can find a wide range of assistive transfer devices online at Abledata, a federal information clearing house on assistive devices for the elderly and people with disabilities (www.abledata.com), or call them at 1-800-227-0216. If you don't have access to the internet, here are vendors who carry the products I've mentioned:

Transfer Bars: The HandyBar is a car transfer that fits in the U-shaped door striker of most cars to create a handle for extra leverage to aide in getting out of a car. Prices range from $45 to $50. Contact Simple Comforts at 1 800-361-1440 or go online at www. SimpleComforts.com.

Swivel Cushions: The cushion helps the user to turn when getting in or out of a car, wheelchair or bed, rotating at 360 degrees. Prices range from $45 to $50. Simple Comforts mentioned above also carries this item.

Installed Transfer Seats: These flip-down transfer seats act as a bridge between a wheelchair or scooter and a vehicle seat. It attaches to the vehicle and can be stowed when not in use. Check out Access Unlimited at 1-800-849-2143 or visit them at www. accessunlimited.com.

 : My Dad watches the news all day. Could this be making him depressed?

 : Daily news reports continuously remind us that we're living under a cloud of war, terrorism, crime and natural disasters that feeds a subliminal message that we're all vulnerable and life is fragile. Despite this depressing "news," we tend to go about our daily lives acting as though life is normal. Your Dad and many of our parents who are retired don't have the diversion of getting on with life as usual – even if it is just a pretense. They don't have school to attend, homework to get done, young kids to get to practice, deadlines to make at work, orders to fill, or customers to please. They've also gone through a war. They know the pain and the hardship that it entails.

Older people who aren't active in their community or family, who have health problems or have experienced the loss of a job, friend or family member, are significantly vulnerable to depression. But what do you look for in depression and just what is it, anyway? Depression is an illness of intense sadness that interferes with the ability to function, feel pleasure, or maintain interest. Researchers have discovered that biochemical imbalances in the brain go hand-in-hand with depression.

It might follow a recent loss or sad event, but the intensity of the feeling and its duration persist far beyond what is healthy. Remember that, because this isn't just psychological; it's also biochemical. You can't simply tell your parent to just "snap out of it" or "look on the bright side." The National Institute of Mental Health offers this checklist of symptoms of clinical depression:

> Persistent sadness, anxiety or feeling of emptiness

> Loss of interest or pleasure in ordinary activities, family or friends

> Decreased energy, listlessness, fatigue, feeling slowed down

> Changes in sleep patterns

> Eating problems and changes in appetite

> Difficulty in concentrating, remembering or making decisions

> Feelings of hopelessness, guilt, worthlessness and helplessness

> Thoughts of suicide or death

> Irritability

> Excessive crying, sometimes without reason

> Recurring aches and pains such as headaches and backaches that don't respond to treatment

If you think your Dad exhibits these symptoms, get him to his family physician to rule out any other physical problems. Studies show that a combination of psychotherapy and carefully prescribed medications can be 80 percent successful in treating depression among the elderly. Antidepressants are powerful drugs, however, and they should be prescribed very carefully and in conjunction with other mental health services. Two websites that are valuable resources on depression are www.nimh.nih.gov and www.depression.org.

Lifestyle changes, including good nutrition, vitamins, exercise and getting out with family and friends are vital to a mentally fit life. I'd also suggest that your father, especially if he is retired and not very active, limit how much televised news coverage he watches. A constant stream of visuals that reinforces how troubling life has become, in addition to how vulnerable his aging body may have him feeling, is simply not healthy. So, yes, your Dad should take a break from the round-the-clock newscasts.

Q: Should I be worried that my Mom's becoming an alcoholic?

A: If your mother is drinking alone, drinking throughout the day, withdrawing from friends or is focused on keeping a supply of alcohol readily available then, yes, be worried. Particularly if she is grieving over the death of a loved one or other major loss in her life, she could be trapped in the vicious cycle of taking a drink to "drown her troubles."

What complicates the problem for your Mom and other older people is that her aging body is more sensitive to the effects of alcohol. Studies show that a 60-year-old will have a twenty percent higher blood-alcohol level than a 20-year-old drinking the same amount. Add to this a mix of medications and decreased food intake common among the elderly and someone who didn't have a problem with alcohol can certainly have one now. Current research shows that nearly one in five older adults is affected by alcohol and drug misuse. Yet few primary care physicians are picking it up: no one wants to ask and no one wants to tell. Many families feel it's too late for the chronic alcoholic, and others are in outright denial that their parent could have a drinking problem. If your mother answers yes to any of the following questions (known as the **CAGE** questionnaire), then she has symptoms of alcoholism:

> ▸ Have you ever felt you should **C**ut down on your drinking?

> ▸ Have people **A**nnoyed you by criticizing your drinking?

> ▸ Have you ever felt bad or **G**uilty about your drinking?

> ▸ Have you ever had a drink first thing in the morning to steady your nerves or get rid of a hangover (**E**ye-opener)?

There are a number of resources that can help you learn how to approach your Mom and her physician to help her gain control of her drinking problem. Part of the strategy should include getting her physically and mentally fit. Your mother might be depressed and the alcohol will only depress her more. Her treatment plan must include getting at the root of her need to drink. Reach out to the National Council on Alcoholism and Drug Dependence Hopeline at 1-800-622-2255, find a family support group by calling Al-Anon at 1-888-4AL-ANON, or research the latest information at the National Clearinghouse for Alcohol and Drug Information website at www.health.org. Whatever you do, don't be afraid to address the issue with your Mom. Looking the other way or hoping she'll just stop on her own denies both of you a healthy, happy relationship with each other, let alone her grandchildren. Alcoholics are at great risk for cascading health problems, hospitalization and an early death. Act on your worries.

Q: How can I get my father to eat better?

 If your Dad is anything like mine, he grew up in a meat-and-potato, smothered in gravy, household. Most of our parents were raised on great ethnic cuisine that was heavy on sauces, spices and salt. America's interest in lowfat food and light fare has been relatively recent, so getting your Dad interested in foods that are user-friendly for his older body might be a real challenge. But, this is a challenge we've got to face head on: According to a report by AARP, four out of five older adults have chronic illnesses that are affected by diet. One out of eight suffers depression with a subsequent loss of appetite, one in four drinks too much alcohol, one out of three lives alone and doesn't feel like cooking and most take medications that require a nutritionally sound body to be effective. Far too many older people are in a rut, eating the same thing day after day.

Tuft's University Center on Nutrition recently came out with a modified food pyramid for adults aged 70-plus. For this age group, two major changes to the typical food pyramid have been made: The bottom of the pyramid "floats" with eight glasses of water and the top has a flag promoting supplements in calcium, vitamins D and B-12. What's with the floating base? Dehydration is a major problem among the elderly. While the rest of us are running around with trendy water bottles, our parents are actually losing their sense of thirst. Let your Dad in on that fact, otherwise he'll just say he's not thirsty. Without enough water, kidney problems, constipation and complications from medications that deplete the body's water supply will quickly take hold.

You might want to stock his refrigerator with small bottles of water, so you can get your Dad into the habit of drinking it. The age 70-plus food pyramid also has little "f-plus" signs everywhere. These stand for fiber, and our parents need plenty of it to keep their digestive track humming along. Nutritionists will tell you to:

> ‣ Find out if any of your parent's medical conditions warrant a special diet.

▸ Try serving small, frequent meals if your Dad has lost his appetite. Or serve him the larger meal of the day when his appetite seems to peak.

▸ If your Dad can't see well, use plain white plates and lay out his food on the plate as if it were a clock. Tell him, for example, that the rice is at 9 o'clock, the chicken at noon and the green beans at 4 o'clock.

▸ Make mealtime a special event with nice silverware and colorful napkins.

If your parent lives alone, organize a visiting schedule among family and friends to have lunch or dinner with your parent. Eating alone, day after day, is a prime factor in older folks not eating well. Home-delivered meals are a terrific way to mix a friendly visit with a meal. To find out about the nearest meal service, call the local Area Agency on Aging or the Eldercare Locator 1-800-677-1116. And if your Dad has physical difficulty eating, call Able Data at 1-800-227-0216, or Independent Living Aids, 1-800-537-2118, and ask for catalogs of eating utensils and devices.

For excellent nutritional advice online, go to:

▸ Mayo Clinic's Health Oasis (www.mayohealth.org). This fun, easy website offers delicious recipes that have adapted for better health. Click on "*Healthy Lifestyle*" and follow the prompts.

▸ The Tufts University Nutrition Navigator (www.navigator.tufts.edu). This site reviews and rates a zillion websites on nutrition and hyperlinks you to them. (Tip: enter "*aging and nutrition*" on the search bar).

 : What preventive health screenings should my parents have?

Most of our parents grew up with the adage, "A stitch in time saves nine." So, perhaps you can convince your Mom and Dad that the same principle applies to their health. A few preventive stitches here and there can save quite a few later – literally. Many of today's health advances are credited to people taking better care of themselves by eating well, exercising and by getting regular check-ups to screen for diseases that frequently affect the elderly. Just consider these statistics:

- **Osteoporosis,** or porous bone, is a disease of low bone mass and structural deterioration of bone tissue. This leads to fragile bones and an increased susceptibility to fractures, especially of the hip, spine and wrist. Nearly 10 million Americans have the disease and women are four times more likely to have it.

- **Colorectal cancer** (cancers of both the colon and rectum) is the second-leading cause of cancer-related deaths in the United States. In 2010, nearly 112,000 Americans will be diagnosed with colorectal cancer and over 50,000 will die this year.

- **Type 2 Diabetes,** often referred to as adult onset diabetes, affects over 12 million people, half of whom don't know they have the disease. Nearly 1 in 12 people over the age of 65 become diabetic; and one in four people over 85 years.

- **Breast Cancer** incidence increases with age: Nearly three out of four invasive breast cancers occur in women over age 50, while the average age at diagnosis is 64. Based on the current life expectancy for women in the United States, one out of nine women will develop breast cancer in her lifetime.

- **Cervical Cancer** incidence has decreased significantly, in large part because of screening for and treatment of precancerous cervical lesions (Pap smears). However, an estimated 11,000 new cases were diagnosed and 4,000 women died of the disease in 2008. Older women are at higher risk, as they tend to stop getting annual Pap smears.

- **Prostate Cancer** is diagnosed nearly every three minutes, accounting for 190,000 new cases each year. It is the most commonly diagnosed cancer in America among men. More than 30,000 American men lose their lives to prostate cancer each year. One in six American men is at lifetime risk of prostate cancer. If a close relative has prostate cancer, a man's risk of the disease more than doubles.

- **Flu** hits between ten to twenty percent of U.S. residents each year, causing an average of 121,000 people to require hospitalization. About 36,000 Americans die annually from the complications of flu, many of whom are elderly.

- **Glaucoma** is now the leading cause of blindness in the United States affecting nearly 3 million people. African Americans, diabetics and people over the age of sixty are at high risk of the disease, which slowly and quietly causes fluid build-up that damages the eye.

Medicare pays for screenings and tests on all of the above conditions. If your parent has a Medi-gap policy, they won't have any out-of-pocket expense. So, there really is no excuse not to take advantage of all of these preventive health services offered by Medicare. Encourage your parents take this list to their next appointment with their primary physician and ask him or her to get these scheduled. The doctor's office should know the eligibility rules surrounding each test.

Q: My Dad thinks losing teeth is normal in old age. Is it?

A: Losing teeth is not a normal part of aging. Decay and gum disease are the major culprits in tooth loss, not getting older. All too often, older people think that the annual dental visit is "kid's stuff." However, people over sixty-five have more tooth decay than any other age group. The good news is that many people today maintain their teeth, and as a result, approximately 50% of people 55 years or older have at least 23 of their 32 natural teeth remaining.

According to the Foundation for Health in Aging, a non-profit organization of the American Geriatrics Society, older people tend to produce less saliva and this means they have fewer protective minerals to help clean teeth; their gums begin to recede, exposing the tooth to decay or infection; arthritis and poor vision make it hard to floss and brush teeth, all of which further complicate daily oral care. The Foundation cites five problems common to older people's oral health: Tooth decay, gum disease, poor fitting dentures, dry mouth and oral cancer.

The bacteria found in plaque give off acid that leads to gum or periodontal disease. Pockets often develop between teeth and gums, trapping food that will decay, thus the need to floss. Symptoms include red or swollen gums that bleed with the slightest irritation. A loose tooth or one that falls out could well be a sign of gum disease, so your father should be examined before it advances any further.

"Dry mouth" comes mainly from the slower production of saliva but can also be linked to medications such as diuretics, antihistamines and anti-depressants. Why is this important? People with dry mouth are more prone to infections and tooth decay. Oral lubricants such as lemon-flavored glycerin drops or artificial saliva can help but again, this is a sign of something going awry and warrants a dental visit.

Oral cancer includes cancers of the mouth, tongue, throat and lips. Red or white spots, sores in the mouth or continuous bleeding are early signs of oral cancer and should be seen by a dentist immediately. Ninety-five percent of cases of oral and throat cancer occur in people 40 and over; and the average age at diagnosis is 60. Oral cancer accounts for nearly 4 percent of all cancers; and it's no surprise that the leading cause of oral cancer is smoking. In terms of preventive dental care, here are some things your Dad can do after he makes an annual visit to the dentist:

> Use a medium soft brush and brush daily. Hard brushes don't make teeth cleaner and can actually be harmful. Long handles are easier to use. Buy a new brush every three months and floss. If it's too difficult, buy the small floss holders with the plastic handles.

> Rinse your mouth throughout the day with warm water (add a teaspoon of salt.)

> Stop smoking.

> If you have dentures, remove them at least six hours per day (most people do this before bed), brush dentures every night, and make sure they fit well. If you have problems with them, don't hesitate to see your dentist, dental hygienist or denturist.

Poor oral health can lead to poor nutrition, which brings on a whole new set of problems. Your teeth, gums and saliva are your first contact with food and start the process of healthy digestion. If your Dad is sending bacteria along for the ride down his digestive track or he shows signs of losing his appetite because it's too painful to crunch and munch, then his oral health will jeopardize his entire body. My guess is that your Dad didn't get a few dollars from the Tooth Fairy for his lost tooth. But, she gave him a better gift – a warning. Tell him to take heed.

: How much water should older people drink?

Water can save your parents from a whole host of health problems, especially those related to kidney disease. Tuft's University Center on Nutrition has become so convinced of the health benefits of water for older people that they have redesigned the USDA's Food Guide Pyramid: Now, the base of the pyramid "floats" with eight glasses of water pictured on the bottom. Why the floating base? Dehydration is a major problem among the elderly.

While the Gen X crowd runs around with trendy water bottles in hand, their grandparents are losing their sense of thirst. As a result, the older generation is having kidney problems, urinary tract infections, constipation and other health conditions linked to a chronic state of dehydration.

The elderly are especially affected by dehydration because many of the medications they take may further deplete the body's water supply without them ever realizing it. All too often, we forget that nearly three-fourths of our body is water. Thus, we need to keep a healthy amount of fresh fluids flowing in and out of our bodies. Water flushes out wastes, regulates our body temperature, carries nutrients throughout the blood stream reaching vital organs, and supports chemical balances. Staying well-hydrated can boost energy and keep the skin moist, which is especially helpful for dry, aging skin. Signs of dehydration include dizziness, weakness, muscle cramps and general feelings of weakness.

So, how much water should your parents drink? Most experts recommend eight glasses of water (8 ounces each) per day. Some refer to it as the "8 by 8" rule.

Does it have to be just water? Not necessarily. Your parents can achieve this higher fluid intake with juices, milk, and teas or coffee without caffeine. Some foods also include water like soups, yogurt, fruits such as watermelon, apples, oranges and tomatoes, and vegetables like lettuce, carrots and cucumbers. But don't think that all fluids are created equal. Alcoholic beverages don't count in your daily intake – they get a big fat zero. In fact, alcohol inhibits the body's anti-diuretic hormone (ADH) so your parents will actually lose fluids. Black tea, green tea, caffeinated sodas and coffee are also known to have a dehydrating effect. Most physical fitness experts recommend starting your day with water. During the night your body becomes dehydrated and can greatly benefit from water first thing in the morning.

Figuring out your parents' best source of water requires a bit of exploration. Would they like to drink bottled water as a way of measuring how much they drink each day? Do they feel their tap water is safe to drink? If not, they could purchase a simple water filter to attach to the faucet or buy a water pitcher with a filter. To make their water intake more interesting, they could add slices of lime or lemon.

Before they start on their new water venture, be sure to check with their physician if they have a kidney condition or other medical condition in which fluid intake should be monitored. Also, take the time to figure out if there are other reasons that your parents are steering clear of water: you might find that your Dad is lowering his intake because getting to the bathroom is a hassle, or your Mom may be cutting down her fluids because she fears incontinence. These indicate other health problems that will only be exacerbated by limiting their fluid intake. So, find out what's going on first and then create a hydration strategy that suits your parents' needs and lifestyle.

: My Dad wants to know if flu shots are free and are they really necessary?

The answer to the first part of your question is "yes." If your father carries Medicare Part B, then he can receive a flu shot from a Medicare provider and pay no coinsurance or deductible. Most Medicare HMOs actually require their subscribers to receive a (free) flu shot. Besides physicians, many senior centers and public health centers offer flu shots. Most Area Agencies on Aging (AAA) throughout the nation offer free flu vaccines. You can track down your local AAA by calling 1-800-677-1116. Remember that October and November are the prime months to receive flu shots.

Now for the second part of your question, are flu shots really necessary? If your Dad doesn't want to be counted among the estimated 36,000 people who die every year from influenza, then it's best he take the shot. Ninety percent of those who die from the flu are 65 and older. Why? Because many older people have other medical conditions that easily become exacerbated by the flu. People with heart disease, lung conditions and diabetes are particularly susceptible. The Centers for Disease Control (CDC) reports that there are about 121,000 influenza-related hospitalizations every year.

Influenza is an extremely contagious respiratory condition easily spread from person to person by sneezes or coughs. Symptoms usually appear within two or four days of infection and you are contagious for three to four days after that. An estimated 10 to 20 percent of the U.S. population comes down with the flu each year. In other words, your Dad has a one in five chance of being exposed to someone with the flu. Pretty high odds, wouldn't you say?

The reason your Dad needs to receive a new vaccine every year is because the virus mutates from year to year. So, the antibodies produced in response to the vaccine decline over time and are very low one year later.

Most of us know too well the dreaded symptoms of the flu: fever, chills, headache, dry cough, runny or stuffy nose, sore throat and muscle aches. It can also cause extreme fatigue lasting several days to more than a week. One of the clearest dangers for older people is the high risk of the flu developing into pneumonia, which can be life-threatening. For that reason, your Dad should ask his physician whether or not he should also receive a one-time vaccination for pneumococcal pneumonia. If his physician prescribes the vaccine, it will be covered by Medicare.

The only people who should not get a flu shot, according to the National CDC Advisory Committee on Immunization Practices, are those who are severely allergic to hens' eggs, have had severe reactions to a flu shot in the past, or developed Guillain-Barre syndrome (GBS) within 6 weeks of getting a flu shot. Side effects are rare, with the most common complaint being soreness around the injection site.

Q: Besides getting a flu shot, what else can my wife do to prevent getting the flu?

 A: Since she's already taken the first step to protect herself by getting her flu shot, let's focus on her immune system. It's no secret to those in their senior years that a good old-fashioned cold seems to hang on longer than it did in their younger years. It's got to do with a tired immune system that just isn't up for the quick one-two punch.

Lymphocytes are essential cells that produce antibodies to battle infections. They become less efficient as we age; putting up a fight for shorter periods of time and there are less of them. Even the body's natural reaction to attacking an infection – launching a fever to burn off troublemaking cells – can go AWOL, allowing bacteria to run amok. One in five people over 65 years with severe bacterial infections won't show a fever.

So, let's get your wife's immune system in tip top shape:

1. **Take a multi-vitamin.** She should choose one that's targeted to her age and gender. If she feels overwhelmed with all the choices available in vitamins, herbs and supplements, then simply choose a good, solid multi-vitamin with the Pharmacopia seal. Research is mixed as to whether or not the herb Echinacea boosts the immune system. Some say it can lessen the duration of a cold and its symptoms. If she does take it, she should do it as soon as she feels any cold symptoms and not take it for more than eight weeks.

2. **Drink water.** Far too often, older people think that tea, coffee and sodas are all the liquids they need. But, actually, all of them can cause damage and dehydrate rather than hydrate. A food pyramid designed specifically for older adults by the Center on Aging at Tufts University illustrates the base of the pyramid as being nothing but glasses of water. For a copy of the pyramid go to my website

at www.lindarhodescaregiving.com and click on "Caregiver Tips." Given the multiple medications older people take, it is essential that they cleanse their body and keep their blood flow circulating so organs stay healthy. Eight glasses of water a day (eight ounces each) should keep your wife in good stead.

3. **Eat for your immune system.** Good nutrition can be a real buddy to a weakened immune system. Fruit and vegetables are at the top of the list, as these foods often double as antioxidants (such as blueberries) which prevent damage to cells. Vitamins C, E and green tea are also antioxidants. Stay clear of high-fat foods and reach for sources of lean protein. It turns out that the amino acids found in lean protein are critical components to revving up your immune system. Fish (salmon), lean poultry, soy products, eggs, beans, and tofu are all good sources of lean protein. Avoid trans fats (read the food labels) often found in processed foods, snacks and margarine, as they'll cause your immune system to work over-time and deplete your ability to fight-off infections. Yogurt, on the other hand, deploys an army of "good" bacteria to detoxify your intestinal tract, staving off potential infections.

4. **Don't forget to exercise.** Being overweight plays havoc with how all of your organs function, which overtaxes an already vulnerable immune system. Studies have shown that people who moderately exercise are four times less likely to come down with colds than their overweight counterparts.

Q: What's the connection between salt and hypertension?

Not until I started reading labels on food did I become aware of how much sodium (salt) is hidden in foods that I thought were healthy. People are pretty surprised when they learn that a healthy-looking garden salad topped with lowfat dressing can pack in more salt than the hamburger and French fries you dutifully passed up. Two tablespoons of Zesty Italian dressing has more than 500 milligrams of sodium. And, who uses only 2 tablespoons?

To put this in perspective, experts recommend that we consume only 2,400 milligrams of sodium a day, but if you have high blood pressure, your intake should drop down to 1,500. Sodium is not inherently bad.

Our bodies need it to regulate our fluids. However, too much of it can cause body fluids to build up.

Processed foods, canned soups, sauces, fast food, spaghetti sauces and salad dressing (even lowfat) can catapult us over the top on the sodium scale. Experts figure that Americans consume two to three times the recommended limit. Most of us think if we ditch the table salt and stay clear of food with visible salt on them such as saltine crackers and pretzels, we're good to go. But, according to Bobbie Mostyn, author of the *Pocket Guide to Low Sodium Foods*, most of us are unaware of how much salt we actually take in. The burden shouldn't just be on consumers to detect high sodium amounts; the American Public Health Association is calling on the food industry to cut down on foods with unhealthy levels of sodium.

So, if you're worried that your parents might be taking in too much salt, what can they do? They should try working with the foods they already enjoy and then analyze the sodium levels. If they are too high, search for ways to prepare their favorite dishes in a way that is safer for their health. Expecting older people to dramatically change their eating habits will only set them up for failure. You also might want to pick up a guide to sodium content, such as Mostyn's. It's a fast and easy way to check out sodium levels of fast foods, condiments and restaurant cooking, along with products to buy at the grocery store. You also can check out the author's website with all kinds of smart tips on sodium tracking at www.lowsaltfoods.com. I know my mother was shocked at how much sodium she was taking in with her favorite salad at a national food chain. She continued to buy the salad, but substituted the dressing. Who knows, your parents might actually enjoy playing "Sodium Sleuth!"

 Q: My Dad isn't sleeping well, but he says older people need less sleep, anyway. Shouldn't he see a doctor?

A: It's actually a myth that older people need less sleep. According to the National Sleep Foundation, our sleep needs remain relatively constant throughout most of our lives; for most people, that is seven to nine hours of sleep throughout their lifetime. It's the stages of sleep that will undergo change.

One reason that your Dad may be experiencing a drop in restful, restorative sleep is that as we age, we experience less of the deep, restorative third and fourth stages of sleep. We also tend to experience less of the fifth stage, R.E.M. (rapid eye movement) sleep – the kind that has your eyes flickering while you're dreaming. All that flickering causes an increased blood supply and the flow of some mighty fine brain chemicals. You can thank these guys for that restored, "go get 'em" feeling when you wake up.

An aging body also produces less melatonin, the hormone that regulates sleep. If your father is in his seventies or eighties, in fact, his melatonin levels may be barely traceable. Other factors that can contribute to poor sleep are getting little exercise, drinking caffeine and smoking.

It's worthwhile to seek ways to help your father sleep more effectively and wake up feeling refreshed. It takes a little work and a bit of re-programming. Here are some tips to share with him:

➤ Develop a regular, soothing routine for going to bed, such as listening to music, reading, taking a warm bath or massaging yourself with skin lotion. Send signals to your mind and body that it's time to sleep.

➤ Stick to the same bedtime and naptime every day. A consistent schedule is critical to setting your biological clock.

➤ Drink very little fluids a few hours before bed time so there's no need to go to the bathroom at night.

➤ Keep daytime napping to a minimum – no more than an hour – and make sure it is early in the afternoon. Avoid dozing off in front of the television.

➤ Avoid heavy meals close to bed time, especially spicy ones. Eating at 5:00 p.m. will give adequate time for digestion. You might want to consider having your largest meal at lunch.

➤ Don't smoke. Nicotine plays havoc with sleep.

➤ Avoid alcohol at bedtime. Although it may appear to make you drowsy, you'll actually awaken early without feeling rested.

➤ Ask your doctor about the side effects of any medications that you are taking. Some will cause sleep disturbances.

If your Dad's sleeping problems persist, he should describe them to his doctor. If he's sleeping, but isn't feeling rested, it could be a sign of coronary artery disease, lung disease, thyroid problems, depression, anxiety or dementia. It's very tempting to simply ask your doctor to prescribe sleeping pills to solve the problem. But, before any such pill is given, your physician should explore what's causing the problem in the first place. Sleeping pills can help in the short term and help stop the cycle of fatigue and exhaustion. But, they are meant to be taken for a short period of time, and certainly not for the rest of your life. Yet, far too many elderly are taking hypnotic drugs as their first choice to getting a "good" night's sleep. Taking these pills for the long haul can cause daytime sleepiness, anxiety, depression, decline in cognitive thinking and falls. Getting off the drug must be done very carefully and slowly. So, if your Dad's doctor does prescribe a sleeping pill, make sure he takes it responsibly and for the short run.

Section Two
Family Conflicts & Relationships

Q: All of this caregiving is getting too stressful. How do I get a grip?

A: There are programs that assist family members to help ease the load of caring for an elderly relative. Of course, it takes time and some organizing to track them down, and I'm sure you feel you don't even have the time to find the help. One of the many pitfalls of caregiving is falling into the trap of, "It's easier to just do it myself." By the time you find someone to help, it's too late or just too much of a hassle. You may also find that the person you are caring for becomes dependent on you and wants only you to help. You begin to think you're the only one who can do it. Once the cycle starts, it's hard to stop. I know. I cared for my husband's grandmother for a year right after my first child was born. She came to trust me and called me her "manager," making it clear that only Linda could take care of her. Between Grandma and the baby, I had my hands full. It was too much of a struggle finding a babysitter for the baby and a caregiver for Grandma; I found it easier to simply stay at home and care for both of them. After a while, a good friend intervened and told me enough was enough. She was right. I was running myself into the ground and had become sick myself. So, from both personal and professional experience, here's what I suggest you do:

➤ Tonight, take the time to list all the tasks you performed today. Then, add any other tasks you frequently perform for your parent throughout the week. Can you categorize some of these tasks? What comes under daily personal care (i.e., grooming, toileting, medications or feeding)? Other categories might be transportation, doctor visits, meal preparation, socialization, exercise and supervision. Put a star next to those tasks that you perform daily or routinely throughout the week.

➤ Make copies of the list, and share it with all of your family members, friends and neighbors who've asked you at one time or another, "Is there anything I can do to help?" See which items on the list they could do, especially those tasks that routinely have to be performed (the ones with a star). Take them up on their offer to help. You'd be surprised at how readily people will respond to a specific task that can be made part of their routine. Even if just a few people respond, this will give you a chance to create a schedule with some downtime for yourself. Do not use the free time to run off and do more errands for your loved one. The idea is to give you the time to re-charge. Go to your favorite bookstore, walk with some friends, get a massage, catch a twilight movie – do something that makes you feel good. If you don't have a large enough circle of family or friends, you can reach out to organizations. Here are some more ideas:

➤ The Faith in Action National Network exists to provide support for millions of Americans with long-term health needs. Volunteers will cook, drive, shop, or just check-in on your parent as needed. You can find information at www.fianationalnetwork.org or call them toll free at 1-866-839-8865. Don't forget to go to your own church, mosque or synagogue to ask for volunteers.

➤ Call your local Area Agency on Aging and ask about the Family Caregiver Support Program. You might qualify for ongoing assistance and even home-modification funds to make it easier to care for your parent. Call the Eldercare Locator at 1-800-677-1116 to find the nearest agency to you.

➤ Call your local senior center and hospitals to find out if they have any support groups on dealing with stress and caregiving. Talking with others who are going through the same thing can really help you put things in perspective and learn how to cope.

➤ Consider hiring non-medical senior care aides who can help you with shopping, watching your parent while you're out, preparing meals and doing many of the non-medical chores that you do all day. Even if they come in once a week, it will give you some free time. You can find them in the Yellow pages under "home health care."

➤ If you're working, ask your employer about any employee assistance programs they might have to help you out. You can also use the Family Medical Leave Act to take some time to provide caregiving. See p. 379.

I know all of this takes some time on your part and you're already feeling overwhelmed. But, doing this will absolutely pay off for you. You must take care of yourself. I've often found that people will help when you ask and if you give them something specific to do.

Q: How can I get my sister to help me care for our Mom? I've hinted that I need help, but she doesn't offer to do *anything*.

 A: The most frequently reported frustration among caregivers is lack of consistent help from other family members. In the National Family Caregiver's Association annual survey three out of four family members felt this way.

It is very common for one family member to gravitate to the central caregiving role. This may be the oldest child, the child nearest the parent geographically, the child without children, the child with a healthcare background or the child with the most flexible work schedule. It is also common for the central caregiver to begin feeling that no one else can really take care of Mom or Dad. I've heard many caregivers say that despite wanting more help, they're the "only one who really knows" what their parent wants and needs. Or, they feel that by the time they explain everything that is needed, they might as well do it themselves. The person who needs the care often feeds into this "only you" syndrome. And, so the cycle begins and the caregiver soon becomes worn down and resentful. Many begin to feel that other family members should just "know" what to do and pitch in voluntarily. They resent having to even ask for help.

Sending hints to your sister is not enough. She may not be picking them up because she genuinely thinks you have everything under control. In the meantime, you're seething in anger and could eventually take it out on your mother. So, let's break the cycle right now. It is your responsibility to share with your sister exactly what is involved in caring for your mother. Most people don't realize how stressful caregiving is until they've gone through it. Just think of how many of us call our parents after our first child is born and ask in amazement, how did you do it?! So, create a picture of what it takes to care for your Mom. Your sister can't do her fair share if she doesn't get the whole picture. I'd start with a two-column list. On the left hand side, write down everything you do:

➤ Making all of her doctors appointments

➤ The medications she must take and how often

➤ The insurance polices and paperwork involved in her care

➤ The bills you pay on her behalf

➤ The transportation you provide and must arrange

- Chores that are done on her behalf

- Food and clothes shopping

- Any medical or health care you provide

- Medical and health care you arrange for a professional to provide

- Any daily living needs you must provide her (e.g. dressing, food preparation)

Then, on the right hand side of the list, identify all of the steps that you take to fulfill each task. I'd also put in parenthesis how much time these tasks take. Now you are in a position to sit down with your sister and share the list. Rather than counting on a "look-at-what-a-martyr-I-am" approach to throw your sister into guilt-ridden action, start by asking her to help you go through the list and provide input on how the two of you can come up with a care plan for your mother. If she lives some distance away, are there things she can do that don't involve being there? Perhaps she can do all of the insurance work, schedule doctor appointments, pay bills and help research any of your Mom's medical conditions. Could she set aside one day a week to relieve you of any of your caregiving tasks? If she can't, could she cover the costs of providing some assistance for that day? When it comes to gifts for Mom, suggest she give gift certificates for home-delivered meals, cab rides, or cleaning service – all of which would assist you, as well.

Once you come away with a care plan, make copies of it so that both of you have it and be sure to update it as your mother's needs change. I'd also suggest setting up a convenient, weekly phone conversation for the two of you to go over your mother's care – that way your sister will feel more of a partner and remain very much aware of what is involved. You need to begin to relate to your sisterly differently – as a partner – before she can start acting like one.

 I've been getting so angry at my parents, as they don't appreciate all that I'm doing for them. What do I do?

 Anger is a completely normal emotion and, in many instances, it can be a healthy reaction to situations that require you to respond assertively to stand up for yourself. In threatening cases, it is an adaptive response to fight when attacked. Some people are quick to anger while others are slow. But, no matter what your response rate, anger is an emotion that you can control. You "own" it. And even though you may feel that your Mom or Dad "makes you angry;" the truth is no one can *make* you angry. *You* make yourself angry. Sure, something your parent does can provoke you, but you get to decide how you're going to respond to that provocation.

So, to better understand what provokes you, let's break your anger down into small parts. Think about the last three or four times you became angry at your parents. Can you recall what you were feeling *before* you saw them? What was your day like at work? Were you feeling pulled in too many directions? Did you need to get to somewhere after seeing them? Were you squeezing in your visit between other family responsibilities? If you were stressed before you opened the door, you sure aren't going to come back out feeling less so. Is there any way you can schedule your visits under less demanding circumstances?

Now, think about what either of them said or did that displeased you. Was it something about the tone of their voice? Did you feel their request was given as an order? Is your Mom's depression bothering you? Are they not doing what you asked them to do? What action did you need to do just before you got angry – was it cleaning up after them? Re-explaining directions for the umpteenth time? Getting them in and out of the car and dealing with parking after a hassle

through traffic? Do you see any kind of pattern towards a certain activity or certain behaviors that "push your button?" Could any of this be related to old, unresolved issues with your parents?

What did you physically feel when you got angry? Was your heart racing, your stomach in knots, your face flushed, teeth clenched, or your head pounding? Anger triggers physical reactions that cause your heart rate and blood pressure to go up and it affects the energy level of your hormones. If you're getting a steady dose of this just about every time you interact with your parents, then you're headed for physical problems of your own. Once you've identified these three components to your anger, you can start developing a plan of action to take control of each.

Here are a few thoughts: It sounds like you're feeling unappreciated and overwhelmed. Being overwhelmed leads to feeling out of control; and being unappreciated leads to resentment. This is a surefire formula for feeling very angry. So, let's start getting some control back into your life. Make a list of all the routine things you do for your parents every week. Assign how much time you spend on each of those tasks. Share that list with siblings (even if they are out of town they can make calls for setting up appointments and dealing with paperwork). Share it with friends who offer to help, but you never seem to take them up on it. Also, create a list of all of your other responsibilities that you perform every week and assign how much time you spend on each.

Sit down with your parents and share both of the lists with them and let them know how much you want to help out and that you've been trying very hard to "do it all." But, now it's taking a toll, not only on you, but on your relationship with them and that's something you hold dear. The three of you can then

tackle your caregiving list as *problem solvers*. Perhaps, you can identify a pharmacy that will deliver pills to save you the trip, a grocery store that makes deliveries, a non-medical senior care service that can take your parents to a doctor's office and run some errands one day a week. If your parents balk at spending the money for this type of service, explain how much it costs you to take off of work; if they truly can not afford it, then perhaps you and your siblings can share the costs or call your local Area Agency on Aging at 1-800-677-1116 and ask about the shared-ride and volunteer programs. The bottom line is that you must find ways to take charge of your caregiving and get others to help – paid or volunteer.

Communication is key to healthy expressions of anger. Dr. Stephen Duncan, a Family and Human Development specialist suggests that the best way to express anger is to use "I-statements with a Feeling-When-Because format." Here's an example, "Mom, **I** feel upset **when** I've taken off of work to drive you to the doctor's **because** what I've done for you isn't acknowledged. **I** feel unappreciated." Notice these are all statements that tell her how you're feeling rather than accusing her of being ungrateful. Who knows, she may be feeling resentful that she has to depend on you and can't get past her own anger to appreciate what you're doing. Or, she's embarrassed about needing your help. Use this as an opportunity to try and understand what's behind her actions that provoke you.

Find ways that are calming to you as soon as you feel the physical signs of anger; it might be leaving the room and taking a deep breath, taking a short walk, envisioning a scene that's peaceful, or calling a friend. When it comes to sharing your feelings, speak slowly and lower your voice and sit down next to your Mom or Dad in a manner that shows you want to solve this problem. This isn't about denying your anger; it's about *listening* to it rather than letting it toss you into a sea of seething.

Q: How do I convince my Mom that I can't keep doing everything for her? She insists on me doing everything and makes me feel guilty if I don't.

A: Sometimes it's hard for parents to realize how quickly all the little things add up: finding a Medicare Part D plan, taking Mom to a doctor's appointment, making pick-ups at the pharmacy, paying bills, keeping up with insurance papers, dropping off dinner, going back and forth to her home and performing household tasks.

According to the National Alliance for Caregiving, one in four adults in the United States provides caregiving assistance to older family members and three out of four do it without any outside assistance. About one-fourth are spending up to twenty hours a week helping a loved one with the activities of daily life and caregiving. For someone who is working, that means holding down another part-time job.

On the "feeling guilty" front, you aren't alone either; a *Home Instead Senior Care* study found that about one-third of family caregivers say they wish they could do more and feel guilty that they simply **cannot**, given everything else they do. Mix a little anger with that guilt and you'll find that many caregivers also report feeling resentful because so much of the caregiving lands on

their shoulders, all the while they need to be a parent, spouse and dutiful employee.

So, now that we've established you are not the only one caught up in the tug of war between being a good daughter and managing your life, let's start working on some ways that we can get your Mom to better understand, and hopefully, appreciate what you *can* do and accept what you cannot.

First, make a list of what you do for your Mom and identify how much time and resources it takes to do each task. Go over the list and identify what tasks you can continue to do and those that could be performed by some outside help. Then, identify the "outside help," which could be in the form of a sibling, a volunteer with a local faith-based group, a neighbor whom you could compensate, or call a local non-medical senior care agency who can perform many of the tasks you are already doing – like preparing meals, providing companionship, picking up and reminding your Mom to take her medications, or getting groceries. In the beginning, you may need to pay for these services so your mother doesn't use cost as an obstacle. Check out whether or not her local grocery store and pharmacy makes deliveries; that way you can simply place an order and they'll do the delivering.

Once you've thought through how you can make *your* life easier in meeting your mother's needs, gain some insight as to what motivates her in insisting that only you can do for her. You might find that she fears strangers coming into her home or she feels a loss of control in managing her life, but having her "child" do things for her places her back in control or perhaps she thinks this is the only way she can get you to spend time with her. Take a look at her history with her parents – was she their caregiver? Is there an unwritten understanding in the family that this is what a daughter does? If you're not living up to the family code, then perhaps, she thinks it reflects badly on her parenting or that you don't love her enough.

Whatever the reason, it's better to find out her emotional needs *before* sharing with her how you'll assist without being the one to "do it all." You could have a conversation that starts off with, "Mom, I've been trying to help out as best I can with the (insert here what you've been doing), but with work and my family, it's been getting pretty tough to handle. Of all the things that I do, what's *really* important to you? Besides focusing on the list of activities she'll give you, probe for and listen to the emotional side of what matters to her.

If your Mom continues to insist that she doesn't want any of these services – including all the free ones you could line

up – then explain to her that, "Mom, I love you very much, but I'm becoming worn out keeping up with my job, the kids and running my own household. It would be so much better when we're together, if I'm able to spend time enjoying being with you rather than running around getting everything done. This is what I can do..." – and then spell it out.

Guilt is a feeling that you own and only you can control. As long as your Mom's needs are being met and she is not in harm's way, you don't need to be "guilt-tripped." If you continue down this path; you'll feel angry and resentful not just to her, but to everyone around you and soon your own health will be at risk.

To find out what services are available in your community, call Eldercare Locator at 1-800-677-1116 or check out what resources and support groups are available from the National Family Caregivers Association at www.thefamilycaregiver.org or give them a call at 1-800-896-3650.

Being a good daughter doesn't mean being a martyr.

Q: Despite having two accidents and being told by his eye doctor that he cannot drive at night, my 86 year old father continues to drive whenever he wants. What do we do?

A: According to Pennsylvania law and the Pennsylvania Department of Transportation, physicians, and others authorized to diagnose and treat disorders and disabilities, must report to PennDOT any individual diagnosed as having a condition that could impair his or her ability to safely operate a motor vehicle. Some of the kinds of conditions physicians must report (if they impair a patient's driving ability) are: visual conditions, neuromuscular disease (such as Parkinson's), cognitive conditions (such as dementia or Alzheimer's disease), heart conditions, cerebrovascular conditions (such as stroke or brain tumor), convulsive or seizure disorders.

It would be helpful if you spoke again to both his eye doctor and family physician. Let them know of your concerns and the recent accidents he has had. Ask the family physician if he or she would conduct a geriatric assessment (including a mini-mental status exam for dementia) of your father to determine if there are medical reasons that impair his driving. His doctor could also refer your father for an assessment by a driving clinic for an impartial and professional opinion on your Dad's driving abilities before the physician files a report with PennDOT.

When a physician submits a report to PennDOT, the agency has 15 days to review the information and they can do one of three things: determine that the driver is medically competent to drive, require more medical information upon which forms are sent to the driver and they must have them filled out by appropriate medical professionals, or they decide the driver is not medically competent to drive and a notice is sent informing them that their license will be recalled in 28 days. As part of their evaluation, PennDOT may also ask the driver to come in for a driver's exam. It's important to note that PennDOT, not the physician, decides whether or not an individual is medically competent to drive.

If all else fails, you can also directly and confidentially contact PennDOT with your concerns. Explain that your father has been restricted by his eye doctor from driving at night, but ignores the restriction and provide details on his accidents. You can call the PennDOT Medical Unit at 1-717-787-9664, or write them at: Pennsylvania Department of Transportation, P.O. Box 68682, Harrisburg, PA 17106-8682. Upon their review, they may send a notification to your father that he has been selected to take a medical and/or driver's exam. If your father ignores the request, his license will be suspended within 30 days for non-compliance.

Every month PennDOT randomly identifies 1,900 drivers over the age of 45 years to acquire a physical exam and eye test to determine if they are medically competent to drive. Of that number, less than one percent is required to take a driver's exam. There are no restrictions in Pennsylvania on older drivers. In contrast, about half of the states do impose some restrictions. For example, Florida requires that all drivers 80 years and over must take a vision exam to renew their license.

You can go to my website (www.lindarhodescaregiving.com) and click on *"Caregiving Tip of the Week"* for a link to a handbook from PennDOT, *Talking with Older Drivers: A Guide for Family and Friends*, that can walk you through the steps I've discussed and much more.

The vast majority of older drivers do limit their driving on their own based on their ability and are safe drivers.

Q: My wife's driving ability is beginning to slip. What can she do to safely stay on the road?

Thanks to a growing awareness among transportation experts who appreciate how important driving is to an older driver's independence, there are many tools available to help your wife remain a safe driver. One out of every three drivers is 55 years of age and older and the vast majority maintain high safety records. And, most are aware that their vision, reflexes, flexibility and hearing are undergoing changes. For some, especially if they are on medications, their thinking skills have also changed.

First, your wife can assess her driving skills and she can include your input, as well. Purchase a CD-ROM from the American Automobile Association (AAA), titled "Roadwise Review." It allows you to measure eight functional abilities that predict crash risk among older drivers. According to the AAA, "Roadwise Review" can help you assess: Leg Strength and General Mobility,

Head/Neck Flexibility, High-Contrast Visual Acuity, Low-Contrast Visual Acuity, Working Memory, Visualization of Missing Information, Visual Search and Useful Field of View.

The Pennsylvania Department of Transportation offers some practical safety tips geared towards older drivers. Here are a few:

▸ Respect your limits: Be sure to get regular medical checkups, including vision and hearing. Be aware that arthritis may affect the range of motion of your neck and pay attention to prescription labels that warn of dizziness and confusion. Be careful of long road trips that strain your muscles, vision and ability to concentrate.

▸ Respect the road: Avoid driving on unfamiliar roads, especially at night and during bad weather. Steer clear of driving during rush hours, and if you can, use less-traveled roads with fewer intersections. Limit night time driving and avoid looking directly into glaring headlights. Map out your destination in advance so you aren't scrambling for directions while you're driving.

▸ Respect your vehicle: Maintain a safe speed and look for hazards ahead so that you have time to make adjustments in advance. Maintain a four-second gap between you and the vehicle in front of you. Adjust the car to your physical needs: position the mirrors, the seat height, your seat belt and the steering wheel so you can comfortably handle the car.

In addition, your wife can save money on auto insurance premiums and feel more confident in her driving if she takes a mature driver refresher course. Older Driver Improvement Classes are offered by:

1. The American Association of Retired Persons (AARP) provides an 8-hour instructional program to improve the driving ability of older adults. Contact the AARP at 225 Market Street, Harrisburg, PA 17101, call at 1-717-238-2277 or go to www.aarp.org.

2. American Automobile Association offers courses and excellent materials. Contact your AAA office and visit www.seniordrivers.org for great resources.

The AAA Foundation for Traffic Safety also offers some terrific free videos available by download. Go to www.AAAFoundation.org and click on "Video Vault." Watch one or all of the resource videos related to safe driving issues. Write to the AAA Foundation at 607 14th Street., Suite 201, Washington, D.C. 20005 to request a copy of safe-driving brochures or you can order by phone at 1-800-305-7233.

Hopefully, these tips will keep your wife safely behind the wheel.

: My Mom's friend just lost her spouse. What should my Mom say and do?

All too often, because we feel uncomfortable with grieving, we tend to shy away from visiting the bereaved, which wrongly sends the message that we don't care. But many people find comfort in being given permission to talk about their loss. You may worry that bringing up the deceased's name is just going to cause tears or unhappiness, so you don't say anything. But never bringing up the spouse will just make the person feel all the more alone. One of the best gifts you can give someone who is mourning is to share fond memories and stories that you cherish about their loved one. Perhaps your Mom could write down a special moment she remembers of her friend's husband as a reflection of what a wonderful man he was – and place it in a card or in a "Memory Box" (such as a small jewelry or keepsake box). She could even collect memories written by other close friends and place it in the box as a gift. This might be nice to bring to her on a visit. Marta Felber, M.Ed., a grief counselor and author of *Grief Expressed: When a Mate Dies*, offers the following "Do's and Don'ts" for talking to someone who is grieving:

DON'T SAY: "I know how you feel." The person in grief may want to scream, "No, you don't! No one knows how bad I feel!"

DO SAY: "I don't know how you feel, but I care about you and that you are hurting." In this way, we validate their feelings.

DON'T SAY: "Just call me if there is anything I can do." People in deep grief can't think straight or focus. They don't know what they need to do.

DO SAY: "Can I get groceries for you or drive you somewhere you need to go?" It's much more useful to offer specific help. Other suggestions: Invite your friend to lunch or dinner, help her with medical or tax forms, or help her go through her loved one's belongings, but only when she is ready.

DON'T SAY: "It will get better." A grieving person knows this intellectually, but in their heart they may feel differently right now.

DO SAY: "It must be so difficult for you. I am thinking about you, caring, loving you" (or whatever you can sincerely say). Remember to stay in the present, where the grieving person is.

DON'T SAY: "Now, now, don't cry." It hurts us to see them cry and makes us sad. But, by telling them not to cry, we are trying to take their grief away.

DO SAY: "Go ahead and cry. It's okay. I'm here." Then sit quietly with them. Hold or touch them. If you feel like doing so, cry with them.

DON'T SAY: "Your loved one is waiting for you on the other side," "God wanted him," "It was God's will," or "God knows best."

Imagine how you would you feel about God after hearing such comments. Be very sensitive. Know the person's faith, and be in touch with your own.

DO SAY: "Feel God's love," or "I will be praying for you," *if* you sincerely will do this.

 : My mother wants to get another dog since hers died last year, but my Dad disagrees. Should we get her a puppy anyway?

 : First off, this needs to be a decision that both of your parents make. Couples often have separate expectations of what they want out of retirement. It sounds like your Mom would enjoy the everyday companionship of a pet, while your Dad is hoping to have some freedom from caring for a dog. Rather than zero in on a "dog or no dog" debate, they would do well to step back and ask each other what kind of lifestyle each would like over the next few years. Hopefully, they'll identify things that they both want and then they can work on ways to compromise where they may not share the same interests.

It sounds like you appreciate your Mom's sadness over not having a dog in her life. Many people (I confess I'm one of them) can't imagine a life without pets. And there's plenty of research backing up why pets are a good thing: People are less depressed; pets offer a welcome distraction from pain, talking to and caring for a pet reduces loneliness and walking a dog encourages exercise.

On the other hand, pets require a great deal of care and attention. And perhaps, this is what concerns your father. He may have been looking forward to a time where he and your Mom could be "free and easy" so they could travel. Yet, your Mom is probably feeling like it's not worth the sacrifice for a few trips a year to be without a dog for most of the year. A possible solution may be an offer made by you and your brother – rather than buying her a puppy – to pay for a pet sitter service, so that when they do travel the dog will be taken care of. Or, the two of you offer to bring the dog into your home while they are away. If this is the case, your Mom would need to agree that she'd use the service and it wouldn't stop her from traveling with your Dad.

If your Dad finds this solution acceptable, then I also recommend not getting a puppy and instead look for an older dog that is already housetrained. Puppies require a terrific amount of work and attention. They also chew everything in sight and that cute little puppy could quickly get on your Dad's nerves, setting off a whirlwind of conflict between your Mom and Dad. It would also be wise to research different breeds and look for a dog that doesn't require a lot of exercise and is small to medium-sized. Unless your Dad doesn't care, they should choose the dog together.

You can find Pet Sitters in the Yellow Pages or go to the website of Pet Sitters International (www.petsit.com) and search for one of their members by zip code. When you interview a pet sitter, find out if they are they insured and bonded, if they've had formal training in caring for pets, what kind of background checks and training do their employees have, do they have customer references (be sure to call!), do they have a formal relationship with a veterinarian for emergencies and is there a veterinarian who recommends them, do they write up daily reports on each visit and leave messages on your voicemail as to how well your pet is doing. On average you'll pay between ten to twenty dollars per visit. Until, your parents work this out...don't buy your Mom a puppy.

 : My Mom is eighty-five and doesn't want to visit our in-laws this Christmas, as it's too much for her. What should we do?

A.: Despite all of the Norman Rockwell images of the holiday season, family events can cause a good deal of dilemmas. College students may want to bring a friend home, a newly engaged couple desperately tries to appease both sets of parents, divorced families argue over who gets the kids on Christmas Eve or Christmas day. Older parents who have enjoyed hosting large family events may be happy to turn over the reins to their adult children, but don't know how to tell them. They don't want to change "tradition."

Life changes. Our needs change. And in response, so does how we celebrate our family traditions. It doesn't mean we have to dispense with tradition, but we may have to tailor it to meet the changing needs of families. In your Mom's case, she really isn't alone. I know of several older friends who have found the frenzy of the holiday season "too much for them," too. They no longer find it enjoyable to be in a crowded room with young children running about with a steady stream of family and friends laughing and talking. It may be difficult for them to hear with all of the background noise and thus, hold a meaningful conversation. They may find the ride too long or the weather too cold to venture out. Some fear falling on wintry days or dread negotiating steps or navigating surroundings they are not familiar with. If this is how your Mom feels and she really would be relieved staying in the comfort of her home, then it would be best to respect her feelings.

It also sounds like your Mom is fine with you going to your in laws – so go and be with them. The goal is for neither one of you to "guilt-trip" the other into doing something you do not want to do. Stay focused on the meaning of the season: it's about celebrating your love of others. It's acknowledged in gifts and spending time with each other. You can do that with your Mom on your own special day, which could be the day before Christmas or after. If you live near each other, then perhaps you can exchange gifts later that day. Talk with her and see what works best. You could also add a few more creative ways to celebrate the day: deliver one of her gifts early and have her open it while you're on the phone with her at your in-laws; if you have children, make sure they call Grandma at different times throughout the day; if you have siblings, ask if one of them can stop by and see her on Christmas Day or find another relative or friend who could visit.

Let her know how much you'd enjoy having her come to your in-laws, but that you appreciate how she'd feel more comfortable staying at home and you want to honor her wishes. And then explore how she would like to celebrate Christmas with you before or after your event with your husband's family.

Q: My Mom needs quite a bit of care and my sister is willing to quit her job to care for her. How should we compensate my sister and prevent potential conflicts, since my brother isn't so keen on the idea?

A: Your Mom and sister would do well to enter into a *Caregiving Contract* or *Personal Service Agreement*. Clearly spelling out what you'll do for a loved one and how that care will be compensated has a number of advantages: It avoids misunderstandings and false expectations; it can head-off arguments among siblings, especially when money exchanges hands, it acknowledges the amount of work and expenses involved in caregiving, and the expenses could possibly be considered legitimate payments applied toward Medicaid eligibility for nursing home care. It can also protect a caregiver if their loved one develops dementia and accuses them of wrongdoing.

Given the fact that your brother has "some concerns," going through the process of writing up a caregiving contract provides him the opportunity to address them before they become seeds of resentment. Some people feel that family should never receive any compensation caring for each other. After all, imagine if your parents handed you a bill at age eighteen for all that they did. But, for some, it's not that simple an equation. The National Alliance for Caregiving reports that over 44 million adults provide some form of care to aging loved ones. On average, this care adds up to about 21 hours of care every week for just over four years. Most families are able to do this without being paid for that care. On the other hand, thousands of family members, mostly daughters, are quitting jobs or reducing their hours to part-time at a significant financial loss. Others have obligations to raise their own families and absolutely need to work. In these instances, if a parent can afford to compensate a relative for providing care so they can remain at home, it's a fair exchange.

Here is what should be covered under a caregiving contract:

1. Identify what tasks the caregiver is to perform. Consider these categories:

   a. Personal Services: Assistance with the activities of daily living such as bathing, grooming, dressing, preparing meals, transferring from room to room.

   b. Personal Health Services: Assistance with taking medications, helping with exercise, scheduling and accompanying care recipient to all doctor's appointments, making sure that doctor's orders are followed, arranging for other health services. Maintaining records on health conditions, medications, allergies and emergency data.

c. Driving: Taking care recipient to all appointments, run errands for him or her and taking him or her to social events.

d. Household Services: Performs or arranges for household cleaning, laundry, grocery shopping; pays bills, maintains records on household and caregiving expenses.

2. Determine a work schedule mutually agreed upon by both parties and how many hours per week of work are expected.

3. Determine wages to cover compensation for care and identify how this will be paid (e.g. weekly, monthly). The wage should be comparable to what local home care companies pay for similar services. Specify that the care recipient is responsible for Social Security payments and that the caregiver is responsible for reporting their income and paying taxes. Will health insurance be provided?

4. Identify what out-of-pocket expenses paid for by the caregiver qualify for reimbursement by the care receiver (e.g. gas and/or a portion of car upkeep if the caregiver is using his or her own car).

You can write up such an agreement on your own or pay a few hundred dollars to hire an elder law lawyer to draft a Caregiver Contract. You can't beat its "peace in the family" return on investment.

 My Dad came to live with us and now he's taking over! What do we do?

 As he tries to find his place in a new household, your father seems to be gravitating back to where he is most comfortable – being your Dad and being in charge. You'll need to coach him into a new role where he can still maintain a position of respect, but can dispense with "giving orders." He also needs to get to know you in a different context, as a parent and a spouse, not just his child. Here are few suggestions to help him with the transition:

1. Set aside some time to quietly talk with him. You might begin with something like, "Dad, during the rush of the move

from your place to here, we really haven't had a chance to talk. We've been living apart for a very long time and each of us has our own routines. What's a typical day like for you?" Be sure to scope out his eating habits, favorite television shows, and past routines such as visiting with friends, reading the paper every morning and so on. Ask him, "Are there things you'd like to be doing that you weren't able to do when you lived alone? "

Listen very closely. As you begin to learn of his daily life routine, you're in a position to see how well your family's routine will mesh with his. You might also pick up some red flags and begin thinking about ways to accommodate his needs without compromising what's important to your family.

2. Now it's your turn to share with your Dad your family's routine. Be sure you've talked this over with your spouse in advance so that all of you are in sync. Describe a typical day in your household to your Dad, explain how you divide chores, and share with him any ground rules that you've established with your kids. You might want to take the opportunity to share with him your basic principles of child rearing. For example, your Dad might be a big tease and thinks he's just being funny making jokes about your kids' haircuts, interests or friends. You might need to explain that teasing often drives a child away or into a shell.

After you've described your household to him, you might want to ask him if he has any suggestions on how he could help support the household culture that you've just described or pitch in with the chores. And you could share how you'll help him maintain the routines important to him.

In your description of how your household works, I'd include one evening a week that you and your spouse go out (as in on a date). If he knows this ahead of time, then he won't feel "left out" or that he is being rejected. You could also give him a gentle warning by saying something like, "Dad, we're going to an event on Friday. Is there anything you need while we're gone?"

3. Talk openly with him about how he'll always be your Dad, but that you're not a kid anymore. Perhaps you could create a new tradition between the two of you by setting up a weekly outing, or watching a favorite television show together. By doing this, you're setting some boundaries on your relationship while reenforcing it at the same time. He won't have a need to constantly show he's still your father by being in charge.

4. While the move is still new, it might be good to have another discussion on what triggers stress for all family members. Maybe everyone makes a list of their top 3 triggers and shares it; then the family figures out together how to make life less stressful for each other. It's best to do something like this now, before real events and real hurt feelings make it tough to have such a discussion that isn't emotionally-charged.

5. If your Dad isn't a "joiner," you may need to be creative and bring people to him or become the bridge for your Dad to connect to some activity or person. If you're active in a church or synagogue, that would present an excellent opportunity for him to make friends there as well. Or, take him to events such as school performances, where he might meet people. You might want to host a small "welcome to the neighborhood" party and invite potential friends. Just like every other member of the family, he needs outside interests so that the household doesn't become his entire world.

6. How you design space in the house for your Dad is extremely important. He needs to have his private space so that he can respect the private spaces of other family members, too. For example, he might enjoy having a small refrigerator and microwave for *his* snacks in *his* room along with *his* own television. But, of course you don't want him to feel physically isolated from the rest of the family. It should be a pleasant space and a personal refuge to re-charge – something that every family member needs.

7. And finally, you, your spouse and your father need to discuss who is going to pay for what. Finances all too often become the lightning rod for unresolved emotional conflicts. So, even though the topic may feel uncomfortable, do it now before you're in the midst of a family feud.

Hopefully, these suggestions will ease the transition for all of you and you'll come to treasure the benefits and joys of a three-generation household.

 : What do you do when siblings disagree on where their Mom should live?

 : One of the toughest things to balance is an older person's independence with their ability to safely live alone. Rather than the family focusing on the solution – e.g. assisted living vs. remaining at home – I'd suggest taking a step back and asking yourselves, "What are we trying to fix?"

All of you, including your mother, should make a list of what she needs. For instance, does she need help with shopping? Paying the bills? Transportation? Cleaning? Getting around the house? Making lunch and dinner? Taking her pills? Is it difficult for her to see? It will be interesting to see if your mother's assessment is similar to the rest of yours. Creating an objective list that all of you can focus on allows you to explore a wide array of options rather than getting caught up in an "either/or" scenario. It also allows all of you to gain a better perspective on how each of you – and your Mom – perceives her needs.

Then, review your mother's medical needs and health conditions. Ask her primary care physician to identify any special needs she may have. It can also be very helpful to get a geriatric assessment, in which a whole team of physicians, nurses and social workers conduct a holistic assessment of your mother's medical, physical, social and mental health needs. You could then share your list of perceived needs and have them help you determine how well your Mom can function living alone. You might also want to go through your Mom's house and identify any safety hazards, especially with regard to lighting, stairs, hallways, the kitchen and bathroom. Once all of you have done your homework regarding her needs, secured her medical and mental health assessment and reviewed the physical state of her living quarters, then you're in a good position to sit down as a team and review all of your information.

Try making two columns on a sheet of paper. On the left hand side list all of her needs that you can agree upon. (If you can't agree on a certain need, then skip over it and work

on the ones that you all do agree on.) On the right hand side of the paper, brainstorm how each need can be met. For example, say your Mom has difficulty taking a shower and one of your siblings thinks this means she belongs in assisted living. To solve this particular problem, you could:

- ➤ Buy a shower chair

- ➤ Install a long hand-held shower head

- ➤ Place railings in the shower

- ➤ Sign up for a personal alert service so she could press a button and have someone arrive to help her if she did fall.

Keep going through the list, staying focused on her needs. For ideas on services to help you meet some of your mother's needs, call your local Area Agency at 1-800-677-1116 and they may even send someone out to assess your mother's needs. If you need some professional help to accurately assess her needs, you might want to hire a Geriatric Care Manager, found in the Yellow Pages under home health or social services. You could also call the National Association of Geriatric Care Managers at 1-520-881-8008 or visit their website at www.caremanager. org to locate someone near your Mom.

At the end of the day, you may discover that your Mom requires such a myriad of services that assisted living may make more sense. On the other hand, you may find that the solutions you've all come up with have alleviated the concerns of those of you who didn't think your mother could continue living alone. The important thing is to not get caught up in an "all or nothing" debate. There are quite a few options and professional people available who can help you assess your mother's needs so that all of you can rally around on what's best for her.

Section Five
PART II

Q: My Mom, who has been visiting with us for a month, is very independent and rather demanding. She now wants to extend her stay and my husband wants her to leave. What do I do?

A: Well, I'm no Dr. Phil, but let me give this a try. Any change in the status quo of family life can prove stressful. Most of us are creatures of habit and enjoy the comfort zone we establish in our households. Even parents who suffered the pangs of the empty nest give a sigh of relief when the kids go back to college after their summer of re-nesting. Here are a few approaches; choose one that feels comfortable for you:

▸ For whatever reason your Mom may want to test you and put you in a position of choosing "Who do you love more – me or your husband?" Maybe she isn't doing it consciously, but tell her that this is how it feels to you. You may want to say, "I won't be placed in this position. I love both you and my husband. Mom, we've welcomed you and enjoyed our time together over the last four weeks." Then, mention some of the nice things you've done together and be sure to include some that also involved your husband.

▸ It might then be helpful to tell her that you and your husband made plans based upon her departure date that you can't change now. You could say something like, "I'm sure you understand, given how active a life you lead, so I'll be taking you to the airport on (the date you had all agreed upon when she came to visit)." If that doesn't seem to work, then how about you and your husband making plans for a little get-away vacation and tell your Mom that if she plans on staying, you'll really be thankful for her to house sit while you're away. This strategy might break the impasse.

▸ If no other family member has ever visited you for such an extended stay, then you can tell her that this isn't about "her," it's about how you and your husband conduct your life. In fact, that is why when you visit her and any other family members, it's never for longer than (say how long).

- ▸ Another approach may be to ask her, "What's really going on, Mom? You've always been such an independent person. This is so unlike you...is there something you're not telling me?" And see what happens.

- ▸ And, finally, you could say that you and your husband also value your space and being independent, just like her. You want this visit to be a memory of good times, so all of you to need to stick with her original departure date. By identifying the date as the one she chose, you'll give her a sense of ownership and by using the term "departure date" you'll make this less confrontational. You don't want to descend into just telling her to "leave."

The bottom line is that this is your home and even though she's your parent, she doesn't have carte blanche to come live with you on her terms. Next year when the topic of a visit comes up, set the parameters around the schedule set by you and your husband and limit it to what works well for the both of you.

Q: My widowed Mom is dating, but she's afraid of getting seriously involved with anyone because of HIV/AIDS. She's over sixty; why should she be worried?

A: One of the fastest growing newly-diagnosed groups of HIV/AIDS is women over fifty. During the last decade, cases in this age group have tripled and the Centers for Disease Control and Prevention report that over 100,000 people over fifty years of age now have HIV/AIDS in the United States. Part of this aging factor is due to new antiviral drugs allowing people who were diagnosed in their thirties to live longer than their life expectancy when the disease first hit in the early eighties.

So, why is AIDS going gray? For starters, no one's talking: older people don't admit to having sex and doctors don't think to ask. Despite Viagra commercials, society still portrays the sixty-plus set as virtually asexual, and, as a result, the awareness level of this tragic infectious disease even escapes health care professionals. Growing numbers of baby boomer divorcees and widows are being thrown into the dating game after 30 and 40 years of a monogamous marriage and aren't very savvy about the practices of safe sex.

Your mother's generation entered their teens without the fear of HIV/AIDS and so they weren't scared into using condoms. The one fear they did have – getting pregnant – sure isn't an issue for them now. But, the lack of condom use exposes them not only to HIV/AIDS, but a whole host of sexually transmitted diseases (STD). Because older people think this is only a young person's disease or only affects the gay community or those who use IV drugs, they never get tested and unknowingly can pass it on. Symptoms of the disease can masquerade as age-related conditions in the form of fatigue, a weakened immune system, skin rashes or swollen lymph nodes, so doctors don't pick it up. As a result, older women are often diagnosed at very late stages of the disease, since in addition; they stay silent about their sex life when in conversation with their physician. African American women have been found to be especially vulnerable to HIV/AIDS.

Add to all of these factors, the off-balance ratio of seven women to each older male among the geriatric set, then it's no wonder your Mom should be cautious about getting "serious" with her friend. Young people have been told countless times to remember that whenever they choose to sleep with someone, they're exposing themselves to everyone else that person has slept with and so on and so on. Anyone along that chain – heterosexuals included – may have been exposed to a partner with HIV. The only sexual history you really know is your own.

So, what should your Mom do? If she truly enjoys, respects and trusts her companion and she believes the feeing is mutual, then physical intimacy may be something they both desire. She could start the conversation something like, "I know we're both thinking about having sex (or "sleeping together"), so let's make it safe for both of us and use protection." If he doesn't have condoms, then your Mom should have a supply on-hand. If he does not want to use them, then your Mom should think twice about continuing the relationship and ask him to explain why. Jane Fowler, who contracted HIV/AIDS after a divorce from a marriage of 24 years and founder of HIV Wisdom for Older Women, is pretty direct about what to do: "If a partner won't use protection, find another partner."

For couples who want an exclusive relationship and stop using condoms, they should each get tested for infectious diseases like hepatitis, sexually transmitted diseases and HIV/AIDS. That way they can start their relationship secure in knowing that they are celebrating their new found love, while protecting each other's health and well-being. The bottom line is that your Mom doesn't need to be scared of intimacy; she just needs to be smart.

My Dad is so impatient with my Mom, who has Alzheimer's. What can I do?

One of the hardest things for some family members to understand is that someone suffering from dementia is not deliberately acting difficult. Far too often – perhaps because of past history, unresolved conflicts or old patterns of behavior – spouses or adult children react to the person with Alzheimer's with a heightened sense of frustration. They find it difficult to give the disease the benefit of the doubt. And so they strike back as if the aggravation is deliberate. Because people with dementia can sometimes go in and out of behaving normally, it may be hard for some family members to distinguish between when "she really means it" and when her behavior is caused by the dementia. As a result, they begin to think that Mom "knows exactly what she is doing" and "she's just out to get me." To make matters worse, the person with dementia can become easily agitated and in a matter of minutes you're in the midst of a firestorm when your Dad adds fuel to the fire with his anger.

Now, how do you cope with your Dad? Perhaps, you could approach your mother's physician and explain the situation to him or her. Ask the doctor to speak with your Dad about the disease and its stages, perhaps showing actual pictures of brain scans. Your Dad needs a third party to validate what you're telling him. A medical explanation should help, but it should be accompanied by a description of how dementia causes behavior changes in people. If you can't get a physician to tell him, then try another professional who he would trust. It might also be helpful to use analogies to explain the course of the disease that would resonate with your Dad (for example, explaining the workings of the brain in "car terms" if he's a car buff).

I'd also suggest that you search for a local Alzheimer's support group, as they will know of the latest medications and treatments that could possibly help to lessen some of your mother's symptoms. They can identify other resources for you and, hopefully, share strategies on how to respond to your mother's behaviors and how to respond to each other. Just meeting other people who are caring for a loved one with Alzheimer's and learning how they manage can be helpful. Perhaps you will meet someone who could speak with your Dad (for example, an older man caring for his wife with dementia, but who's coping with it more positively).

To find a support group anywhere in the country, go to www.alz.org. Also, feel free to give their 24-hour Helpline a call at 1-800-272-3900. An excellent resource book is *The 36-Hour Day*, authored by Nancy Mace and Peter Rabbins.

Q: My wife has Alzheimer's and I've been caring for her at home for seven years. My physician thinks it's time to place her in a skilled nursing facility, but it makes me feel guilty. What should I do?

A: First of all, you are to be admired for the care you have given your wife so that she could stay at home alongside you during the past seven years. Caring for a loved one with Alzheimer's disease is one of the toughest challenges anyone can ever undertake. It's a heart wrenching journey as you watch someone who was vibrant and interactive drift away from you. It's harder still when they go through stages of paranoia, accusing those closest to them of stealing from them, hurting them or viewing them as total strangers not to be trusted.

Two well-known researchers in the field of dementia coined the term the "36-hour day" to highlight the round-the-clock care that people with Alzheimer's require. Caring for someone with this disease is very wearing on both your physical and emotional health. Though friends and family will tell you to take a break and may even offer to watch over your wife, my guess is you probably didn't take them up on it as much as you could. Oftentimes, caregivers believe that they are the only one who can provide the care and the person with dementia reinforces this by acting agitated if anyone else takes

their place. Sometimes, just finding someone to come in to care for a loved one seems like an overwhelming task in itself, so caregivers just resign themselves to a nonstop marathon of caring.

But, there are consequences and it sounds like your doctor has picked up on them. Caregivers are at greater risk than the general population to suffer a host of health problems due to the wear and tear of stress. High blood pressure is a prime target leading to heart problems, diabetes and stroke. And, whatever underlying health conditions you have now, they will likely worsen. I am sure your wife wouldn't want to see you risk your health and even your life – caregivers who lose a spouse after a long and debilitating illness have a much higher fatality rate within the first year of their loved one's death. So, let's start with this premise to begin easing your feelings of guilt: Your wife, if she could, would be looking out for you. If you've ever flown, then you have heard the directions from flight attendants telling you that, if you are traveling with children, place the oxygen mask over your face first, then your children. It goes against every parent's instincts, but it makes perfect sense. If you're out of breath and become unconscious, then you've placed your children in peril. You can't help them.

If your physician, family and friends have been encouraging you to place your wife in a setting that can meet her extensive needs with 24-hour care, then they are likely correct and are looking out for you. Professional and compassionate staff who are very skilled in helping Alzheimer patients achieve their best level of functioning could actually help her improve, resulting in greater "quality time" between the two of you. You'll be more rested, less stressed and you won't have to tend to other caregiving tasks – you can just focus on being with her. It would be best to find a caregiving facility that is close to you so that travel won't pose a hardship. If you do not have access to the internet, ask a friend, family member or librarian to go to Medicare's website on nursing homes. It is called "Nursing Home Compare" and you can look at quality of care reports on every facility in the country at www.medicare.gov. I also offer a free nursing home navigator workbook on my website at www.lindarhodescaregiving.com that walks you through the questions to ask when searching for a facility. Be sure to ask about what special programs they offer residents with Alzheimer's disease.

It's time for you to put on the oxygen mask. And it's okay.

Section Two PART II

Q: I'm overwhelmed trying to figure out which doctors take Medicare, what's covered and what isn't and how to track down services to help me care for my wife. The internet is a help, but that's confusing, too. Where do I turn?

 A: Medicare recently created a new website that acts like your very own GPS (Global Positioning System), navigating you through a maze of rules and programs wrapped in red tape. It also acts as a gateway to hundreds of websites that can help you with specific problems, so you're not surfing the net endlessly on your own.

Say, for instance, you want to know which of your wife's doctors accepts Medicare or she needs to find a new doctor, for example, a nephrologist for a kidney condition. All you have to do is go to www.medicare.gov/caregivers for the new "*Ask Medicare*" feature. On the home page, simply click on the "*What doctors take Medicare*" link. You'll be asked to enter your zip code and how many miles you're willing to travel to see a doctor. Then you'll be asked to pick a specialty, such as a "*nephrologist*," and voila! You'll get a list of physicians who take Medicare near her and all of the contact information necessary to make an appointment. You'll even learn where the physician received his or her medical degree. You can also just enter a doctor's name to learn whether or not he or she takes Medicare.

Now, let's say your wife needs a wheelchair and you're not sure if Medicare will cover it. This time you'll click onto, "*Is it covered?*" and you'll be asked to enter either her policy number or her state. A menu will appear identifying a wide range of "coverage topics" and you choose the one that's most relevant. In this case, it's easy, as you'll choose "wheelchair options and accessories" and you'll learn exactly what is covered and how to go about getting a wheelchair for your wife.

If she needs to find a home health care agency to come in and assist her recovery from a stroke, for example, then you'd click the link on "*Get In-Home Services.*" You'll find out what's covered by Medicare, a list of home health agencies near her and their contact information. Plus, you can find out how well that agency performs on certain quality measures identified by Medicare. You can do the same for nursing homes and assisted living facilities. You can even compare drug plans all at this one website.

Feeling stressed out? Then visit their section on "Overwhelmed? Get Help" where you can join an online support group, view blogs from other caregivers or find a support group that meets near you. You'll also be sent to links that will help you find a geriatric care manager, along with legal and financial resources, as well.

The Department of Health and Human Services reports that at least 44 million Americans provide care for a chronically ill loved one, most of whom are elderly and rely on Medicare. So, the agency decided that the best way they could inform and empower family caregivers was to create a website that would act as a "GPS for Medicare," as explained by Rima Cohen, a special adviser at HHS. "It's meant to make information readily available, and presented in a format that is easy to understand." So, give it a try. It should save you a lot of time and a few headaches. For those of you without access to the internet, ask your local librarian to help you get on the site. You might also request help at your local senior center. To get your questions answered on coverage, billing and other matters, you can always call Medicare at 1-800-633-4227.

: How do I tell my sister that Mom is too stressed out watching her kids?

A: Given the results of a study in the *Journal of Public Health*, your instincts are exactly right about reaching out to your sister. In a study of nearly 14,000 women caring for grandchildren, epidemiologist Sunmin Lee with the Harvard School of Public Health found that "providing child care just a few hours a day greatly increased risk of heart disease." The risk of heart disease for grandmothers providing as little as nine hours of child care per week is a dramatic 55 percent higher than for grandmas free from the wear and tear of watching the grandkids.

The researchers suspect that the chronic stress from childcare is at the root of the problem. In most cases, Grandma's adult child is working and relies on her to watch the children, making visiting with the grandkids a duty rather than an option. On days when Grandma doesn't feel well, she still feels obligated to watch the kids so that her daughter or son can go to work. On the other hand, grandparents who are free from the duties of routine child care (routine is the operative word here) get to enjoy spoiling the grandkids on short visits while gleefully handing them back to their parents before the dear cherubim "disintegrate."

In addition, Lee and her colleagues suspect that stay-at-home grandmothers are generally in poorer health than those who remain in the workplace and thus aren't available to offer childcare for their grandchildren. Add the stress of childcare to common aging health conditions of arthritis, diabetes, high blood pressure and heart disease and you've created a formula for disaster. No wonder they're twice as likely to have a heart attack. Caregiving grandmas also find it very difficult to make time for themselves: they don't make regular health care check-ups or get to their doctor when they're sick; they don't exercise or find the time to follow healthy lifestyle habits.

So, where do we go from here? Depending on your relationship with your sister, you may begin the discussion by talking about your mother's general health. The results of a recent doctor's appointment may be very helpful to focus on, so that it's not just about your impression. You may need to enlist the support of your mother's physician, as he or she may not be aware of her stressful lifestyle. Don't blame your sister or act like she's taking advantage of your mother. Chances are that your Mom isn't letting on as to how stressful watching the kids has become. You could also tell your sister about this study and share a copy with her (Go to www.globalaging.org/health/us/babysitting.htm for further information on the study.). Offer to help your sister find other child care arrangements, as this is seldom an easy thing to do. Perhaps your sister can begin by just cutting back your mother's child care duties to two days a week. Of course, you should also include your mother in this discussion. Reassure her that in no way do you feel she's inadequate at child-rearing. Instead, you and your sister want to protect her health and give her the added time to enjoy herself during her retirement. You also want to create opportunities for her to simply enjoy the kids the way that most grandmas do without the daily pressure of being responsible for them. There's a good reason Mother Nature makes it nearly impossible to bear children after fifty – follow her lead.

Q: Will we be over our heads if we bring Mom in to live with us?

A: To be sure that your solution of your mother moving in with you is the best move, make a list of the observations that have caused you to reach this conclusion. For instance, is she acting confused or forgetful, eating poorly or seeming depressed? Is she not taking her medicines properly? Is her personal hygiene deteriorating? Are the bills stacking up along with other mail? Is she physically not able to get around? Then, get your Mom to her physician to do a complete geriatric work-up and share your observations with the doctor. Why? It's important to find any underlying physical problems that might be contributing to the behavior and symptoms that have alarmed you. Her confusion might simply be due to a medication she is taking. If this is rectified, living independently may still be an option for her.

Once you are better informed, I suggest making a list with three columns. The first column is for the activity involved in caring for your mother. In the second column, estimate how much time it will take to perform that activity, and in the third column identify who will do it (e.g. you, your husband, a relative, a friend or a paid person). There are also ripple effects to these activities that require time and resources, such as extra grocery shopping, more laundry, more trips to the pharmacy and more cleaning. Be sure to take these into account as well. Here is a list of activities that you should consider:

- **Eating.** Will you have to prepare all meals? Is she able to feed herself? Is she on a special diet?

- **Bathing.** Will she need assistance in showering? Help with daily grooming?

- **Using the toilet.** Will she need help going to and from the bathroom? Is she incontinent?

- **Dressing.** Can she get dressed on her own?

- **Medications.** Will she need to be reminded, or will you need to administer them?

- **Transportation.** How often will she need to see a doctor or therapist? Will you do the scheduling?

- **In-home therapies.** Any daily therapies? What daily medical care does she need?

- **Finances.** Will you be taking over all of her finances? Bill paying?

- **Supervision.** Can she safely be left alone or is she confused, prone to wander or fall? Does she sleep at night?

Once you've done your "assessing" on both counts – your Mom's needs and your ability to provide the time and resources – then you are in a good position to make an informed decision as to whether it is in everyone's best interest for your Mom to come and live with you. Caring for your mother is a wonderful thing to do. Just make sure that your expectations are realistic and that you and your spouse are prepared for the venture.

 My Dad has Type 2 Diabetes and he gets angry at my Mom when she tries to monitor his diet. What should she do?

 Being told that you have Type 2 Diabetes is tough because it also means you need to change your lifestyle. It means altering your diet for starters, and that isn't easy for any one. Old habits are hard to break, but in your father's case, those habits can prove deadly. Many people who acquire diabetes in later life go through stages of denial, depression and defiance. At first, your father may think that if he just stops eating cookies, he'll be good to go. Then, he may become quite depressed because he'll need to keep up with his blood pressure and sugar levels, take medications and insulin shots, along with giving up some of his favorite foods and exercise. Deep down, he may feel this is the beginning of the end and it is all downhill from here. This can make him angry, giving way to defiantly ignoring doctor's orders and his loved one's best intentions.

So, how can we help your Mom not be seen as a "food cop?"

1. **Make this a joint adventure.** Your Mom will benefit from healthy foods and exercise, too. If they both start taking walks, plan meals, and decide that this is a sign to take control of their lives for healthy aging, then the chance of success for each of them doubles.

2. **Let your Dad take control.** He may need some time to absorb his diagnosis. If your Mom takes over telling him what to do, he'll just resent her. In Dr. Barry Jacobs' book, *The Emotional Survival Guide for Caregivers* (Guildford Press), he finds that patients who have been told they have diabetes, "don't just snap to it," in fact, "most people take up to a year to really adapt to necessary changes." Your mother could say something like, "Honey, I know this must be pretty hard, so please tell me how I can be your partner in this? I don't want to be on your case, but it hurts me to see you do things that the doctor told us will harm you." And then let him come up with ways for her to help.

3. **Be informed.** Your Mom and Dad need to meet with the dietician, nurses and doctors on his medical team and read the material they give you. It is also worth a trip to the bookstore and library to better understand the disease. Your first stop on the internet is the American Diabetes Association at <u>www.diabetes.org</u> or give them a call for materials at 1-800-342-2383.

4. **Join a support group.** Local hospitals offer support groups, which is a great way for your parents to meet others who are coping with diabetes. Call your local chapter of the American Diabetes Association and they will gladly tell you how to contact support groups near you.

If all else fails, ask his physician to recommend – or better yet – prescribe a therapist who can help them learn how to negotiate with each other regarding your Dad's choices. Your father needs to recognize that this isn't just his problem. All of you deeply care about him, so his lifestyle choices as a diabetic matter very much to the whole family. It's the cost of being loved. And if I were your Dad, a little bit of "policing" is a price I'd be willing to pay.

Q: How do you talk to someone who has Alzheimer's disease?

A: Alzheimer's is one of the most devastating diseases any individual or family can face. The disease makes those suffering from the disease feel like they are in a constant state of being lost – nothing is familiar to them, not the room they live in, the furniture, the faces they see every day, their daily routines and even their own family members. Imagine how you feel when you're driving along and realize you're lost. At first, you may feel angry and frustrated that you can't figure out the directions; you may feel irritated with the unfortunate "backseat driver" who tries to help out. And then, there's the fear that grips you when you've steered your way into parts unknown with threatening danger at every turn. For someone with Alzheimer's, the analogy is all too real. They feel frustrated, confused and fearful in a world of strangers doing things to them or giving them "backseat" directions. It's no wonder they exhibit anger or appear agitated.

So, how do you talk to them? How do you break past the fear, the anger and the confusion? *Talking to Alzheimer's* by Claudia J. Strauss is full of terrific advice. It would have been a great help to me during the year I cared at home for my children's great-grandmother. Here are some of Strauss' suggestions, which you can share with all of your family members when they visit your loved one with Alzheimer's:

1. Calm down before walking in to visit. Your goal is to get yourself emotionally ready and to be at ease. Take some deep breaths, envision your favorite quiet place or call up the feeling of someone rubbing your shoulders or back. Relax. Why? You'll want to convey a sense of peacefulness and readiness to enjoy your loved one when you enter the room. You're creating an oasis during your visit. You'll want to give off "good vibes," as that's what he or she will pick up. It's best to enter the room with something like, "Hi, Dad, it's me, Linda, your daughter," so he won't have to guess or be embarrassed.

2. Your loved one's reality has changed. Setting him straight on facts and dates is not helpful. It will probably agitate him and remind him that he's losing his grip on reality. If he thinks his mother is still alive or that his son is still small and needs to be picked up from school, simply show that you're listening rather than argue (nod or say, "I hear what you're saying," or give a noncommittal "uh, huh," if you prefer not to lie.).

3. Expect a lot of repetition. Your loved one is struggling to remember the last conversation he had. He lives in the moment. Every time he asks a question, it is new to him, so you must act as if it is a new question to you, too. Answer in a tone of voice that is reassuring.

4. Ask questions that have a yes or no answer. An open-ended question like "How is your day going, Mom?" is an exception, as it is in the here and now.

The one thing you want to avoid are questions that require retrieving information from memory. You don't want to put your family member on the spot so that she becomes embarrassed or angry with herself for not being able to remember. Strauss' overall message is, "Don't let the person become the disease. Worrying about what you say or do makes it much more difficult to convey love, respect and that you like being with them." The book is full of examples of what to say and how to respond to a great number of common situations. It would make a great gift for any family or friends facing the care of a loved one with Alzheimer's.

 My wife just learned she has cancer. She's seems unusually quiet about it. Is this normal?

When people first learn they have cancer, their emotions can run the gamut. Some people shut down emotionally while others explode. Initially, whatever comes most naturally will probably be what's best for that individual until they are able to catch their breath and begin the process of coping with cancer. Your wife's withdrawal right now may be a kind of shock-absorber while her mind begins to process this life-changing event.

There appears to be three major phases in reacting to a cancer diagnosis: the initial response, a period of distress and then adjustment. The initial phase can be as short as a few days or up to a few weeks during which people report feeling shock and disbelief or outright denial. Once people get beyond the shock of their initial reaction to the diagnosis, they then go through a period of distress calling up a wide array of emotions: some people get angry, some ask "Why me?", some become sad and depressed, some feel guilty that they brought this onto themselves, others become anxious and fearful of impending pain, the effects of the treatment and not knowing whether or not they'll pull through. All of these emotions are normal responses with a new cancer diagnosis. So, give your wife the space and permission to feel them.

But, there can be a point where your spouse's distress becomes unhealthy and is downright debilitating. She won't be able to move onto the next phase of adjustment which will compromise her treatment and hopeful recovery.

Here is what to watch out for:

Consuming Anxiety. Research has shown that cancer patients who are anxious personalities have a harder time adjusting to the disease than their less anxious counterparts. If you're overly anxious, you'll more likely feel overwhelmed and that your life is out of control, rendering you helpless. Typical emotions in reaction to a cancer diagnosis will be extremely heightened, causing even higher levels of psychological stress.

Guilt: It's My Fault. All of us are plagued at one time or another with the "should haves" or "what ifs." Asking ourselves these questions can be a learning experience, but if we dwell on them for too long, especially when there are no clear cut answers, the soul searching can prove deadly. Okay, maybe you should have gone to the doctor sooner, you should have stopped smoking, stayed out of the sun or you should have listened to your wife about your high fat diet. What if you would have had that colonoscopy last year or didn't skip your mammogram? Whatever

your answer, the reality is that you have cancer and dwelling on what you could have done differently will not get you better. Move on, let it go and take control. Guilt paralyzes.

Clinical Depression. Cancer patients can expect feelings of sadness and loss over their circumstances, causing them to feel mildly depressed. Belonging to a support group, talking to another cancer survivor, or a social worker can help most people cope with feeling blue. But about one in four cancer patients will become clinically depressed where persistent feelings of hopelessness, worthlessness and helplessness consume them. If your wife starts showing these symptoms; talk with her doctor about psychotherapy and prescription medication. Sometimes the effects of chemotherapy and other drugs may contribute to her depression. Don't accept that depression is just a normal part of having cancer.

Holding it in. Psychologists refer to this as "emotional suppression." My Irish grandmother called this being stoic – a good thing in her world. But research shows that cancer patients who don't discuss their feelings are at very high risk for anxiety disorders and depression which will work against their recovery. They will quietly sink into hopelessness and disengage from those around them. It's is very important for their doctor to get them to talk about what they are feeling. The National Comprehensive Cancer Network offers an excellent tool – a Distress Barometer for physicians at www. nccn.org. So, if your wife stays quiet much longer, alert her doctor and urge her to start sharing what she feels.

The cancer ride is an emotional roller coaster and one of the best ways to handle its ups and downs and twists and turns is to gain as much knowledge as you can about the cancer and how to treat it. Lifestyle changes like nutrition, meditation and exercise can give her a sense of control, which is something she badly needs right now.

Q: When should we tell our grade-school-aged children that Grandpa is dying of cancer?

A: It's natural for parents to want to spare their children from pain. We spend a lifetime trying to protect them from every accident conceivable and our hearts ache as we watch them go through their first break-up. Yet, we all know that we do them no favor if we raise them in an overprotective bubble. If we do, they'll be without the protective gear to navigate the rough and tough terrain of life's journey. Your father's impending death is now part of your children's journey. There is no detour. They'll look to you and your spouse for a compass to guide them along this path. Most experts in childhood bereavement will tell you that children know more than you think. They pick up on your body language, the teary eyes of family members, the whispered conversations, the look in Grandpa and Grandma's eyes. At this age, your children need to know what's going on, so that none of them will be plagued with "if only I had known, I would have..." for the rest of their lives.

To answer your question, I read two excellent books on the subject recommended by The Caring Place, a center for grieving children. The first, *How to Help Children through a Serious Illness*, by Kathleen McCue, tells parents that nearly all children have three universal concerns:

1. Young children may believe that they had something to do with causing their loved one to die. For example, they may have secretly wished them "dead" when they were being disciplined. As a result, she cautions that children need to be told that nothing they did or didn't do could have caused what's happening to Grandpa to make him die.

2. Young children need to know that whatever their loved one has, it is not

contagious. They need to know they won't catch it, and that their parents won't catch it.

3. Young children who face the death of a parent also need to know who will take their parent's place. In other words who will do the "Daddy" or "Mommy" things? In this instance, your kids need to know how your family will function in the face of their grandfather's impending death: how you may be spending more time away from home, how Grandma may come to live with you for awhile, how you'll be spending time at a hospital or that when they visit with Grandpa they'll be meeting people from hospice. McCue also recommends giving your children something to do – as she puts it "they're entitled to help."

In Dr. Dan Schaeffer's book, *How Do We Tell the Children?*, he offers a checklist of actions to consider (For those of you with younger children, please see his book for recommendations during different stages of childhood.):

1. It's better to "control the message" by explaining to your children what is going on; otherwise, they will be confused and anxious, and imagine many things that aren't true. Never lie to a child or make something up so that they'll feel better.

2. Do not be afraid of using the "d" word (meaning death or dying). Terms like "passed away," "gone on," or "left us," cause children great anxiety and confusion, as in, "Is Grandpa on a trip?" "Is he coming back one day?"

3. Explain death in a simple, straightforward manner, for example: "Dead means that a person's body stops working, he won't be able to talk, walk, move, see, or hear because none of the parts work. He won't feel any pain."

4. Allow the child to ask questions; don't be surprised if they ask a lot of mechanical questions like "Why is he cold? Where will they put the body? Can he hear me?"

5. Never describe a dead person as "sleeping." Aside from being inaccurate, it will frequently cause anxiety around sleep in children.

6. Let them know that it is okay to cry and feel sad – an especially important message for boys.

From all that I've read on this subject and through personal experience, one resounding message comes through – you cannot protect your children from the cycle of life. Soften the harsh reality with the embrace of love, shared tears and the reassurance that their family circle will help them through this sadness. But, sad it will be.

Q: How do we set up a family meeting to decide what's best for our mother, who just had a stroke?

A: Sharing the decision-making is a smart way of handling such a life-changing decision for your Mom and your siblings. Each of you has a different relationship with her, different life experiences and thus, different perspectives on how to handle your Mom's care. In order to maintain peace among you and avoid conflict down the line, it is helpful to discuss your mother's care openly as a unit. But, if your family is already at loggerheads, I'd suggest getting a professional facilitator to hold the family meeting (a social worker, psychologist, priest, rabbi or minister.) Even if you all need to pitch in to pay for someone, it will be well worth it. If you're doing it on your own, here are my suggestions for a productive family meeting:

Everyone needs to do some homework. You'll accomplish more if everyone brings important information to the meeting. Just like organizing who brings what to a family reunion, each of you needs to volunteer to bring the results of an assignment to the meeting. Someone needs to gather your Mom's medical information – type of stroke, her prognosis for recovery, other medical conditions that require care, medications and any other information about her health. Someone else should tackle all of her financial and insurance information and another should research the range of housing options and medical care available to meet her needs. If possible, share the results of your assignments ahead of time.

Create an agenda. Each of you should identify the three most important things you'd like to discuss at the meeting. Organize the agenda around these issues. Chances are you'll find some overlap.

Identify a facilitator. One of you should be in charge of organizing the agenda and keeping the discussion on task.

Everyone attends. If all of you can't get together in one place, it's worth setting up a conference call. If your family is small enough, you can easily do a three-way call, which is much cheaper than travel.

Chances are most of you have had experience in being part of meetings so you're aware of the following basic rules (it might feel a little strange to be somewhat formal with each other, but a few ground rules do help):

- ▸ Follow the agenda that you all agreed upon.

- ▸ No cutting in. Wait until someone is finished talking.

> No accusations. (as in "you always side in with him.")

> When you have something to say, it should reflect what you think, not what you think others think. So, start the sentence with "I...".

> Stay focused on your Mom's needs. Rally around what's best for her. So, that means you need to leave old scores behind.

> If you're not clear on a point your sibling has made, ask him to clarify it. (Don't stay silent, assuming he meant something he didn't.)

> If you want to make sure you've understood him, try something like, "This is what I heard you say (then repeat what you think you heard). Is that right?"

> Create next-action steps as you complete each item on the agenda. Identify any other information you need to make a decision. Wrap up the meeting with everyone clearly understanding what you've decided as a group and who will be responsible for what, going forward. Create a list of those duties and share it before you disband.

Functioning as a group will make it much better for your Mom and easier for all of you to work as a team. If all of you are online, take advantage of the convenience to exchange information on websites, send pertinent attachments, and e-mail each other and the staff in charge of your mother's care. This will be a very trying time for all of you, but if you openly communicate with one another, then emotions of anxiety, guilt, grief, anger, or frustration won't be able to play havoc with your relationships.

 : My uncle told me he's thought of committing suicide and I think he's being seriously neglected by his sister, who is his primary caregiver. What do I do?

 : If you suspect that he is being seriously neglected, then you are the one person who can make a difference in your uncle's life and, hopefully, make it worth living. Let me offer a few steps to consider.

First, give a call to your local Area Agency on Aging (AAA) and ask to speak to the Protective Services caseworker. You can find your local AAA by calling the Eldercare Locator at 1-800-677-1116. Explain the situation and stress how concerned you are that your uncle will harm himself. If you can, cite the dates on which he has threatened suicide. You will be filing a "Report of Need" that remains confidential and allows the protective services team the right to intervene. The Protective Service caseworker will likely go and meet with your uncle and his sister. They will be able to assess his needs (both physically and mentally) by arranging for a comprehensive geriatric assessment to determine whether or not he has dementia or any other health issues affecting his ability to live on his own. The Area Agency on Aging will also be able to sort out the legal and financial issues surrounding your uncle. If he is capable of making decisions for himself, then he can decide whether or not to seek supportive services to remain living at home or explore assisted living. The geriatric assessment may determine that he actually needs nursing home care, which can also be arranged. If his sister has Power of Attorney, allowing her to handle his finances, the Area Agency on Aging will work with her to make the financial arrangements. However, if he is considered competent by the social workers, then he does not need his sister to make these decisions and the power of attorney can be revoked.

Second, I'd also let the Protective Services caseworker know that you believe that his sister is negligent about caring for him. This places his health and well-being at risk and could be assessed by the caseworkers as "caregiver neglect" on the part of his sister.

Third, if you do not want to call protective services, you still have the flexibility to intervene. Even if his sister has power of attorney, she can't prevent him from seeking care. So go visit your uncle, build some rapport with him and see if he would go to a doctor's appointment with you.

Once a physician assesses your uncle's mental and physical state, you are in a better position (along with a Protective Services team) to make an educated, compassionate decision about his care. It would also make it difficult for his sister to prevent anyone else from providing the care he needs, once a professional medical opinion is rendered.

Fourth, you could also talk to an Elder Law attorney and ask what options you have, but I'd start with protective services workers at the Area Agency on Aging. No matter what you do, get involved.

Q: Can my sister use her Health Care Power of Attorney to prevent us from visiting with our mother?

A: The short answer is no. Your sister cannot use her health care power of attorney to restrict your visits. She is, however, empowered to make health care decisions on behalf of your mother *any time* your mother becomes incompetent. The key word is "incompetent." The health care power of attorney kicks in when your mother is incapacitated and unable to make health care decisions on her own. It is valid only *during* her incapacity. People usually grant this type of permission to a loved one whom they believe will make good medical decisions *when and if* they become incapacitated.

A Health Care Power of Attorney is used to make decisions involving health care facility admissions and discharges, medical treatments, organ donations, and the movement of the patient. For the durable health care power of attorney to be legal, your mother had to be competent when she signed it. Many states have laws that spell out procedures for determining when someone is legally competent. You don't need to be a lawyer because, in this case, the word "attorney" means "designated agent."

However, it sounds like something else is going on with your sister. Perhaps she feels like she's losing control of her household with everyone (no matter how well-intentioned) coming and going to see Mom. There might be unresolved family conflicts, or she might feel that surprise visits agitate your mother. Rather than argue about visiting rights, try exploring what your sister wants to accomplish by restricting your visits. Your mother should be included in this discussion.

Offer to set up a visiting schedule that gives your sister a break and ask her to share how each of you could assist with appointments and outings. Let your sister know that you respect the privacy of her home, but you'd like to find a happy medium so that all of you can share in being with your Mom, just like her. Hopefully, in time, your sister might find that a few visits now and then lifts your Mom's spirits and that's what all of you should be working toward.

Section Three
Lifestyle

: My husband will retire next year and I'm worried as to how he'll handle it emotionally. Any tips?

For starters, your husband should know that what he's facing is no longer his father's kind of retirement. It is more like entering a new life phase, life shift, transition or, as some experts call it, "rewirement." Most of the books on retirement planning focus almost entirely on finances. Sure, money builds the foundation for retiring, but life after work is about so much more.

Far too many new retirees don't prepare for the substantial shift in how they'll perceive themselves once they have retired. It's easy to get caught up in the excitement of having free time, no time clocks or deadlines and the ability to travel or pursue hobbies. But, within about a year, the adventure of every day being a "Saturday" wears off and people begin to question their identity. It's easy to see why. Just think of how most conversations with strangers start, "So, what do you do?" All of a sudden, you're not able to throw out a job title and all the cache that goes with it. It is how our society judges people and assigns value. So, it is no wonder that the Ameriprise Financial group found in their survey of retirees that 40 percent of them were unhappy within the first five years of retirement and recall feeling much better about life when they were working. At work they felt a sense of purpose, enjoyed the camaraderie with their co-workers and fell into a comfort zone that daily routines and structure bring. To prevent your spouse from joining the ranks of the discontented, John Trauth and Alan Bernstein, in their book, *Your Retirement, Your Way* (McGraw Hill 2007), offer four "must do" steps in planning a satisfying retirement and changing one that isn't:

First, identify those tasks and projects you've done where the experience just flowed when you lost track of time and thoroughly enjoyed what you were doing. These are the kinds of experiences you want to repeat in retirement. It would also be wise to take personality inventories to help you get a better sense of what satisfies and excites you at this stage of your life.

Second, remain connected to your family and friends. People who stay socially active and engaged have been proven to live healthier lives and stave off depression. If you're thinking of moving away, consider how you'll re-create a socially active life and stay connected to family. Some retirees are moving towards family so they can enjoy being grandparents.

Third, eliminate the things that make you unhappy. Make two lists: a "To Do" list of things you want to do in your retirement and a list of "Stop Doing" list of the things that make your life stressful. Take advantage of your non-structured life and the absence of the demands that your former job required; don't substitute a new set of stressors for old ones.

Fourth, renew meaning and purpose in your life by finding ways to make other people happy. Baby Boomers especially are attracted to this ethos of giving back through volunteering. There are selfish reasons to help out, too, as people who volunteer also enjoy healthier lives.

Retirement planning experts offer a number of other strategies to emotionally prepare for retirement. Among them are: write out your vision of your retirement in five year increments, identifying what you'll be doing, where you'll be living, where you'll travel, whether you'll be working and what hobbies or interests you'll be pursuing. Share your vision (especially with your spouse), family members and friends to get their feedback and start making plans around it. If you are thinking of moving to another state then before you sell the house, spend a few months there during different times of the year. Allow yourself the freedom to try out your ideas – trial and error can be a good thing. Retirement is about lifestyle and not simply the end of a work life. Just like you can experience three or four careers in a lifetime, so too, can you enjoy different lifestyles during your retirement. You can decide to consult, start a small business, go back to school, work part-time, join the Peace Corps, become a nurse, train for the Senior Games or take the first twelve months off and kick-back.

The overlying message among all of these advisors is to start envisioning the next twenty to thirty years now, and see those years as dynamic and changing. Most of their advice is based upon an optimistic projection of the future. I'd also advise that both of you think through how you'll provide for each other should one or both of you become ill.

Q: My Mom had a part-time job she loved, but gave it up to take care of my Dad. He recently died and she won't go back to work because "it would make her feel guilty." Is this normal?

A: What she is experiencing is a form of what psychologists refer to as "survivor's guilt," often experienced by those who have survived some catastrophe in which others died. It stems from feeling guilty that they did not do enough to save those who died or they aren't worthy of being one of those who did survive. For example, people who escaped out of the twin towers on September 11th reported feeling survivor's guilt and some, to this day, can't shake feeling guilty.

Losing a spouse is also catastrophic – it may not involve many other people and the death may even be expected, but the end result is a dramatic loss that deeply affects one's sense of self and the world around them. Add an intensive year of caregiving, as in your Mom's case, and she'll feel another kind of guilt coming from a sense of relief. All of a sudden, the stress of taking your father to one doctor after another, keeping up with his medications, helping him bathe, eat and dress all the while she loses sleep, feels tired, and in her darkest moments feels resentful at life's turn of events – has stopped. She's been freed. If she allows herself to feel happy that she's no longer a caregiver, she may feel like she's betraying your Dad. She might even think that by going back to work, she's acknowledging that his death is actually a good thing.

You and I know this isn't the case, but it's hard for your Mom to see clearly through a storm of conflicting emotions. Nor do we see the exacting toll that caregiving plays on those we love and ourselves. The "Evercare Study" with the National Caregiver Alliance revealed some pretty alarming results: three out of four caregivers found their health failing and couldn't find time to get to the doctor, most felt aches and pains, eight out of ten weren't getting enough sleep, felt drained and depressed, and six out of ten admitted they weren't eating right. So, chances are your mother's health isn't in the best state of affairs, either.

Now, it's your turn to do for your Mom like she did for your Dad. Tell her you "want to look out for her. Just like Dad needed to let her help him, I need you to do the same with me." Explain to her how she needs to heal, not only in her grieving, but in recovering from a very long year of caregiving. Take her to her doctor to get a good physical check-up that should also include a heart-to-heart talk about how she's feeling. If she shows signs of clinical depression, her physician should treat it.

She may need you and her doctor to give her "permission" that going back to work is really about getting well; it's about *her health*. Being active, getting out of the house, and engaging socially with others are the best antidotes against depression. Assure her that your father would want her to be well and as her daughter, there's nothing more important to you than her well-being. If you frame it this way, you'll help her feel less guilty so she can escape its paralyzing grip on her. Going to work will also give her a sense of purpose that can fill the void she's feeling right now with no one to take care of and not being needed.

She may need to let her co-worker and supervisor know that she may have to ease into her old job. Advise your Mom that it would be helpful if she also let them know how they can best support her; they might think that bringing up your Dad will make her feel sad or if they don't say anything your Mom will feel they don't care. If she's having a particularly hard day (it might be your parent's anniversary), let a coworker know and tell them how they can help. This should ease her anxiety over any unrealistic expectations that she can only go back to work if she's at one hundred percent.

Going to work might very well be just *what the doctor ordered*. And that's something your Mom should be able to accept after a year of following them for your Dad.

 : We'd like to take my Dad on vacation despite his health problems. How do we make this work?

 : The best vacations are usually the ones where you've taken the time to plan and do your homework. So, let's begin researching your vacation options. First, all of you must want to go on this vacation. If your Dad is being dragged into this, chances are you'll have a dismal time. If he really wants to stay at home, then make a list of all the tasks that you would expect someone to do in your absence, such as shop, assist with physical therapy, make meals, make sure he takes his medications, and goes to doctor's appointments – whatever you do now. Then call a local home health or senior care agency, describe what you need and have them identify the properly skilled person to care for him. If his care is light, then perhaps a reliable family member or friend can come and live with him while you are away. If you, your husband and Dad want to make a go of it, here are some things to keep in mind:

- Find a place where the weather is agreeable for all of you. It's best to look for moderate climates.

- Cruises make for a great family vacation that can meet each individual's needs and those of a whole family. There are cruises that will accommodate a wide range of medical needs. In fact, there are cruises that are fully equipped and medically staffed for dialysis patients, diabetics, and those who are oxygen dependent. Some cruise lines offer nursing and attendant care. A website that can help you identify such cruise line packages can be located at www.medicaltravel.org or call them at 1-800-308-2503.

- All of you should make a list of the kind of activities you'd like to do on the vacation. Be sure to share your likes and dislikes. Use this list as a guide to develop a mutual itinerary and also to identify ways that everyone can go off on their own sometimes. You don't have to be constantly together.

- Family resorts offer another alternative for a vacation package catering to multiple generations. Most travel agents or the American Automobile Association will know of such family-friendly resorts. They often have individuals available who can stay with your Dad while you and your husband enjoy other activities.

- Take all of your Dad's medications, check if you'll need a refill during vacation and fill it before you leave. If you are flying, be sure to store the medications in your carry-on bag rather than risk their loss if the luggage is detained or stolen.

- If your Dad needs a scooter, a wheelchair or other cumbersome equipment to get around, ask the hotel where you'll stay if they can provide or rent it for you. Or call medical equipment companies listed in the Yellow Pages in the area of where you'll be staying to find out how you can rent whatever you'll need.

- Be sure to notify hotels of any conditions that your Dad may have and ask to have the room near the elevator or on the first floor.

- Choose activities and a vacation length that isn't too physically demanding.

- Take the time to call ahead to restaurants and hotels to make sure they are handicap-accessible.

- Take breaks – whether driving a long distance or planning a long day – pace the day for your father.

- Check with your Dad's health insurance and find out if there are any policy restrictions when he is out of the service area.

- Be sure to buy trip insurance in case you need to cancel at the last minute.

- Some families, if they can afford it, bring a caregiver on the vacation to attend to their parent.

Q: My husband and I want to go on vacation, but we cannot leave his mother alone. Any suggestions?

A: You could set up a "mutual vacation," wherein she takes a "vacation" at a quality assisted living facility while you and your husband go out of town. Many assisted living facilities are delighted to have a short-stay guest, often referred to as "respite care." She may enjoy all of the attention and dining out every day, along with the security of having her physical needs met. Just make sure this option is okay with her, and you both should visit the facility ahead of time. She should not feel like she is being abandoned or "set-up" for eventually placement in what she may consider a nursing home. A refundable deposit is required by most facilities, depending on the length of stay. Here's how one person described the experience of vacationing this way:

"We personally visited several retirement communities, eliminated some on sight and others because they did not provide the flexibility we needed. The one we ultimately chose had neither a minimum nor a maximum period for so-called "respite" care. We planned our loved one's vacation so that she entered the facility a day or two before we left town, and extended two or three days on the other end. That way, if adjustment problems arose, or medication problems surfaced (that happens!) we would be around to see to the problem. At the other end of the vacation period, we had a couple of days to unpack and "re-enter" without coping with caregiving needs. During the vacation period, we made arrangements for drop-in visits by friends of the family. We also planned the mailing of cards so that the week was pretty much covered by mail each day. We arranged for the newspaper to be delivered to her so that she had her own paper for crossword puzzles, etc. We arranged with a local florist to have a fresh arrangement sent at midpoint to cheer up the room and remind her that we were thinking of her. (For a man, some florists will make up and deliver "snack baskets" with little boxes and bags of this and that). As a bonus, when the time came for her to enter assisted living full time, she related to her very pleasant 'vacations' rather than feeling threatened or, at worst, abandoned."

Thus, with some thoughtful planning and homework, you can enjoy a vacation while your mother-in-law is safely cared for. If your loved one does not need 24/7 care, you might want to consider bringing in someone from a non-medical senior care agency. Taking a break from caregiving, whether it's a vacation or simply enjoying an afternoon to yourself, is far beyond a luxury – it's essential. Have a great time.

Ever since our Dad died, we feel Mom could really use the companionship of a pet. Is a dog a good idea or just too much of a hassle?

A: There's plenty of research heralding the benefits of interacting with pets: People are less depressed, pets offer a welcome distraction from pain, talking to and caring for a pet reduces loneliness and walking a dog encourages exercise. Sure, their love and affection requires some work, but you can make this easier than you may think. That being said, get your mother a pet *only* if she wants one! If so, it makes more sense to get her an older, housebroken dog; you'll also want to make sure that the dog is used to a crate, so that when she goes out during the day she won't have to worry about her new friend wreaking havoc throughout the house. Older dogs can be found through newspaper ads, the Humane Society and non-profit pet adoptions groups listed in your phone book.

Your next step is to make sure that walking the dog won't become an athletic or hazardous event for your Mom. Get her a dog whose size she can manage and make sure that where she walks the dog is obstacle-free. You might want to build a long handrail alongside a walkway. Or install a dog-door (a small, secure opening that is cut into an existing door) that leads to an enclosed back yard. That way, if your Mom isn't feeling up for a walk, the dog can easily go in and out without her. These are pretty inexpensive and you can find them at most discount retail and pet stores. You can also make life easier by keeping your Mom stocked with 25-pound bags of dog food to save her from frequent shopping trips and heavy lifting.

Your Mom might be worried that if she becomes hospitalized or wants to take a short vacation, no one will be around to take care of the dog. She might not realize the benefits of "Pet Sitting Services." I've used it myself and it's a great way to leave your best buddy behind feeling safe and happy in his own home. You can find them in the yellow pages of your phone book under Pet Sitters or go to the website of Pet Sitters International (www.petsit.com) and search for one of their members by zip code. Here's what to ask and look for in a good, reliable pet sitter:

> Are they insured and bonded?

> How long have they been in business?

> Are they a member of any professional association, e.g. Pet Sitters International (PSI)?

> Do they have any formal training in caring for pets? Do they own pets?

- What kind of background checks and training do their employees have?

- Do they have customer references? (Take numbers and call).

- Do they have a formal relationship with a veterinarian in case of an emergency? Is there a veterinarian who recommends them?

- Do they come to your home before the first pet sitting assignment to meet the pets and gather detailed information about their care?

- If so, watch how they interact with the pet and how much attention they give to finding out details on how to care for your pet.

- Do they write up daily reports on each visit and will they leave messages on your voicemail on how well your pet is doing?

- Do they run their service as a professional business, e.g. presenting you with written materials and contracts?

On average, you'll pay ten to fourteen dollars per visit and two dollars for each additional pet. Perhaps you and other family members can tell Mom that you'll chip in for the service or give her gift certificates.

Your Mom may also be worried that she'll become attached to the dog and then have to give him up if she needs to move into an apartment or assisted living. But, there are facilities that welcome pets as long as the resident is able to provide the care. Even nursing homes today have dogs and cats that either live on the premises or visit as part of pet assistive therapy programs. All in all, with a little bit of planning, there really isn't that much of a hassle in your Mom having a dog, but you do need to make sure that this is something she wants. The rewards of owning a warm and cuddly companion are pretty darn high. If she's not up for a dog, consider a cat or even a chatty bird.

Is there a private test that my Dad could take to help him assess his driving ability?

 Actually, the American Automobile Association offers older drivers a screening tool, *Roadside Review*, to help them identify problem areas in their driving ability. It's called the "AAA Roadwise Review" and members can purchase it for less than ten dollars at local AAA offices.

This user-friendly CD-ROM can be used on any computer, so your Dad can take this review at home or go to a local library to use a computer. This innovative tool is the product of six years of research spearheaded by the National Highway Traffic Safety Administration (NHTSA) and the National Institute on Aging. In pilot tests they found that drivers exhibiting significant losses in the capabilities tested by *Roadwise Review* were two to five times more likely to cause a motor vehicle crash than drivers without any losses in the eight key driving abilities measured by the tool.

Here are the eight safety abilities that your Dad can assess using the *Roadwise Review* screening tool:

1. **Leg Strength and General Mobility:** ability to brake and accelerate under regular conditions and to respond in emergencies.

2. **Head/Neck Flexibility:** ability to check blind spots when you back up, change lanes or merge into traffic.

3. **High Contrast Visual Acuity:** ability to detect pavement markings, read road signs and spot hazards in or near the road.

4. **Low Visual Acuity:** ability to maintain lane position and drive safely in rain, dusk, haze and fog.

5. **Working Memory:** ability to follow directions, remember traffic rules and regulations and make good decisions while driving.

6. **Visualization of Missing Information:** ability to recognize and anticipate a threat or hazard even when part of it is hidden from view.

7. **Visual Search:** ability to scan the driving environment and recognize traffic signs, signals, navigational landmarks and hazards.

8. **Visual Information Processing Speed:** ability to pay attention to what is in front of you, while also detecting threats at the edge of your visual field.

At the conclusion of each of the eight tests, your father will receive a summary of results and advice on steps he can take to address any "driving issues" that may come up. There are a good number of visual, medical and physical rehabilitation devices and techniques that can be used to keep him driving safely. If substantial problems are identified, then he'll be advised to see a physician, an occupational therapist or a Certified Driving Rehabilitation Specialist. If your Dad has no measurable loss in ability in the eight tested areas, he can use these results as a baseline to track any changes over time.

People who've taken the *Roadwise Review* have found it "very well set-up, easy to follow and move through." Others say it's actually fun and they like the thought of taking it privately. If they've done well, they have more confidence in their driving and if they haven't, they are given concrete action steps to prevent an accident in their future.

Is the test worth taking? The statistics sure tell you it is: Although older drivers are more likely to wear seat belts, less likely to drink and drive and less likely to speed; they are more likely to be hurt in a car crash suffering debilitating injuries and longer recovery times than all other populations. They also experience the highest crash death rate per mile except that of teenagers. The most common factors in crashes involving mature drivers are: failure to yield right-of-way, improper left turns, confusion in heavy traffic, in-attention, complications while backing up, failure to maintain a proper speed, and hesitation in responding to new traffic signs, signals or pavement markings.

It's really a great way for any older driver to assess their driving skills. So, give your local AAA a call and ask to order the *Roadwise Review* CD-ROM. Also, visit the AAA website for more safe driving information for older drivers at www.aaapublicaffairs.com.

 The whole scare over the H1N1 flu got me thinking about what we should do in case of a pandemic. Any tips?

 Hopefully, with better preparation and antiviral drugs, we won't experience a pandemic as bad as the flu of 1918, which caused 50 million deaths worldwide. But, experts say it's just a matter of time before we face a virus with that level of potency. Here's what experts advise you can do to prepare for a flu pandemic:

Communications

1. Stay informed by calling the CDC hotline at 1-800-CDC-INFO (1-800-232-4636), or go online to www.pandemicflu.gov. Listen to newscasts and read your newspaper to stay up-to-date and learn where antiviral medicine will be given to the public.

2. Identify how medical care will be provided to you. If one of you is sick; will it be a family member, a qualified neighbor, or do you have a home health agency lined up? Should you stay with family members during the pandemic and who will provide transportation if you can't drive?

3. If you have chronic health conditions, then create a list describing each with the name of specialists and contact information. Make a list of all medications and dosage levels you take, along with any allergies you have. Bring this information to a public health center giving out antiviral medicine during a pandemic.

4. If you require ongoing medical care, such as dialysis or chemotherapy, ask your health care provider how you can receive this care during a pandemic. What is the provider's emergency preparedness plan?

Supplies

1. Store at least a two week supply of water, based upon one gallon of water per person per day. Half of it can be used for food preparation and sanitation, while the other half you drink. Stay hydrated.

2. Stock up on ready-to-eat canned meats, fish, fruits, vegetables, beans and soups that don't have to be heated, in case of a power outage. Choose protein bars, peanut butter, nuts, crackers, and canned juices and don't forget food for your pet.

3. Keep a 30-day supply of medications that you must take to stay well in case you cannot get to a pharmacy, or if they are closed. During Hurricane Katrina, many elderly people died because they did not have their medications with them.

4. Keep standard emergency supplies on hand, such as a portable radio, batteries, flash lights, a manual can opener, garbage bags, paper towels and toilet paper.

5. Supplies especially relevant to the flu are: Kleenex, antibacterial hand washes and wipes, pain relievers, fever reducers such as Tylenol, over-the-counter remedies for nausea and diarrhea, cough and cold medicines, vitamins, fluids with electrolytes and a thermometer.

6. Have some cash safely stored at home should banks or ATM machines be closed and keep the gas tank in your car near full.

7. If you don't have a cell phone, get a no-contract phone with prepaid minutes.

Even if you escape the pandemic flu this season, you'll be prepared for the next power outage or bad winter storm if you follow these suggestions. It's not like your investment in time and supplies won't pay off. One last thing; make sure you've had your pneumonia vaccine.

Q: My Dad, who is widowed, has been dating someone who he really cares for, but is worried about becoming sexually intimate. Any advice for him?

A: Probably one of the last taboos in our society is discussing sexual intimacy among older people. It's a topic rarely discussed and when it is, it's usually in the context of jokes or even disgust. Yet, later life certainly doesn't mean that all of a sudden someone becomes asexual. In contrast, our sexual drive remains with us throughout our lives. It changes, evolves, refines and matures. The way someone expresses their sexuality after sixty years may be different, but it's still there.

To respond to your request, I researched several excellent articles on the subject and listened to a webcast on "Sex and Aging" with three distinguished physician panelists from Columbia University and New York University Medical Center. Let me share with you some of the major themes and points that experts on the topic suggest that may address some of your father's worries:

➤ Most older people experience interest in sexual intimacy well into their eighties. It continues to be a source of expressing closeness, love, respect and enjoyment. It remains an important measure of quality of life.

➤ Sexual intimacy doesn't always equal sexual intercourse. Many people can derive great pleasure in touching, stroking, holding, kissing and cuddling. One of the more serious losses of aging is the loss of physical intimacy when one loses a partner and no longer experiences the simple pleasure of just being held or touched. There's no need to place undue pressure on yourself or a partner by believing that, if you're not having intercourse, then it means you're not having sex and that makes your relationship inadequate.

➤ When older people start a new relationship in later life, they may feel uncomfortable with their body (especially women), or apprehensive about exploring their partner's. They were probably very comfortable with the sexual rituals they had with their former spouse, but now they must create new rituals with a new partner and they may feel awkward. But, the time to communicate is right from the start as you both create this new way of relating. Be open and specific as to what feels good to you and ask what feels good to your partner.

➤ For many older people, engaging in sexual activity just before going to bed may be too stressful, as they may be exhausted and need to relax to get a good night's sleep. This may also interfere with sleep, anxiety or other medications. One of the benefits of retirement is that people can consider other times of the day to share their intimacy when they may feel more energy to enjoy each other's company.

➤ If a partner has health conditions that has him or her concerned about lovemaking, then they should see a physician who can help answer questions about when and how to engage in sexual activity after an illness (e.g. heart attack) or with a condition (e.g. lung disease). If you experience discomfort, erectile dysfunction or if you feel something is amiss, bring it up and ask your doctor, "What can we do about this?"

➤ Women may find after menopause that they experience vaginal dryness, which can make intercourse painful, as can the thinning of the vaginal walls. Dryness can be helped by over-the-counter water based lubricants such as KY jelly, however, petroleum-based lubricants such as Vaseline should be avoided because it can cause infections.

➤ Giving each other a massage is a relaxing way to slowly increase sexual arousal and relieve aching muscles. Atmosphere is important: dimmed lights, relaxing music and getting out of a "sick room," where someone recovered from an illness helps set a romantic mood that's welcome at any age.

➤ Safe sex is important at all ages. One of the fastest growing groups among HIV/AIDS is women fifty years of age and older. Some experts suspect that, unlike young women, older women are embarrassed to ask their partner to use a male latex condom, thinking it may insult him or they're embarrassed to use a female condom. Don't be.

➤ Sensuality and intimacy offers a life-affirming expression between two people that can be very rich, deep and fulfilling. It celebrates life in the moment and in late life, it can be all the more rewarding.

Q: My husband has finally decided to get a hearing aid, but doesn't know where to begin. Any tips?

A: First, he should see his physician or a specialist who treats ears (otologist or otolaryngologist) to make sure that his hearing loss isn't due to a medical condition. The law requires consumers to have a physical examination within six months prior to buying a hearing aid. He'll be given a written recommendation by his doctor to give to a hearing aid vendor or he can waive an examination, but that would be ill-advised.

Hearing Aid centers, audiologists and ENT (Ear, Nose & Throat) physicians offer hearing examinations. They'll offer comprehensive testing by a licensed audiologist and fittings by a hearing instrument specialist. Tests are performed in a sound-controlled booth while your husband wears earphones. Typical tests include pure tone air conduction (how well he hears at different frequencies), speech reception threshold (what decibel he begins to understand speech) and word recognition tests. At the conclusion of the testing, he should receive a copy of his audiogram with a clear description of what the results mean.

Depending upon his type of hearing loss and his lifestyle needs, he'll be introduced to a variety of hearing aids: Behind-the-Ear (BTE) fits snugly behind the ear with small tubing molded to fit the outer ear, Open Canal Mini-BTE are smaller with a small tube extending to the speaker in the ear canal, In-the-Ear (ITE) fits directly into the external part of the ear, In-the-Canal (ITC) fit partially into the ear canal and is barely visible and Completely-in-the-Canal (CIC) aids are molded to fit deeply within the ear canal and are the smallest, most invisible of hearing aids.

Before buying, here is what your husband should ask:

1. Do you offer a variety of hearing aids from different manufacturers? Or, do you deal with just one? You may find more options in the kind of aids offered and pricing with a range of manufacturers.

2. What services and products are included in the price? You may be quoted one price for a package of services, so ask them to break out the separate charges for testing, evaluation, fittings, and follow-up appointments. With this information, you can compare products and pricing more easily.

3. May I have a copy of my audiogram? If you want to get a second opinion, take your test results to another hearing aid vendor

and find out what type of aid they suggest. You should not have to be retested to be given the second opinion.

4. What is your return policy and warranty? According to Pennsylvania's Hearing Aid Sales and Registration Law, you have the right to a thirty-day money-back written guarantee, refunding the purchase price of the hearing aid and accessories to you. However, they can charge you a "restocking fee," but it can not exceed the lesser of 10 percent of the purchase price or $150.00.

5. Can you help me with financing and insurance? Medicare does not cover hearing aids, but some of the exam and diagnostic testing may be covered. Many centers offer payment plans or they will call your private insurance company to determine what is covered. If your husband is a veteran, he may qualify for hearing aid assistance, so call the Veterans Administration at 1-800-827-1000 to find the center nearest him and get benefit information. An excellent website hosted by the Hearing Better Institute at www.betterhearing.org offers guides you can download and an extensive list of financial resources. AARP provides a free consumer guide on hearing aids at www.aarp.org; just enter "Consumer Guide to Hearing Aids" in the search bar on the home page.

Q: Is it just me, or are newer cars being made with brighter headlights? My daughter says it's due to aging. What's the story?

 You and your daughter each have part of the story right. Here is what's going on: Most people over fifty find themselves complaining about glare from headlights just like you. Your eyes adapt to darkness by way of tiny muscles located in your iris that control the size of your pupil – the wider the pupil, the more light comes in. As you age the muscles are weakened so the pupil won't be able to regulate how much light goes in, nor will it be able to adapt quickly to dramatic changes in the intensity of light. This process is known as "dark adaptation" and for the older eye, this becomes a real challenge and that's why you'll find going from light to dark more difficult. And, it also explains why the eye can't quickly adjust to the high intensity of bright headlights.

All that being said, headlights on some of the newer cars are brighter. These are known as high-intensity discharge (HID)

lights and omit twice the light of halogen headlamps. They also produce a blue-white light compared to the yellow glare of regular lights. Drivers behind the wheel of HIDs like them, but drivers on the receiving end can find them blinding. Fog lights used when it isn't foggy also pose problems for oncoming traffic. Another contributing factor toward glaring headlights is the higher positioning of the lights on SUVs that appear directed right at your eyes.

Experts believe that the typical driver fifty years-plus needs twice as much light to see well after dark because they need more light. That's because they need more light to compensate for less light passing through their pupils.

The National Safety Council and the American Automobile Association offer a number of strategies that can help your "mature" eyes better adapt to the dark:

1. Clean your car's headlights, tail lights, turning signal lights and windows at least once a week. A thin layer of grime on your headlight can reduce its light up to ninety percent! Smudges on the inside of your windshield will catch and refract light restricting your ability to see.

2. Make sure your headlights are properly aimed, so that you're getting the full effect of the lights. Anytime your car is inspected or being worked on, ask the technician to align the lights. Studies show that half of cars being inspected have headlights off-kilter.

3. Smoking while you drive actually decreases your vision due to the smoke's nicotine and carbon monoxide.

4. Drive a safe distance behind other cars. You should be able to stop inside the illuminated area of your headlights.

5. To avoid the glare of oncoming traffic, especially if the driver has their high beams on, focus on the right edge of the road toward the white line and use it as a steering guide.

6. Whenever you are out in the sun, wear sunglasses. Intense and bright sunlight bleaches the photoreceptors in your eye, lengthening the time it takes for your eyes to adjust to the dark. Don't hasten the process of aging going without "shades."

7. If you wear prescriptive glasses, ask for AR (anti-reflective) coating on the lenses. This transmits more light at night, improving your vision and helps distinguish fine details during the day.

8. The AAA cautions consumers about buying "night driving" glasses that supposedly block the wavelengths of light attributed to glare. No matter what their tint, they do reduce the amount of light reaching your eyes overall, which will impair your vision. Never wear sunglasses for night time driving.

There is another precaution you can take, and that is to gradually reduce your night driving to lessen your risk for accidents. Be aware, too, that twilight is one of the most difficult times of the day to drive because it requires your eyes to constantly adjust to the growing darkness.

Hopefully, these strategies will keep you safely on the road for years to come.

Q: How can my parents downsize their home?

 Remember when you first looked at a college dorm? Downsizing all of your worldly possessions into a tiny room seemed insurmountable. Now fast forward to your Mom or Dad's life as they try to downsize from the family homestead to an apartment or assisted living facility. It's not just the emotional transition, but also the practical challenge of downsizing that makes the move so daunting. There's so much "letting go," deciding what to sell, what goes to charitable organizations, and what's given to family and friends. Then, there are the innumerable choices – how will the furniture fit into the room? Where will the pictures hang? Just the thought of making all of these decisions stops many people dead in their tracks: They stay put even if they're unhappy or have become hostage to a very large house.

With good, old necessity being the mother of invention, a relatively new service has emerged that can help your parents make all of these decisions and much more. "Professional Organizers" will certainly help in downsizing from a full house to apartment living. Finding an expert might prove a bit difficult, as this is a rather new field. Some realtors now offer real estate consultants who can organize the move, sell the furniture and help your parents assess just how much space they will have in their new apartment for new and old furniture. You can also call the National Association of Professional Organizers at 1-856-380-6828 for a referral, or visit their website at www.napo.net. Also try the Yellow Pages under "Organizing Services."

I asked professional organizer Alice Winner if she'd share some of her tips on how to help parents downsize their homes to make a smooth transition into new, smaller living quarters. Here's what Alice recommends:

> First, your parent must want to do this. Don't launch a de-cluttering, downsizing attack without their full support. Initiate

the topic gently by asking if they'd like some help in getting ready for the move.

- Begin by asking your parents to make a list of what they want to keep, give away or perhaps sell. Place stickers on the back of each item, noting if it is to be sold, given to someone or will be part of the move. Don't criticize their list, even if it appears unreasonable.

- Start with what's in the basement. Chances are they don't have strong emotional ties to what they've been storing down there.

- Break down moving tasks into small segments over a reasonable period of time. Rather than set aside a whole day to clean an entire area of the house, clean out one kitchen drawer, one closet, or one dresser drawer in an afternoon. If you tackle small projects throughout a week, you'll accomplish more.

- Begin getting rid of paper clutter. For example, check with your accountant on how long your parents need to keep cancelled checks and start shredding what they no longer need. Newspapers, magazines and books can be recycled or, if valuable, given to local senior centers and libraries.

- Separate financial and legal records from memorabilia. Don't worry about identifying or categorizing the memorabilia, just put it in boxes.

- If they have lots of pictures on the wall and will soon have less wall space, have them identify those that would look nice in a good photo album.

- If there's a large piece of furniture they can't quite bring themselves to part with, ask if they can envision it stored temporarily in someone else's home until they can make a final decision on what to do with it.

- Take photos of furniture that has special meaning that will be given away or sold.

- Ask your Mom or Dad to tell you the story behind pieces of furniture, glassware, vases, or paintings that are being passed down to other family members. Write it in on a piece of paper and place it inside the item or tape it to the back of it. Now, other generations can enjoy the story.

A very helpful book is *Making the Move: A Practical Guide to Senior Residential Communities*, by Lettice Stuart. She recommends that your parents choose five of the most important pieces of furniture they must have to feel at home in their new place. (I can see Frasier's Dad sitting in his beloved duct-taped rocker!) Another great book is *Living Transitions: A Step-by-Step Guide for a Later Life Move* by Sue Ronnenkamp. You can order it through her website at www.livingtransitions.com.

Q: Any tips on getting my mother to go online and use email?

A: Believe it or not, seniors are one of the fastest-growing groups signing up for internet service. So, perhaps some of your Mom's peers might be your best bet to convince her that she's missing out on something. Find out how many of her friends are using the internet and talk with them.

Senior centers, community colleges and neighborhood groups are offering classes on using computers and the internet. Many of these programs offer free classes on how to use a computer, send emails with attachments (including family photos) and use the internet. Anyone can walk in and get help in setting up a free email account. Darlene Simmons, who never used a computer before she took a class, can't say enough about how it changed her life. "It's a whole new highway of communication for me," she says. "I'm now emailing to my grandson, and I've learned how to send electronic greeting cards. My daughter is living in Germany and email has been a godsend." She's also enjoyed more contact with other relatives, is getting 80-year-olds in her church to sign up for classes and has posted her own poetry on the internet.

Having a close relationship with her grandkids of all ages (especially those in college) might be the incentive to get your Mom involved. When she's visiting, have your kids sit down and show her what they could do together, for example, play games (such as checkers) over the internet or have her help them with homework assignments. I recently ran into a grandmother who was thrilled at finally finding a way to connect with her teenaged granddaughter through email; kids at that age are much more likely to email news about their life than to telephone.

Research has shown that many seniors just aren't convinced that the internet is relevant to them. Perhaps you could tap your Mom's interest in a hobby and show her what she can do on the internet to further her talent. Or, if she takes quite a few medications or has a health condition, you can show her how to access helpful information online. And, then there's the shopping!

One way to start her off might be to get her and a friend to sign up for a class at a local senior center where she won't feel threatened. Or, you might acquire an older computer with a modem (or purchase an external modem) and bookmark a few sites of interest. A good site that is easy to navigate is AARP's at www.aarp.org. Show her how to use email using a free, trial account so she doesn't have to worry she'll be throwing her money away. If she has a computer or netbook, you could also get her an inexpensive web cam and sign her up with Skype (www.skype.com), a free service that allows her to talk for free anywhere in the world with a user who has also signed up with Skype. She'll be able to see her grandchildren while she talks with them – all for free.

Are Continuing Care Retirement Communities a smart move?

If your Mom and Dad can afford it, CCRCs (also known as life care communities) are a great housing option. They usually offer the total range of care on one campus; independent living apartments and homes, assisted living apartments and intermediate and skilled nursing care.

Your parents will be offered a wide range of activities; golf, swimming, exercise equipment, physical therapy, banking services, educational courses and transportation. If they become ill, they're able to receive most of their health care on-

site and once they recover, they can go back to their original residence.

For people who like living in a community of folks their own age and like the security of a one-stop approach to long-term care in a campus setting, a CCRC is a perfect match.

So, what should your parents be looking for? First, they need to check out the CCRC's financial solvency. Since your parents will be investing most of their life savings into the CCRC, you'll want to make sure that the company has a solid past and strong future. In many states, the Department of Insurance regulates and license CCRCs.

CCRCs must give prospective residents a "disclosure statement" containing information about the financial status and operation of the facility. It should include the names and addresses of all persons responsible for the operation of the facility, financial statements showing assets, liabilities and operating expenses, clear details of all fees, and its association with any other organizations. Be sure to ask for it along with a copy of their latest inspection report. CCRC's basically offer three types of agreements:

1. **Extensive Contract:** This includes unlimited long-term nursing care for little or no substantial increase in your parents' usual monthly payments.

2. **Modified Contract:** This includes a specified amount of long-term nursing home care. Once your parent has used the limit, then he or she is responsible for paying the bill in full. Remember: Medicare doesn't cover nursing home care.

3. **Fee-for-service:** This covers independent and assisted living services only. No nursing home coverage is included; your parent is required to pay the bill out-of-pocket or carry long-term care insurance.

Your parents will be asked to sign a very detailed contract. It's smart to have both a lawyer and a financial consultant read it over for you. But, before they get that far, your parents should spend some real time at the CCRC; going there for lunch and dinner, attending events, and staying overnight for a few days to really get a feel for the community. Here are some questions your parents should ask:

➤ Who makes the decision as to what level of care I'll need, if I should become ill?

➤ What kind of refund policy do you offer and under what circumstances?

➤ Are there health insurance requirements? (e.g. Will the CCRC purchase long term care insurance on my behalf? With what company?)

➤ What is the payment schedule? Will I own or rent my residence?

➤ Are you accredited by the American Association of Homes and Services for the Aging? (This is voluntary, not all CCRCs opt to go through the accreditation process, however, it's a good quality marker. You can view a list of accredited CCRCs in the country by going to www.ccaconline.org. Continuing Care Accreditation Commission).

If you'd like a directory of all the CCRCs in the state, contact your state's Insurance Department, as they will likely provide you with a complete directory with a brief description of each facility, their entrance fee and monthly fees along with contact information. Check out your state's government home page to see if their Department of Insurance provides a directory online.

: How can I handle caregiving when my parents live in another state?

First you need to go to where your parents live and do a little advance work. It's sort of like advance teams for political candidates. It's their job to scope out the town, know the hot button issues of the locals, get everybody's name right, know who to invite and brief the candidate. They can really make or break an event. Think of this as a campaign to help your parents make it on their own. They're the candidates and you're the advance team. Here are some pointers:

> **Get to know the neighbors.** You'd be surprised at how much neighbors do for each other. On your next visit, go over to the neighbors and give them your contact information and ask for their phone number. If you're lucky, these are folks who knew you when you were growing up, but chances are, either the neighbors or your parents have moved. Ask the neighbors to check in with you if they become concerned about your parents, especially if they live alone. Stay in touch with those neighbors, even if it's just a matter of sending them cards on the holidays.

> **Get to know the mail carrier.** Now, here's someone who probably knows more about your parents' routine than you do. Getting the mail for many older people is the highlight of the day, and they wait for a quick chat along with their mail. If Mom's not there, seems disoriented, or her mail piles up, it's her mail carrier who will pick up the warning signs and take action. If you'd like the mail carrier to pay a little extra attention to your parents, contact their local post office and let them know you'd like them to keep an eye out for your folks.

> **Get to know the bankers.** It's probably a good thing that many parents are part of a generation that hasn't taken too fondly to automatic teller machines. An ATM sure won't give you a call that Mom just took out a large sum of money or that a stranger has been accompanying Dad to the bank. Introduce yourself to the bank manager and ask him or her to alert you of any concerns.

> **Get a phone schedule going with your siblings.** A friend of mine happened upon an idea to keep up with his Mom who lives several hours away. He noticed that when he talked to her on Sundays, she'd often just heard from his sister and

brother, too. Rather than get a triple-dose of her kids in one day, he thought it would make more sense if each of his siblings agreed to call on separate days throughout the week. Now their Mom gets a call just about every day from one of them, which is more fun for her, as well as providing a frequent check-up on how well she's doing.

> **Get to know your parents' best friends.**
Your parents' friends can let you know if something's up and that, perhaps, you should look in on your parents. My mother lives in Phoenix and I've gotten to know her buddies pretty well. We've shared phone numbers, and I try to stop by and say hello when I'm out there. One time I called one of them to look in on my Mom when she had the flu. My Mom didn't want to bother anyone, but I knew she needed someone to get her medicine and good, old chicken soup. Friends are your best eyes and ears, and they'll likely have your parent's best interests at heart. Take the time to nurture your relationship with your parents' friends.

> **Get to know the home health services network.** Be sure to scope out the home health services and non-medical senior care agencies in your parents' community, so that if you need them, you can spring into action. This can buy some time, just in case you can't get there right away. You'll want to explore the levels of care they provide, the costs, and what is covered under what circumstances. Find

out if they can send a nurse to assess your parent's situation and let you know if more medical attention is needed. This could be especially helpful if you think your Dad has more than a regular case of the flu or you're worried that his diabetes has gotten worse.

> **Get to know the Area Agency on Aging.** Get to know the staff at the local Area Agency on Aging. They can help you track down a host of human services for your parents. To find the agency in your area, call the Eldercare Locator at 1-800-677-1116 or go to www.eldercare.gov. If you prefer to call, then the next time you're visiting your parents, bring back an extra copy of the local phone book. You'll find the yellow and blue pages of government and social agencies especially helpful. If you're online, you can always check out www.yellowpages.com.

Q: Any suggestions on how to make long distance caregiving easier?

 Caring for a parent who lives out of town presents a whole host of challenges. If we're talking about your Mom, for example, she likely enjoys her friends, her surroundings and her whole network of acquaintances – from the retail clerk at her favorite store and the teller at the bank to her doctors and card club friends. All of these are very valuable for her social well-being, but of course, when she is not well, she'll need you. Here are a few tips to help:

1. **Meet with your mother's primary physician.** Go to one of your mother's appointments with her general care practitioner. Explain that you live out of town and it would be very helpful if, during your Mom's subsequent visits, that the doctor calls you as he or she shares results and directions with your mother. If your mother sees other specialists, request that her physician become the "command center" so that her care is coordinated. Ask if her doctor would be willing to exchange email with you as an efficient way of learning about your Mom's health status and for you to inform him or her of changes, as well. Introduce yourself to the nurse manager and give her all of your contact information and ask that it be placed in your mother's chart. Develop a relationship with the doctor and staff. Before you leave, make sure your Mom has signed a consent form that allows the doctor to speak to you regarding her health status, especially if she is hospitalized. Bring home a list of her medications, all of her physician's contact information and a copy of medical records that detail any of her medical conditions.

2. **Get to know the neighbors and your Mom's friends.** On your next visit, go over to the neighbors and give them your contact information and ask for their phone number. Ask them to check in with you if they become concerned about your Mom. Stay in touch with these neighbors and her friends, as they can become your eyes and ears when your Mom is in need. Also, decide among close friends and relatives who will be the first-responder in a health crisis to take hold of the situation until you arrive.

3. **Get to know the home health services and aging network.** Be sure to scope out the home health services and non-medical senior care agencies in your Mom's community so that, if you need them, you can spring into action. This can buy some time, just in case you can't get there right away. You'll want to explore the levels of

care they provide, the costs, and what is covered under what circumstances. Find out if they can send a nurse to assess your mother's health and let you know if more medical attention is needed. This could be especially helpful if you think she may have the flu or you're worried that her diabetes, for example, has gotten worse. It also provides you a reality check, so you aren't jumping on a plane for what turns out to be a false alarm. The local Area Agency on Aging can also help you find a wide-range of human services for your Mom. To find the agency in your area, call the Eldercare Locator at 1-800-677-1116 or go to www.eldercare.gov.

4. **Treat yourself to outside help.** Don't burn yourself out by thinking that you are the only one who can help your Mom. Set up a support system and use it. If you have siblings, be sure to share the responsibilities and the expenses of hiring someone to come in and assist your mother when needed. Make travel easy on yourself by watching for low airfares that can give you a break from long drives. If your Mom needs quite a bit of care that requires managing doctor's appointments and more, then you might consider hiring a geriatric care manager.

 I'll be visiting my parents and would like a list of things to do to make their home fall-free. What should I consider?

 Good idea, since the odds are pretty high that one of your parents will fall within any given year. One in three women sixty-five years and older fall annually and after age 85 years, half of them will fall, while one-third of men in the 80 to 84 year old age group will fall. All too often, a fall leads to a life-changing event brought on by a broken hip and fractures that strip people of their independence. And here's the startling fact: one half of the injuries caused by falls results in death.

The "Home Safety to Prevent Injury Action Plan" by the Administration on Aging and "Rebuilding Together" has created the following checklist to keep your parents safe.

A Checklist for Preventing Falls in Your Home:

Stairways

› Make sure all handrails are unbroken and are securely fastened.

- Both sides of the steps should have handrails.

- Check carpet and rubber mats on the steps: are they secure and not frayed?

- Place brightly colored adhesive tape on the edge of each step, so Mom can see the contrast and know she's at the edge of the step. If carpeted steps are old, easy to slip on or frayed, consider removing the carpet.

Floors and rugs

- Make sure all floorboards are even.

- Secure all rugs, including area rugs, to the floor with tacks, non-skid pads or double-sided tape. Do they really need that area rug?

- Use non-skid floor wax.

Bathroom

- Be sure they can move safely in the bathroom and that they can get in and out of the tub or shower.

- Remove soap build-up in tub or shower on a regular basis.

- Place non-slip strips in bath/shower.

- Install adjustable height shower heads.

- Mount grab bars at the toilet, bath and shower on walls with secure reinforcements to prevent the bars from coming loose.

- Make sure that the shower curtain isn't held up by a tension rod – it will fall if someone grabs it. Install a rod that's bolted to the wall.

- Buy a raised toilet seat and install handrails alongside the toilet (if getting up and down is difficult).

- Attach a liquid soap dispenser in the shower. A bar of soap that drops to the floor could cause a fall in the attempt to retrieve it.

- Set the water at a safe temperature (120°F or lower); many older people lose their sensitivity to temperature and scald themselves.

- Secure bath mats with non-slip, double-sided rug tape.

Kitchen

- Arrange items that are used frequently within easy reach.

- Keep a sturdy step stool handy. It should have a grab bar at the top to hold onto.

- Replace standard dials on the stove with large, easy-to-read, dials. Make sure the "off" button is very visible (consider marking it red).

- Buy sturdy, fire-retardant pot holders and oven mitts and keep near the stove and oven to discourage the use of small towels or aprons as pot holders.

- Make use of Lazy Susans (circular trays that hold food and spin), so that dishes, pots, pans and cooking materials are easy to reach. You don't want your parents reaching too high or too low, which may throw one of them off balance.

Lighting

> Place nightlights in hallways, bedrooms, bathrooms and stairways.

> Install light switches at the top and bottom of stairs.

> Place a lamp (and telephone) near the bed.

> Keep lighting uniform in each room and add lighting to dark spaces.

> Install sound or movement-activated lights that go on and off automatically when someone gets up in the night.

All rooms

> Move newspapers, boxes, electrical and phone cords, plants, and furniture out of traffic areas, especially hallways.

> Store clothing, bed coverings, and other household items where you can easily reach them.

Outside of the house

> Repair holes, uneven joints on walkways.

> Arrange to have leaves, snow, and ice removed from stairs and walkways. Make sure they have a supply of salt or sand.

> Check outside lighting in entryways and other walk areas.

> Both sides of steps should have handrails and be securely fastened.

If you'd like to find out if your local Area Agency on Aging offers or knows of programs that provide low or no-interest loans, tax credits or other programs for home modifications for those who are older or disabled, call the Eldercare Locator at 1-800-677-1116, or visit their website at www.eldercare.gov. "Rebuilding Together" is a national organization that repairs and modifies homes of older, low-income homeowners to help them age in place. You can reach them by calling 1- 800-473-4229 or check them out at www. rebuildingtogether.org.

 How can I help my Dad track down his old military buddies?

 If you saw "Band of Brothers," "Saving Private Ryan," or a host of similar movies, you certainly understand how meaningful it would be for your Dad to re-connect with the guys in his unit. My Dad, who was stationed

in Italy, had been talking for years about trying to find his buddies. By chance, he saw a reunion announcement for his unit in *The Legion* magazine. He went to the reunion, and when he returned, showing us pictures of his old buddies, it unleashed a flood of stories from the war that he'd never told us before. The event meant the world to him.

The U.S. Department of Veterans Affairs has made it pretty easy for you to help your Dad pursue his quest: Go to the VA's website at www.va.gov. On the home page, go to the Burial and Memorial Benefits section and click on the sidebar: *Locating Veterans*. The site will give you directions on how to write a message to your Dad's comrade(s) and

then send it to your VA regional office. The regional office will take the next step and forward it to your Dad's buddies. (Because of privacy requirements, the VA can't simply release the information directly to you or your father.)

At the website, you can also view a complete list of all the reunions being held for each military branch throughout the country. Besides using the VA's resources, try www.switchboard.com. All you'll need is the full name of your Dad's military buddy to get an address. You might have to write to everyone who has the same name because your Dad might not know what town his buddy lives in, but it's well worth the postage.

Q: How do we get my father to talk about his experiences in World War II?

A: Since the attack on September 11th, we've come to appreciate the real meaning of the word, "hero." The glitz of sports heroes pales before the true heroism of firefighters and police officers who fought to save lives and died trying. But, chances are you have heroes in your own family circle and what better way to celebrate their contribution to our freedom than to create an oral history to pass down to your children and theirs?

Tell your Dad that the Veterans History Project, which was passed into federal law in October 2000, directs the American Folklife Center at the Library of Congress to collect and preserve audio and videotaped oral histories, along with letters, photos, diaries and maps of veterans of America's wars for all branches of service. Their seasoned interviewers report that it's best to have a list of questions that you work from and to simply tape the interview on audiocassette.

If you're pleased with your oral history, they would love to have a copy of it. Give them a call at 1-202-707-4916 to find out how to send it in. You can also visit their website at www.loc.gov/folklife/vets for a list of questions to ask and full details on the project. I looked over their list of questions and the *Oral History Workbook* of the Nieman Enhanced Learning Center. Here are some questions from these two excellent sources that will set you on the right track:

Getting started:

- What were you doing just before you joined the armed services?
- Were you drafted or did you enlist?
- How old were you?
- Where were you living at the time?
- Why did you join?
- Why did you pick the service branch you joined?
- Do you recall your first days in service?
- What did it feel like?
- Tell me about your boot camp/training experience(s).
- Do you remember your instructors?
- How did you get through it?
- Did you make buddies at boot camp?
- What were they like?

War experiences:

- After boot camp, where exactly did you go?
- Do you remember arriving and what it was like?
- What was your job/assignment?
- What were your rank and serial number?
- What were your living conditions like?
- Did you see combat?
- Were there many casualties in your unit?
- What was the objective of your unit?
- Tell me about a couple of your most memorable experiences.

Daily life in the war:

- How did you stay in touch with your family?
- What was the food like?
- Did you have plenty of supplies?
- What equipment did you use?
- How did you handle fear?
- Was there something special you did for good luck?
- What did you do when on leave?
- Where did you travel while in the service?
- Do you recall any particularly funny or unusual event?
- What did you think of officers or fellow soldiers?

- Describe some of your buddies in the war.
- Did you ever think we might lose the war?

Life after service:

- Do you recall the day your service ended?
- Where were you?
- What did you do in the days and weeks afterward?
- Did you work or go back to school?
- Did you make any close friendships while in the service?
- Did you continue any of those relationships? How long?

- Did you join a veteran's organization?
- What did you go on to do as a career after the war?
- How did your service and experiences affect your life?
- What do you want your grandkids to know about this time in history?

For great examples of interviews, stories and other links to World War II oral histories and projects, visit www.tankbooks.com. Don't let next Veterans Day come and go without recording your hero's contribution to world history.

 : How do I get my Dad onto the World War II Memorial Registry?

 : If you want the whole nation to know what your Dad did in the war, here are two ways to do it: the WWII Folklife Project, sponsored by the Library of Congress, and the WWII Memorial Registry. Here is how your Dad can go down in history as being part of the Greatest Generation:

World War II Memorial Registry

You can easily enroll your father in the WWII Memorial "Registry of Remembrances" by phone or by going online. I registered my Dad by phone and was extremely impressed by how easy it was. Just call 1-800-639-4992 and wait to speak to a customer service representative. She'll want to know your veteran's branch of service, rank, where he served, his hometown, and when he went into the service. You can also add a few words about his activity during the war. If you're going online, go to www.wwiimemorial.com and click on the side bar *"WWIIRegistry"* and then on *"Register an Honoree."* Any U.S. citizen who contributed to the war effort, whether he or she was a veteran or back on the home front, is eligible for the Registry. So, if your mother was also active on the home front, register her, too.

At the World War II Memorial in Washington DC there are four computers at the Pacific Arch where you can look up your honoree's name and a short bio will appear. Of course, you can also see it online by going to www.wwiimemorial.com. (It takes a few weeks for them to verify the information before it is viewable on the web.)

For a fee of $10.00, you can also have his photo displayed. Send a photo digitally by going to www.wwiimemorial.com/photo or mail it to WWII Memorial Processing Center, P.O. Box 305, Calverton, New York 11933. Write on the back of the photo the ID Number and Account Number you received when registering your father.

The Veterans History Project

This project is operated by the Library of Congress at the American Folklife Center. Their mission is to collect and preserve first-hand stories of veterans who fought in wars of the 20th Century, with a special emphasis right now on WWII vets. They are also very interested in accounts from civilians who were actively involved in the war effort, such as USO workers, flight instructors, industry workers and medical volunteers. If you have access to the internet you can download their Project Kit, which will help you assemble all of the material the Library of Congress would like to receive (e.g. photos, audio tapes, letters, and official papers). Go to www.loc.gov/folklife/vets/ to find out more information and download the kit. You can also call 1-202-707-4916 to get the Kit. The Folklife Center submits the names of all those who submit their histories to the National Registry of Service. The Center plans to digitalize all of the submissions and make the findings available to historians.

Q: Is a personal alert system a good idea and how do they work?

A: Many people fear, when living alone, that they won't be able to get to a phone to call for help. If this concerns your parent, or if he has a condition that raises the likelihood that such a situation could occur, then looking into a "personal medical alert or alarm system" might be a good answer. Most of these systems are listed in your Yellow Pages under "Medical Alarms." An internet search using key words *personal alarms* and *elderly* will bring up a good number of services. There are essentially two options: your parent can sign up for a monthly service plan or purchase a system outright. Here's a brief overview on how each system works:

Monthly Service Plans

Most of these systems operate using two primary components: a small wireless, waterproof pendant and a base console connected to your parent's phone line. Most people wear the pendant around their neck so their hands are free, while others like wearing a wristwatch-type pendant. The pendant should be waterproof so you can wear it in the shower or bathtub where accidents are common. In the event of an emergency, you press the activation button on the wireless pendant. This activates the console to immediately phone an emergency response center operated by the service you subscribe to. Within seconds, a two-way, hands-free conversation is established between you and the company's emergency operator via a highly sensitive two-way speakerphone.(Some also offer digital service with 900 MHZ capacity, similar to your cordless phone).

The emergency operator has pre-programmed information on you, including medical history, prescribed medications, your location, preferred hospital and who else should be contacted (family, neighbors, doctors). If the operator is able to talk with you, he can direct the operator to call a series of contacts (your child, a neighbor, a friend) who can come over immediately. However, if the operator is unable to make voice contact or thinks the situation requires medical help, they'll contact emergency personnel. With most of these plans, you will pay a monthly fee ranging from $30 to $80, depending on what options you choose. Many companies also charge a one-time installation fee. You don't own the console and need to return it when you de-activate the service. Here are some basic questions you should ask:

▸ What kind of training has the staff had who receive the calls?

- What formal relationships does the service have with the local emergency response services in the community?

- If English is your second language, is there an interpreter available?

- What is the company's average response time?

- If the operator places calls to non-emergency contacts, such as a family member, how long do they wait for a response?

- Do they maintain contact with you until someone arrives?

- Is there a trial period for the service? Or minimum contract period?

- What kind of range will you have with the system? Can you activate the system from your mailbox? How far in the yard? What about the basement?

- How long has the company been in business? Would you be able to speak to a few customers?

- If you're not satisfied with the service, are there any advance notices or de-activation fees?

Be sure to test the system to determine its range throughout the house and how far you can use it outdoors, such as to the mailbox.

Buying the Equipment

There also are companies that will sell you a system that you will own. It usually comes with two components: a transmitter and a phone dialer. The transmitter is the usual waterproof pendant; when you push the button, it sends a radio signal to the phone dialer that will dial pre-programmed numbers of first responders (your child, a neighbor and/or 911). If no one answers the first call, it automatically goes to the next number.

With this system, you pre-record a message stating that you need help, giving your name, address and basic medical information. So even if you are rendered speechless from a heart attack or stroke, the emergency operator will still have all the information he or she needs to respond and reach you. These systems usually come with a speaker-phone to activate a brief, two-way conversation. Prices vary depending upon how sophisticated a system you buy. All of these systems offer a variety of features, and with technology changing every day, be sure to research the latest advances to meet your particular needs and budget. It can certainly offer you and your family peace of mind - and besides, it makes a great gift for the holidays or a birthday. My mother has one and it has definitely given her a sense of security.

Q: What should my parents have in a Disaster Supply Kit?

A: Whether being prepared for an electrical outage, storm, an evacuation due to a fire, a hurricane or even a "Red Alert," it is wise for older people to have a Disaster Supply Kit. Having extra food and medicines stored can also be helpful if your parents live alone or reside in an isolated area. A simple bout with the flu could incapacitate them enough so they aren't able to leave the house.

The American Red Cross, the Federal Emergency Management Agency (FEMA), and the Centers for Disease Control all offer check lists of what you need to include in your Disaster Supply Kit. To make this easier, I've created two categories: supplies your parents need to take with them in the event of an evacuation and those they need to have on hand if they need to "shelter in place." I've given special attention to items relevant to an older population. The goal in both instances is to have enough supplies to remain self-sufficient for a short period of time.

EVACUATION SUPPLIES FOR YOUR DISASTER SUPPLY KIT

It's best to store these items in a duffle bag, backpack or a light travel bag with wheels that will be easy for your parents to transport. The items in the evacuation bag, of course, will also be used if your parents are told to remain in their homes. It is recommended that they have a week's supply of the items in the evacuation bag. However, I recommend that your parents have a 30-day supply of their medications. During a disaster, stores may be closed, transportation shut down or supplies may be limited. Ask your pharmacist how long and in what conditions these medications should be stored and ask your physician about prescribing an extra 30-day supply.

List of supplies for the evacuation bag:

> Small, battery operated radio with an extra set of batteries

> Cell phone (If your parents don't have one, it might be a good idea to purchase a basic phone with a simple plan for emergencies)

> Flashlight and extra batteries

> A manual can opener

> Extra set of eyeglasses and/or contact lenses and cleaning supplies

> Hearing-aid batteries

- Extra wheelchair batteries or other special equipment

- Supplies for dentures

- 3 day supply of food that won't spoil (e.g. ready-to-eat canned meats, fruits, vegetables, smoked or dry meats such as beef jerky, canned juices, bouillon cubes or dried "soup in a cup" mixes, canned or powdered milk, peanut butter, jelly, crackers, nuts, health food bars, trail mix, cereals, cookies

- Plates and utensils

- 3 day supply of water (one gallon per person per day) and pack of water purifying agents

- Insulin supplies and dietetic foods, if appropriate.

- One change of seasonal protective clothing and sturdy shoes.

- One blanket or sleeping bag per person.

- A first aid kit (buy a prepackaged kit with a first aid manual).

- Sanitation supplies (e.g. towelettes, prescribed ointments for skin, personal hygiene items that you use every day)

- Extra set of car keys

- Cash, credit cards or traveler's checks

- A whistle

- Non-prescription drugs (aspirin and non-aspirin pain reliever, anti-diarrhea medication, antacid (for stomach upset), syrup of ipecac (used to induce vomiting if advised by a poison control center), laxative and vitamins.

- Place the following lists in a self-sealing plastic bag: style and serial numbers of medical devices such as pacemakers, doctors and emergency contacts, prescription medications including dosage, allergies and medical conditions.

- Place copies of medical insurance and Medicare card into self-sealing plastic bag.

Action steps to prepare for an evacuation:

- Identify an out-of-town contact person for family members to call and share messages.

- Plan how you will evacuate or signal for help.

- Plan emergency procedures with home health care agencies or workers.

- Tell others where you keep your emergency supplies and evacuation bag.

- Teach others how to operate any necessary equipment.

- Label equipment like wheelchairs, canes or walkers.

- Shut off water, gas and electric if instructed to do so.

- Keep the fuel tank of your car full and a signal flare in the car

- Use emergency routes specified by authorities (short cuts could be hazardous).

SHELTERING IN PLACE SUPPLIES

This list is in addition to the supplies previously cited for your parents that should be contained in their Evacuation Bag. It is based upon the assumption that your parents would remain homebound for at least one week without electricity, gas or water.

List of supplies for sheltering in place:

- Same type of foods as those cited for the Evacuation Bag, however, have enough stored for at least a full week, place in containers (e.g. heavy-duty plastic bags or self-sealing plastic bins) and keep them cool and dry.

- One gallon of water per day per person. (half for drinking and half for bathing and food preparation)

- Shut-off wrench to turn off household gas and water.

- Plastic sheeting and duct tape to secure a safe room (If this would be difficult for your parents to put up, perhaps do it now except for the door.) Of course, this should not be a room that is being used now.

- Flashlights with extra batteries. (Consider keeping a flashlight in each major room, e.g. the kitchen, living room, bedroom and bathroom.)

- Camping stove or grill for cooking if going outside is permitted.

Action steps for sheltering in place

- Your parent should know how to turn off the water, gas, and electricity

- Determine a safe room to be sealed off with plastic and duct tape.

- Replace stored food and water every six months.

- Exchange numbers with a neighbor who would be willing to look in on your parents in the event of an emergency.

- Make arrangements for pets or have enough supplies in place for them.

For great information on how to prepare for each type of disaster, go to the American Red Cross website at www.redcross.org or call your local chapter located in the phone book.

Q: We'd like to help a co-worker who is caring for her mother. Any suggestions?

A: I've often thought that there ought to be some sort of "Lamaze" movement for families when they take care of older relatives. We heap all kinds of information, good wishes and tips on expectant parents for bringing in a new life, but when we're bringing in a "wisdomed" life – we're on our own.

How about you and your co-workers hosting a "caregiving shower" for your friend during a lunch hour? Make it festive with a cake and refreshments. Here are some ideas for gift-giving:

Give her gift certificates for:

> Taxi services so that she doesn't have to deal with the hassle of parking.

> Cleaning services so she can go home to a clean house.

> Take-out dinners from restaurants.

> A massage, manicure or other treatment at a local spa.

> A home health services aide to spend time with her mother so she can take a brief break.

> Phone cards for long-distance calls to family and friends.

Do some homework for her:

> Call to find pharmacies and grocery stores that deliver to her home. If there is an extra charge for the service, pay it in advance.

> Check out available local senior services by calling the Area Agency on Aging 1-800-677-1116. Gather a list of services and present them to her in a nice notebook.

> Buy her some helpful books on caregiving.

Give her coupons for your time to:

> Come to her home and sit with her Mom for a few hours while she does whatever she wants.

> Perform helpful tasks such as calling to set up appointments, internet research on various health conditions, or organizing her Mom's contact and medication list.

All too often, caregivers are not aware of the many services available to them. Your colleague will be forever grateful that you gave some time and effort to help her get through the maze of health and aging network services – not to mention some Tender Loving Care.

: We are holding a family reunion and I want to create an oral family history. Where do I begin?

What a great idea! A family reunion poses a perfect opportunity to sit down with older members of the family and ask them about how things were "back in the day." Most of them will love telling stories about their childhood, how they learned to make a living, raise a family and overcome obstacles along the way. They relish being asked to pass down some words of wisdom to the younger generation and the mere act of asking them about their life story allows them to feel valued. The act of creating an oral history is just as valuable for you, the interviewer, as you develop a sense of roots to their past.

Now, how do you go about it? It's best to have a series of questions prepared ahead of time. If you're able to send these out before the reunion, even better. You might also suggest that family members bring memorabilia to display on a table.

You can use a tape recorder, or even better, a video recorder. Besides individual interviews, you'll find that trading memories *among* family members can also be fun. For example, you could tape an exchange between aunts and uncles about particular family events or what life was like growing up with their parents or grandparents. You could film them looking at old photographs while they tell the stories behind them; include a shot of the actual photo or some other memorabilia, such as a piece of jewelry, documents, ethnic dress or family Bible, that becomes a focal point for discussion.

A family history video that blends interviews with old photos makes a perfect birthday gift for your parents. And, if videos aren't your thing, a lovely scrap book can achieve the same goal. There's a very nice, easy-to-use book, *How to Tape Instant Oral Biographies*, by Bill Zimmerman, that lists some questions, beyond the typical fact-finding ones:

> ➤ Is there a story behind how you were given your name?

> ➤ Who were the first family members to settle in this country and what brought them here?

- Do you know of any stories about what life was like for them?

- How did your parents meet?

- How did your parents make a living?

- Is there any particular hardship that they faced?

- Was there any special "saying" that your Mom or Dad used? What did it mean?

- What beliefs did your parents try to teach you?

- Talk about any special traditions we celebrate in our family.

- Do you recall any special home remedies that your Mom or grandmother used?

- What was your hometown like when you grew up? What do you miss most about it?

- Did you have a nickname and how did you get it?

- How do you think your friends would describe you as a teenager?

- If married, how did you meet your spouse?

- How did you know your spouse was "the one?"

- Any suggestions on how to enjoy a long marriage?

- What goals did you set for yourself in your twenties? How did those change and why?

- Did you go to war? Where were you stationed? Can you describe the day you were called up?

- If you've had children, what are the three most important things you've taught them?

- What would you say are your major accomplishments in life?

- Any big surprises in your life or special hardships? How did you get through them?

- What should we pass on to the next generation about our family?

Creating an oral history is truly one of those gifts that keep on giving. You'll never regret taking the time and effort to do one.

Q: I think my Dad would feel better if he volunteered, but where should he start looking?

A: Not only can volunteering help your Dad feel better about himself, it can be downright lifesaving. Turns out that in a study reported in *Psychological Science* by researchers at the University of Michigan, older people who give social support and help others have a higher survival rate than people who don't get into the act of giving. Sure proves that you can't argue with the old saying, "It is better to give than receive!" Now that we know volunteering might be just what the "doctor orders" for your Dad, the next step is figuring out who you call and how you find a great volunteer experience. But, before he even picks up the phone, he'll be ahead of the game if he spends some time thinking about answers to the following questions:

- Would I like to learn something new and try something totally different?

- Would I like to apply my current knowledge, experience and skills?

- What are my strengths, skills, experience and natural gifts?

- What is it that I really enjoy doing and what is it that I dislike doing?

- Do I like working on my own or with a group of fellow volunteers?

- Would I be able to take a hobby and turn it into a volunteer experience?

- Do I want a variety of volunteer experiences or just a consistent one?

- What would make me "jump at the chance" to volunteer?

- Am I willing to travel to where I'll volunteer, stay close to home, or stay at home?

- How much time do I want to give, what days and time of day?

Most Volunteer Coordinators will ask him similar questions to find the best match for him. The following three "gold standard" volunteer agencies are found nationwide. These groups will also connect you to other volunteer programs.

RSVP (Retired Senior Volunteer Program)
(National: 1-800-424-8867)

This program has been around for decades and is very experienced at placing retirees (people aged 55 years-plus) in volunteer opportunities with hundreds of local groups within any community. They also provide their volunteers with supplemental car, accident and liability insurance while they are on assignment. If necessary, they'll even help out with transportation needs. When your Dad calls RSVP, he'll be asked where he lives so they can connect him to his Area Coordinator, who will either talk with him on the phone or set up a face-to-face interview. Their goal is to customize the volunteer experience to create something meaningful for each volunteer. RSVP has volunteers ranging from dispatchers, friendly visitors, and tax preparers, to mentors, school tutors and computer trainers. If your Dad thinks he's too old, think again – hundreds of their volunteers are over 85 years old.

THE VOLUNTEER CENTER (United Way)
(National: 1-802-388-7044)

Heidi Neuhaus, as a Director of a Volunteer Center sponsored by the United Way, recommends volunteers "do something that's close to their heart." She also advises them to shop around, meet the people they'll be volunteering with and for and then decide what they'd like to do. "With budget cuts that non-profit agencies have faced, the need is even greater for volunteers," beckons Neuhaus. Programs like the Contact Helpline and the Domestic Abuse Hotline are staffed by volunteers. Unlike RSVP, their program is open to all age groups. They, too, will interview your Dad to find the best match.

THE AREA AGENCY ON AGING
(National 1-800-677-1116)

Thousands of older people throughout the nation volunteer by distributing home-delivered meals. "They deliver a lot more than just a meal," claims Shirley Gallagher, a retired Area Agency on Aging Director. "They're our eyes and ears whenever someone living alone needs help." Besides offering home-delivered meal opportunities, the Area Agency on Aging can have your Dad volunteering as an ombudsman's assistant in nursing homes, a friendly visitor in personal care homes, a driver, or a dispatcher. Just like the other volunteer agencies, the Area Agency on Aging will tailor something to meet a volunteer's needs or refer them to whomever can. When your Dad calls, tell him to ask for the Volunteer Resource Coordinator.

And finally, don't forget your local newspaper; most have a Volunteer Connections section listing all kinds of volunteer opportunities.

Q : We are moving away; how can my parents make long-distance grandparenting work?

A : According to a survey by AARP, 66 percent of grandparents have at least one grandchild who lives more than a day's drive away. So, it's going to take some creativity and disciplined effort for your parents to maintain a close relationship with their grandchildren. Thanks to land phones, cell phones, the internet, the ancient art of letter-writing and the good, old post office, they can stay in touch and even create new traditions to make this move a positive adventure.

First of all, Grandma and Grandpa need to reassure your children that they'll find new, fun ways to stay close and, of course, they can look forward to great visits together. The children will be anxious enough leaving their school and friends behind, so they don't need their grandparents to add to the anxiety. Here are a few ideas for your parents to share the journey and cross the miles:

- If they don't have a computer and don't know how to use the internet, now is the time to jump into their grandchildren's world of communication. I'd tap your parents' motivation to stay in touch right now, and you, the kids and the grandparents go off together to a computer store and get set up.

- Set up a routine of a weekly or bi-weekly call so that the children can look forward to talking to their grandparents.

- Read stories to each other over the phone. My nephew and I love reading his favorite series, *Captain Underpants* (I'm not making up this title), over the phone.

- Get a digital camera and email pictures of daily life, from showing off a homework assignment, to something the dog did, to just making a funny face to scare Grandma. The same goes for them. If digital isn't their thing, buy them a bunch of single-use cameras and have them mail each one to you to develop.

- Write letters. There is nothing like getting mail from those you love – especially from grandparents.

- Be sure to make pictures or copies of homework assignments and artwork to mail to Grandma and Grandpa to put on the refrigerator.

- Most schools have assignments where you need to interview someone and write a report. Grandparents are a great source.

- Check out digital picture frames that will send a constant stream of new photos to your parents.

- You can also buy clocks and picture frames that have embedded computer chips. Your kids can record their greetings to Grandma and Grandpa. And, your parents can do the same for the kids.

- When your parents visit, schedule a trip to school so that your children can show off their new school, new teachers and friends. Take pictures.

- Grandparents can send care packages with some of the kids' favorite candy, books, articles in magazines – little things that let them know they're thinking of them everyday.

All of you can make this work. But you'll need to make a conscious effort to create and sustain new ways of communicating before you slip into a routine of typical bi-annual visits. It's been said that "absence makes the heart grow fonder." Let this absence make their hearts grow fonder still.

 : How can we make the outside of my mother's house safer?

 : Your first step is to help your Mom identify whatever makes her feel insecure when she leaves and re-enters the house. It might be helpful for you to come home with her from an outing, so both of you can identify what is making her feel less safe about her surroundings. Perhaps there's poor lighting, it takes too long to unlock the door, or the entrance is too dark. Some of her safety concerns may come from feeling vulnerable physically. The fear of falling and breaking a hip plagues many older women. Icy sidewalks or steps can pose a very grave threat to your Mom. Once you have a better sense of what makes her feel insecure and after you've surveyed the environment outside of her home, here are some things you might consider:

Movement sensitive lighting. Perhaps it's time to install new lights that are sensitive to any movement directly outside of her entryway. For any would-be intruder, the automatic light signals that someone is home. The other advantage is that the light will be on for her when she comes home. She should also have timers that control outside lights and one in the bathroom throughout the night. Timers offer an inexpensive way to burglar-proof the house and they are easily installed.

Clearing the way into the house. If your Mom's without an automatic door opener, now would be a good time to get her one. There are also systems that turn on a radio a few minutes before she enters the house so that the noise will alert a burglar to escape. Wherever she parks the car should be well lit. Make sure that the pathway to and from the house is clear of any obstacles so that she won't trip over them. Repair or lay a new sidewalk and add a railing along the walkway so she won't have to fear falling. Relocate tall bushes to another part of the yard if they create a good hiding place for an intruder.

Cold Weather preparation. In cold weather, always make sure that she's well-stocked with rock salt to tackle icy sidewalks. Better yet, hire a service or responsible neighbor to maintain her driveway and sidewalk throughout the winter.

Take a Cab. If your Mom likes to go out in the evening, but doesn't like coming home alone, treat her to cab rides. Most cab drivers, if asked, will wait until she is safely in the house before they leave.

Keyless Entry or New Locks. Make sure the lock to the door can open easily and quickly. She may become nervous if she has to work with a lock or a key that's become difficult to negotiate. You can install a keyless lock available at any hardware store.

Security Systems. Investing in a security system not only protects your Mom, but also provides her with peace of mind. You'll need to make sure, however, that she can easily operate the system so she's not constantly triggering the alarms. Be part of this decision so she isn't sold something more complicated or extensive than what she needs. And don't forget the simple things: installing a peephole in the front and side doors, an intercom so she won't have to open the door to any stranger and placing decals on the windows to look like she has an alarm system.

Can you give me a crash course on caregiving for my parents?

Helping your Mom and Dad navigate aging is rarely smooth sailing. But, an eye on prevention and thoughtful planning can help them weather the high winds ahead. Here's how:

Eye on Prevention
Whenever you visit, look around the house: Are household bills piling up and mail left un-opened? Do you see scorched pots and pans? Is the house more unkempt than usual? These could be early signs of dementia,

depression, vision problems or mobility issues. Is the refrigerator stocked with fresh fare or do you see moldy and expired food? Are your parents less interested in eating? Have they been losing weight? Poor diet can exacerbate chronic diseases, weaken the immune system and lead to dementia.

Nearly one in three elderly are headed for a fall every year and half will die as a result. Are stairways well-lit and handrails securely fastened? Are throw-rugs, clutter, and electrical cords out of the way? Is the bath mat non-slip and are grab bars mounted securely in the shower? Is there enough room to safely move around in the bathroom? And about those pills they are taking: are they organized or strewn all over the house? Are expired pill bottles mixed in with current ones? Is either parent taking more than 3 medications? Confusion, dizziness and mistaken signs of dementia can be caused by prescription drugs or from taking the wrong combination.

Planning for high winds

Get a geriatric assessment. Anyone over sixty-five should have a physician trained in geriatrics with an interdisciplinary team perform an overall work-up. The aging body is complex and deserves a specialist. Many local hospitals offer assessment clinics.

Create a support system

Meet the neighbors and ask them to call if they think your parents need you. Make a contact list of their doctors, pharmacist, and home health care providers. Read over their insurance policies to know what services are covered under what circumstances, so you can be prepared to quickly respond when the need arises. Make sure they have a living will and durable healthcare power of attorney – you can't respect their wishes if you don't know what they want.

Here are three top resources to guide you:

Prescription Safety

Adverse drug reactions are estimated as the fourth leading cause of death among the elderly. Research medications your parents take by going to www.medlineplus.com. Encourage them to use pill tracker containers and create a list of all their current medications, what it's for, who prescribed it and dosage. Make copies so they can take it to all of their doctor appointments every time they go!

Medicare's Website

Every year your parents have to decide what Medicare prescription plan they'll join (Part D) and if they want to stay in traditional Medicare or opt for a managed care plan. It can be very confusing. You can help them by visiting www.medicare.gov for answers. You can compare plans, learn what Medicare covers and research nursing homes right from your computer.

Eldercare Locator

Area Agencies on Aging offer all kinds of

community services and benefits that can help your parents remain at home. Call 1-800-677-1116 to find one nearest them or go to www.eldercare.gov.

If you'd like free forms for tracking medications, creating a contact list and a medical biography for your parents, go to my website at www.lindarhodescaregiving.com and click onto "Free Caregiver Forms."

Q: My wife has become so afraid of falling that she's going out less. Any ideas on how to deal with her fear?

A: Chances are your wife had a nasty spill or a fracture not too long ago and now she feels less steady. One bad fall can make anyone feel pretty vulnerable and fragile. And, it's no wonder: There are over 300,000 hip fractures each year, many of which require surgery, and if you're older with multiple health conditions, then complications can arise. A challenging recuperation can play havoc with a once active lifestyle and it's likely that your Mom has seen a friend go through the ordeal.

But, she doesn't have to live in constant fear. She can take charge by controlling her environment, getting in physical shape and learning how to fall like a skydiver. Yes, you read that correctly.

A recent study by the University of Michigan's College of Engineering found that how you position your body in mid-air before you hit the ground can dramatically reduce the risk of fracturing your hip by up to 70 percent. Parachutists are trained to fall in a crouching position and then leaning so that the outside of their lower leg hits the ground first followed by rolling onto their backside. If you land this way,

the researchers discovered that the hip only receives 25 percent of the force necessary to break it. Okay, that sounds well and good. But a fall happens so fast, so how can you possibly think about how you're going to land? Experts say you have seven-tenths of a second from stumble to impact when falling on a non-slippery surface. That's plenty of time to position your body for a fall, claims Dr. Ashton-Miller, who has learned this first hand as an avid skier. But it means you need to train your brain to fall in skydiver fashion. One way to do this is by repeatedly visualizing yourself falling the way I described earlier. You can check out a simulated video on how to fall by going to my website at www.lindarhodescaregiving.com.

Other than turning your wife into a skydiver, here's what she can do to get her confidence back: Exercise to build muscle strength, take calcium to build bones, keep up with eye exams, learn Yoga or Tai Chi to gain balance, take time getting out of bed, watch out for medications that cause dizziness, and when walking on sidewalks frequently look down for cracks and holes. On the home front, go through the house, making sure that steps and hallways are free of clutter and are well lit, install grab bars in the bathroom and make sure that outdoor walkways are in good repair. One out of every three people aged sixty years or older has a home accident in the United States, so staying at home isn't the answer.

 My Mom forgot she had a pan on the stove and caused a small grease fire. What can she do so this won't happen again?

 Your Mom sure isn't alone: seventy percent of all kitchen fires start because someone has left the stove unattended and it happens every eight minutes throughout North America, making stovetop fires the number one cause of house fires and home fire injuries. Most of them start as a result of food or oil igniting and quickly spreading. Stovetop fires are the leading cause of people losing their homes due to fire.

Here are the most common stovetop safety tips suggested by fire prevention experts:

1. Stay in the kitchen, especially when you're heating oil, frying, grilling or broiling food.

2. Don't store things around the stove like dish towels, potholders, or cook books.

3. Clean your stovetop of all grease; it doesn't take much to ignite it.

4. Turn pot handles toward the center of the stove so you won't accidentally knock over a boiling pan.

5. Always have a fire extinguisher nearby along with non-flammable oven mitts.

6. Roll up your sleeves when cooking and don't cook in a robe with large open sleeves.

If a pan catches on fire, turn off the burner, grab an oven mitt and SLIDE a cover over the pan. Do not place the lid directly on top of the pan as fire will escape around it. Never throw water on the fire, as it will make it worse.

Recently, the *Today* show on NBC featured several great safety products:

Products to prevent fires:

Safe-T-Element Cooking System: This system reduces the extremely high heat of electric burners. It is controlled electronically and offers four cover plates that are installed over your existing electric burners. A control unit caps the highest temperature at 662°F. The system runs about $200.

Motion Sensor "Stove Guard:" This electronic system senses when you have left the kitchen. It shuts off the stovetop and turns it back on when you return. It runs about $310.

Products to stop fires:

A **Fire Extinguisher** should always be within easy reach of the stove. Home Depot carries the "Home Hero," a very easy-to-use model with an ergonomic handle and a one-button push system.

The **"Kitchen Safety Blanket"** offered by Kovenex runs about $30 to $35 and all you do is throw the blanket on top of any stovetop fire and it immediately snuffs it out.

"Williams Pyro Stovetop FireStop" Secured under the stove vent hood, this product simultaneously triggers an alarm and releases bicarbonate of soda, a totally harmless, but effective, fire-extinguishing chemical. These run about $55 for two canisters.

Most home improvement stores carry the products mentioned.

And, did I say to stay in the kitchen while cooking?

 My parents would like to renovate their home so they can remain there as they age. Are there any resources to help them redesign their home?

 Over the past decade there has been a terrific movement in senior housing known as "Universal Design." The concept is rather simple – create living spaces that everyone at any age can enjoy. "Universal design simplifies life for everyone," according to the Center for Universal Design, "by making products, communications and built environments more usable by as many people as possible at little or no extra cost." People, regardless of age, ability or situation, benefit from this type of housing and living space.

AARP is a very active proponent of universal design, showcasing and promoting livable spaces for people to "age in place." You can check out their website dedicated to sharing resources and tips on this type of housing design at: www.aarp.org/families/home design. You can also find Certified Aging-in-Place Specialists that can help you remodel your home with universal design expertise at the site.

According to AARP and the Center for Universal Design, homes built upon universal design principles most commonly feature:

1. No-step entry into the home, often achieved with slight slopes in the landscape rather than building ramps. Entry ways that are protected from the weather, while unlocking doors with sensor lighting.

2. One-story living where dining, preparing food, taking a bath and sleeping can all take place on one floor.

3. Wide doorways that are 32-36 inches wide, making it easy for wheelchairs, walkers and strollers to pass through, along with wide hallways between 36-42 inches that do the same.

4. Maneuvering space in bathrooms that allow for a 60 inch diameter turn in a wheelchair. Adequate blocking around toilets and tubs for the future placement of grab bars.

5. Curb-less showers with trench drains where water flows across the shower floor into a gutter. In this instance, no one needs to step up or step down into the shower. A wheelchair can easily enter this type of shower.

6. Kitchens with full-extension pull-out drawers, adjustable height shelves in wall cabinets and single lever water faucets. Knee space is available at kitchen counter tops or at the sink for sitting while preparing food. Glare-free task lighting overhead and under counters is featured.

7. Home automation of motion detector lighting in garages, entrances and basements. Doorbell intercoms and audible and visual alarms for doorbell, baby monitors and safety alarms.

For more information and ideas on how your parents can make their home livable for years to come, visit the website of the Center for Universal Design at www. centerforuniversaldesign.org. At the site you can also access free "Technical Construction Sheets" and a host of publications on how to design and remodel rooms. You can also order their publication, *Affordable and Universal Homes: A Plan Book,* and booklets on bathrooms, bedrooms, kitchens, decks and patios. Call them at 1-800-647-6777.

PART III

Navigating
Legal & Money
Matters

Section One
Money Matters & Insurance

Q: What should we look for in a long-term care insurance policy?

A: Long-term care policies usually offer one or all of the following kinds of care:

Nursing home care: This means skilled nursing care at a long-term care facility. Some nursing homes also provide custodial care and assisted living, which would not be covered under the skilled nursing care provision of the policy. So, don't assume that if the care is provided by a nursing home, the care is automatically covered. Be sure to ask for clarification. Nursing homes are licensed by the state and, if the facility is Medicare-certified, then they are also monitored by the federal government. Nursing-home care is the major reason most people buy long-term care policies. It's no wonder when people can expect to pay $70,000 a year.

Home health care: These are services provided at home and include occupational, physical, respiratory and speech therapy, nursing care, social work, and nursing assistant services. This benefit is very helpful, as it gives your parent an alternative to nursing-home care.

Personal or custodial care: These services provide help with the activities of daily living that are non-medical, such as assistance with bathing, transferring in and out of beds and chairs, meal preparation, and medication reminders.

Respite care: This is temporary care to relieve a caregiver who provides full-time care to the insured person. For many companies, this is an add-on to a regular policy.

Most companies divide care into three levels: Skilled care that requires doctor's orders and is provided by physicians, nurses and registered therapists; intermediate care that requires trained personnel who are under the supervision of a doctor or nurse; and custodial care that requires non-medical personnel to help with the tasks of adult daily living.

If you live alone and do not have family members close by, then you might want to consider the benefit of custodial care. You could be recovering from a bad flu and not need a registered nurse, but could use someone to cook your meals, shop, get your prescriptions filled, give you a bath, monitor your health and alert a family member that you need to get to the doctor.

Custodial care, in many cases, can prevent you from going down a slippery slope that could have been prevented. Make sure the agent clearly spells out what the company defines for each level of care and have them tell you who decides if that level of care is needed.

Most companies require that you cannot perform at least two activities of daily living (ADL) tasks before coverage kicks in (eating, bathing, using the toilet, walking and dressing). They frequently send out a company nurse to assess your condition. Ask the insurance agent about any restrictions surrounding hiring help (e.g. whether you can hire a relative who is a nurse's aide). And, what is the appeal process if you disagree with the level of care decision the company made?

Be sure to get "compound-inflation rider coverage," which means that the daily benefit will increase over time. Say, for instance, that you buy a policy today that pays out $110 per day because that's the average cost of a nursing home in your area. In 20 years, if you calculate a modest 5 percent inflation rate, then that nursing home cost would rise to $292 – over twice the amount you'd receive. With the rider, your premium will cost more, but inflation protection is an important feature.

Also, be sure the policy is a tax-qualified one. Federal law now allows individuals to deduct a portion of the premium. Check to see if your state has a 30-day "free look" provision for a long-term care policy so you can cancel

it within thirty days of enrolling if you change your mind.

One other thing I'd recommend is to choose a policy that allows you to redirect your benefits from home care to nursing home care and vice versa. For example, if you exhaust your nursing home benefit, but have untapped home health care benefits, the company should add the home health care amount to your nursing home care.

The Shopper's Guide to Long Term Care Insurance offered by the National Association of Insurance Commissioners (NAIC) for less than a dollar includes a nifty worksheet to help you compare "policies. Go to <u>www.naic.org</u> and click on the "*Publications & Data*" bar, then go to "*Consumer Information*" to find the guide available for purchase. Long Term Care Quote is a national resource center and independent agency specializing in long-term care insurance that offers easy-to-understand, free comparative quotes to consumers. Check out their website at <u>www.longtermcarequote.com</u> or call them at 1-866-773-0291.

Q: My parents saw an ad for a new health insurance plan, but it sounded too good to be true. How can they tell?

A: The first red flag is that it's "too good to be true." Scam artists are very savvy at telling consumers what they want to hear. Insurance fraud experts caution that if the deal seems too good – like you'll get full coverage, no pre-existing conditions, cheap premiums, no medical exam or detailed questions to answer – then you are likely being scammed.

The Coalition Against Insurance Fraud has been reporting a spike in health insurance scams due to high unemployment, as people scurry to find health insurance. Add the passage of the new health care reform law, and James Quiggly, the Coalition's President forecasts, "you have a perfect storm of vulnerabilities." People are confused as to what the new law covers and when it takes effect. "Confusion," warns Quiggly, "is a crook's best friend."

And, confusion sure surrounds the recently passed health care reform law. Not even lawmakers seemed to know what was in the bill. So, right after the law was passed, hustlers were going door-to-door, claiming that there's a limited open-enrollment period to buy health insurance. One ad appeared on cable television stations showing a picture of the president urging people to call during a very limited enrollment period to get the new coverage. It has since been shut down.

Other than the "deal seems too good to be true," the Coalition Against Insurance Fraud offers eight warning signs of fraudulent health insurance:

1. Intrusive sales tactics that invade your privacy through unsolicited phone calls, door-to-door sales, faxes, and emails. The "agents" are usually very aggressive and the marketing material doesn't show legitimate contact information.

2. Pushy sales representative who urge you to sign up immediately or you'll lose their special deal.

3. Vague answers that are fuzzy about coverage details, brochures that are too simplistic, agents who seem ill-informed or avoid answering your questions by telling you "everything you need to know is in the brochure," or are unwilling to show you the actual insurance policy.

4. Requirement that you have to join an "association" or "union" to buy the

coverage. Typically these groups are fake and create an illusion that the phony plan is legitimate.

5. Slick internet sites present a professional-looking website urging you to buy "coverage" online quickly and easily. They get your credit card or bank account numbers, leaving you without a policy and your money.

6. Slow response is the norm. You won't receive your insurance card or policy promptly after signing up.

7. Suspicious payment delays. The hospital complains that your plan hasn't paid your medical bills. When you call, they give excuses of "accounting glitches" or "processing errors."

8. The "federal oversight" con game claims that the insurance plan doesn't require state licenses because they are regulated by ERISA or another federal law. Almost all plans require state licensure.

Experts advise that you go slow and know exactly what you're buying by taking the time to read the policy before you buy. If you want to know if a company is licensed to do business in the state, visit the PA Insurance Department's website at www.insurance. state.pa.us and go to "Services for Consumers" and then "How to Choose a Company." Or, you can call their Helpline and leave a message at 1-877-881-6388, and a representative will get back to you with an answer.

 We are paying for most of my Dad's medical expenses. Are there any tax deductions we can claim?

Yes, you can. The first thing you want to do is to see if you can claim him as a dependent. You and he need to meet two tests to be eligible for the dependent care deduction: your father's income must be under a certain limit set each year by the IRS – you do not need to include his Social Security income. He must, however, include income from pension benefits, interest and dividends from investments or withdrawals from any retirement savings plans, like IRAs. On your end, you need to prove that you cover more than half of your Dad's costs for housing, food, transportation, medical care and other necessary living expenses. By the way, a parent does not need to live with you to be declared as your dependent. But, since your father does live with you, the IRS will also allow you to include a percentage of your mortgage, utilities and other shelter-related expenses and count those toward meeting the "more than half of your Dad's expenses" threshold. If you father qualifies as a dependent, then you'll be able to claim him as a personal exemption to further reduce your taxable income.

Medical expenses offer you another series of deductions even if your father doesn't qualify as a dependent. In this instance, your best resource to find out what you can deduct is IRS Publication 502, *Medical and Dental Expenses*. To claim these deductions, you still need to show that you pay for more than half of your father's support, but he does not need to meet the dependent income test. If your Dad's medical and long term care expenses exceed 7.5 percent of your Adjusted Gross Income (AGI), then you can claim those medical deductions that exceed this amount. The IRS also allows you to include your medical expenses in this total. For example, if your adjusted gross income is $40,000, then you are able to deduct medical expenses that exceed $3,000, which is 7.5% of your (AGI) of $40,000. On the other hand, if both of your medical expenses came to $2,600, you are not allowed to deduct any of these medical expenses because they are not more than 7.5% of your adjusted gross income.

Here are just some of the medical expenses you can deduct: transportation to medical appointments, including ambulance transport, long-term care insurance premiums, prescription drugs, Medicare Part D premiums, privately hired in-home health care, nursing care, chiropractor visits, dental treatment, hearing aids, eyeglasses, nursing home care, and out-of-pocket medical expenses resulting from surgeries and procedures. You can also deduct changes

you've made to your home to care for your father, such as: constructing ramps, widening doors, installing railings, modifications to the bathroom, kitchen, stairways, and entrance or exit ways. If a capital improvement will actually increase the value of your home (e.g. installing a stair lift or adding a new room to the house), then the cost of the improvement is reduced by the increase in the value of your property.

If you'd like free help filing your taxes, be sure to look into AARP's Tax Aide program of terrific volunteers who will walk you through the kinds of deductions we've discussed and actually help you file your tax return. Many sites have the capacity to even file your return electronically. Call 1-888-227-7669 to find a tax counseling site near you or go to www.aarp.org/taxaide. These will be operational from February 1st through April 15th.

: My parents have decided to pre-plan their funeral; do you have any tips to offer them?

A: Most experts will tell you that pre-arranging a funeral is a smart consumer choice, especially if you'd like to keep funeral expenses to a minimum both financially and emotionally. For far too many families, making choices on funeral arrangements – picking a funeral home, the kind and cost of the casket, where services are held, what kind of memorial service is held, cremation or burial and who decides what among family members – can be a prescription for everlasting conflict.
There are three basic types of funerals:

First, the "traditional funeral or full service funeral" is the most common and usually the most expensive. It involves a viewing and/or visitation, a formal funeral service at a secular or religious venue, use of a hearse to transport the body to the funeral site and cemetery, burial, entombment or cremation of the remains. The full service funeral also factors in costs of the casket, cemetery plot or crypt, embalming, dressing the body, rental of the funeral home for the viewing or service and limousines to transport immediate family members.

The second type of funeral is a "direct burial," upon which the body is buried shortly after death, oftentimes in a simple container.

Since no viewing or visitation is involved, embalming is not necessary. Families may opt to have a memorial service at the graveside or at another time and place. There is usually an additional fee if a service is arranged by the funeral home for the graveside. Costs for direct burial involve the funeral home's basic services fee, along with charges associated with transportation, tending to the body, purchase of a casket or burial container, cemetery plot or a crypt.

The third type of funeral is "direct cremation" wherein the body is cremated shortly after death without the need for embalming. The ashes are placed in an urn or container and family members decide if the remains will be kept at home, scattered or buried. You may opt for visitation at the funeral with or without the remains present or hold a memorial service some place else. Direct cremation is usually less costly than the "traditional," full-service funeral and includes the funeral home's basic services fee, transportation, care of the body and crematory fee. Of course, you'll also be charged for an urn or other container. If the remains are buried, then you'll incur the costs of a cemetery plot or crypt.

Funerals are pretty expensive propositions: A traditional funeral, including a casket and vault will cost an average of $6,000, but that figure doesn't includes all the extra expenses such as flowers, obituary notices, acknowledgment cards, limousine and receptions, which can run thousands of dollars, making most funerals add up to well over $10,000. Add to this, the powerful emotional pull of wanting to do "one last thing" for a loved one and you can see why overspending on funerals is such a high risk for many families.

THE FUNERAL RULE

There is a federal law known as the "Funeral Rule" enforced by the Federal Trade Commission (FTC) that protects consumers from making unwary choices and purchases of funeral services. Many funeral providers offer a variety of packages that reflect common goods and services that make up a funeral. Most people don't realize, however, that they can pick and choose particular items they want, rather than accept everything sold in a package.

According to the Funeral Rule:

1. Consumers have the right to choose the funeral goods and services they want with some exceptions that may be required by law.

2. Funeral providers must state this right in writing on the general price list. If state or local law requires you to purchase any particular item, the funeral provider must disclose it on the price list and cite the reference to the specific law.

3. Funeral providers may not refuse or charge a fee to handle a casket you bought elsewhere.

4. Funeral homes that provide cremation must make alternative containers available.

The Federal Trade Commission offers an excellent consumer guide titled, *Funerals: A Consumer Guide* on planning for a funeral that would be very helpful for your parents. You can find it at www.ftc.gov/funerals or call for a copy at 1-877-FTC-HELP (1-877-382-4357).

 : Could you offer a list of consumer tips on making arrangements for a funeral?

 : As described in the previous "Question and Answer," the Federal Trade Commission offers some excellent advice for families who are faced with the burial of a loved one. Here are some highlights from their publication, *Funerals: A Consumer Guide*:

1. **Shop around in advance.** Compare prices from at least two funeral homes. If you're squeamish about going to funeral homes, they must provide this information to you over the phone. Remember that you can supply your own casket or urn. Outer containers are not required by state laws; however, certain cemeteries may require it. You can actually go online these days to look for caskets at deep discounts. To locate casket stores and online stores visit www.casketstores.com and click on "*Store Directory*" or see www.funerals.org/caskets/htm.

2. **Ask for the General Price List (GPL).** The law requires funeral homes to give you written price lists for products and services. Make sure this list includes all of their products and services, not just those chosen for "packages." It's also smart to ask for a casket price list before you look at them as the least expensive may not be available in the display room.

3. **Avoid emotional overspending.** It's not necessary to have the most elaborate casket or the most high-end funeral to honor a loved one.

4. **Recognize your rights.** Laws regarding funerals and burials vary from state to state. It's a smart move to know which goods or services the law requires you to purchase and which are optional.

5. **Apply your smart shopping strategies that you use for other major purchases.** You can cut costs, for example, by limiting the viewing to one day or one hour before the funeral, or by dressing your loved one in a favorite outfit instead of expensive burial clothing.

6. **Plan ahead.** It allows you to comparison shop without the frenzy and grief immediately following a death, creates an opportunity for family discussion, lifts some of the burden from your family and prevents potential conflicts.

7. **If you prepay:** You may wish to make decisions about your arrangements in advance, but not pay for them in advance. Keep in mind that over time, prices may go up and businesses may close or change ownership and prices may even go down. Review and revise your decisions every few years.

8. **Make your wishes known.** Let your family know of your wishes and where you have stored all of the information and directions regarding your funeral.

Those who plan their funerals ahead of time certainly reduce the odds of grieving family members financially over-extending themselves. They also lessen the opportunity for disagreements over the details of the funeral service. It truly is a parting gift.

Q: I think my Mom is getting into serious credit card debt. What do I do?

A: Your Mom certainly isn't alone. Most people are shocked to find out that the fastest growing group filing personal bankruptcy in the country is the elderly. They're the generation known for their thrift, but faced with a slow economy, a fixed income, medical bills and the skyrocketing cost of prescription drugs, older people find plastic may be their easiest way out. Since many older people own their homes and have had a life-long pattern of living within their means, credit card lenders jump at the chance to give them unsolicited cards.

A recent Harvard study on consumer bankruptcy reported that the number one reason older people fall into bankrupting debt is medical bills. Out of pocket expenses and expensive maintenance drugs drive them over the edge. Others find it tough adjusting to life on a fixed income and so they bridge the gap with plastic. After years of working hard, they feel they deserve vacations, the right to spoil the grandkids or pay off expenses that their adult children are juggling. The plastic puts them back in charge. It's all too seductive.

So, now what? First, let your Mom know she isn't alone and she shouldn't be ashamed.

Tackle this as a chance for your Mom to cut wasteful, high interest costs and to strike a blow against the credit card companies that have been luring her in. Show her how they've been taking advantage of her. Don't make it personal or about her mistakes.

Here are some tips from debt counselors:

> Review the bills and her spending patterns to identify where she's overdoing it.

> Create a monthly budget.

> Review the credit card statements and total up what she is paying each month in interest and fees. Chances are she'll be shocked and angry.

> Pick out one credit card for her to keep. It is tough functioning in today's world without a credit card. Or, better yet, get her a check debit card. Talk with her about what she would use it for and suggest she leave it at home otherwise; it's too tempting to have it with you at all times.

> Stay clear of impulse buying (including TV home shopping channels).

> Don't pay off the credit card debt with her "nest egg" savings.

- Shop around for the best rate on cards that consolidate paying off other cards. Go to www.bankrate.com to find comparative rates on the best credit cards for paying off loans, cards that give the best rebates and those that are friendly to folks who pay the entire balance off every month.

- Check the statements every month for errors, penalties and fraudulent billing. Many predators count on the fact that seniors often just look at the bottom line and pay the bill.

- Contact the creditors, explain your mother's situation and set up a payment plan. Most will respond to your initiative to pay off the debt.

Debt counselors often advise that the first step out of debt is preparing a realistic budget. Assess how much money comes in from all of your Mom's sources of income and then create a list of fixed expenses, such as rent or mortgage payments, car payments, and insurance premiums. Then, make a list of her monthly expenses like food, telephone and utility bills and prescriptions. Finally, create a list of discretionary expenses, such as clothing, gift giving and entertainment. If your Mom is in serious financial trouble, then going to a debt counselor is the best alternative. For help finding one, contact the National Foundation for Consumer Credit, a national network of non-profit budget and debt counseling agencies. To find a local agency near you, call 1-800-388-2227 or visit their website at www.ngcc.org.

 Friends of my parents just filed for bankruptcy and it has my parents worried about their own situation. What should they do?

 This is becoming one of the saddest developments of growing older in today's economy. In 2010, AARP's Public Policy Institute released their first round of research from their Consumer Bankruptcy Project. The findings are sobering: bankruptcy filings among people 65 years and older has more than doubled since 1991 and among those aged 75 to 84 years, the rate has gone up a staggering 433 percent. In contrast, filings by younger people have declined.

The next phase of the AARP project is to find out why these bankruptcy rates are climbing at such an unprecedented rate. Experts believe that rising out-of-pocket medical expenses are a prime suspect, along with the high costs of living expenses, such as rising food prices, housing, utility bills, gas and oil prices. I also believe there is another factor at work and that is the ripple effect the economy has on family. A significant number of older people are cashing in their life savings to help their adult children cope with financial hardships caused by losing jobs to downsizing, layoffs or outsourcing to other countries while they struggle to raise a family. Grandma and Grandpa are coming to the rescue.

But, it's not just the high cost of living feeding these bankruptcy rates. Rather than starting retirement with a nest egg, more and more people are entering their golden years in the red. Elizabeth Warren, co-author of the study and a Harvard Law professor puts it this way, "Our culture has normalized debt. So now, instead of going into retirement loaded with assets, Americans are hitting their retirement years loaded with debt." But, what they soon find out is that managing that debt once you are on a fixed income can become near impossible, especially if you are in the midst of a recession. And, then there's the fact that we are all living longer which means that most people will be stretching their assets to the limit, if not exhausting them. Relying solely on Social Security checks is very difficult, making the lure of credit cards irresistible.

If your parents are worried about their finances, then now is the time to meet with a financial counselor who can help them manage their debt so they can maintain their quality of life and not live in fear of what their friends are going through. There are non-profit Consumer Credit Counseling Services (CCCS) throughout the country that offer budget counseling and education, housing counseling (e.g. pros and cons of reverse mortgages), financial literacy classes and debt management plans. Nearly all of the educational programs are free and, for a small fee, they'll manage your debt by paying your monthly bills and negotiating payment plans with creditors. To find a CCCS nearest you call 1-800-388-2227 or go visit the National Foundation for Credit Counseling's website at www.nfcc.org.

Q: My Dad is thinking about taking an early retirement. Is there a downside to this?

A: There are three options your father can consider when it comes to drawing on his Social Security benefits: he can retire at age 62, but this is considered "early retirement" so he'll face a permanently reduced rate in his benefits, he can retire at his "full retirement age," which will be 66 years without any reduction, or he could retire as late as age 70 and receive special retirement credits added to his benefits because he delayed his retirement.

Many people don't realize that the magic age of retirement at 65-years is changing to compensate for the huge baby boom generation about to retire. Anyone born between 1943 through 1954, for example, will reach their "full retirement age" at sixty-six years, not sixty-five like his parents experienced. Retirement benefit calculations will be based upon your father's average earnings during his lifetime of work under the Social Security system. For most current and future retirees, the 35 highest years of earnings will be averaged to calculate benefits.

If your father is in good health, there are some very positive reasons to keep working. First up, he won't be tapping into his nest egg of savings, so if he enjoys a long life, it will last longer and its assets will continue to grow. He can continue to save and hopefully, invest in a 401(k) plan with contributions from his employer. If his employer provides health insurance, then he'll be saving a good deal by not having to pay for his own health insurance until he reaches the age of sixty-five years when Medicare kicks-in. Your father can also use these few additional years of working to pay off all or most of his debt which can dampen any retirement when you find yourself living on a fixed income.

According to Alicia H. Munnell, director of the Center for Retirement Research at Boston College, Social Security today will replace about one-third of the typical 63-year-old's pre-retirement income. That means – if you hope to have a healthy retirement for twenty-five to thirty years – you certainly can't rely on Social Security alone to meet your income needs during the "golden years." T.Rowe Price Associates suggest that for every year you postpone your retirement, you'll be able to increase the dollar amount of your withdrawals from savings by thirteen percent.

If you father does plan to continue working, he needs to know that there are limits on how much he can earn each year and he should check with Social Security to learn the amount. Even if your father works following his full retirement age, he'll still need to pay Social Security and Medicare taxes on his earnings. The same is true if he is self-employed. Overall, experts advise that if you enjoy good health and your family tree celebrates parents and grandparents who've lived into their 80s or 90s, then delaying taking your benefits until full retirement age or later could be a very wise move. This will protect you from outliving your savings, pensions, annuities and other assets – some of which may have limits on how long they will be paid.

The Social Security Administration (SSA) offers a tool kit on retirement planning and several "calculators" to help your father estimate how much he'll realize in benefits at different ages for retirement. Just go to www.ssa.gov or give them a call at 1-800-772-1213 (TTY 1-800-325-0778). You can also visit the local Social Security office.

Whether or not to retire early is a very important decision with life-long ramifications, so be sure to have your Dad take advantage of the financial guides available from SSA and groups like AARP (www.aarp.org), who offer "Roadmap to Retirement (1-888-687-2277). Your father may also do well to talk with a financial planner specializing in retirement.

 : I worry that my Dad has a serious gambling problem. What should I do?

 : Gambling addiction among the elderly is growing nationwide, yet it remains hidden under the innocent guise of "fun, travel and recreation." The New Jersey Council on Compulsive Gambling developed the first senior outreach program in the country and reports that well over half of the revenue Atlantic City casinos earn comes from older adults. There are several reasons older people are vulnerable to the lure of gambling. For many, it is the first time in their life that they have disposable income. Your Dad might feel he deserves to have fun and doesn't have to worry about supporting his family anymore, so what's the harm?

Casinos heavily market to their senior patrons. Your Dad will be made to feel important and the VIP treatment can go a long way to fill the void of loneliness or provide feelings of power and excitement.

The elderly face the dangerous consequence of gambling away their life savings without the ability to recoup it. Research studies indicate that about five to seven percent of people who gamble become addicted.

The National Council on Problem Gambling offers ten warning signs of gambling addiction:

1. Have you often gambled longer than you had planned?

2. Have you often gambled until your last dollar was gone?

3. Have thoughts of gambling caused you to lose sleep?

4. Have you used your income or savings to gamble while letting bills go unpaid?

5. Have you made repeated, unsuccessful attempts to stop gambling?

6. Have you broken the law or considered breaking the law to finance your gambling?

7. Have you borrowed money to finance your gambling?

8. Have you felt depressed or suicidal because of your gambling losses?

9. Have you been remorseful after gambling?

10. Have you gambled to get money to meet your financial obligations?

And, here are some questions to ask yourself: Is your father spending an excessive amount of money or time on gambling? Has he lost touch with friends or picked up new gambling buddies? Is he always short of money? Does he have unexplained debts or disappearances? Is he unable to pay for prescriptions and utility bills? Is he secretive about his finances? Does his mood depend on whether he won or lost?

For specific information on how to help your Dad, call the National Council on Problem Gambling at 1-800-522-4700 or go to www. ncpgambling.org. You can also check out Gambler's Anonymous at www.gamanon.org or call 1-718-352-1671.

: How can my parents beat "out-of-pocket" medical expenses?

A : So many retirees complain that they feel like they are being "nickel and dimed" everywhere they turn. According to a recent study by the Rutgers University, Division on Aging, older Americans spend 19 percent of their total income on out-of-pocket medical expenses every year. Half of these dollars are spent on drugs and dental care. Older people who are in poorer health find that they spend nearly one-third of their income on health expenses. Here are seven ways your parents can begin saving money:

1. **Find doctors who take "Medicare Assignment."** Medicare "assigns" how much it will pay for services for a given condition or procedure. If a doctor takes as payment in full the amount that Medicare "assigns," then that means the doctor takes "assignment." In other words, the doctor won't be sending your parent a bill for the balance between what the doctor charges and what Medicare reimburses. If the doctor doesn't take assignment, then he or she is permitted to charge up to 15 percent more than what Medicare would have paid the doctor.

2. **Secondhand Equipment.** Many senior centers have programs in which previously owned wheelchairs, quad canes, walkers, crutches, and other durable medical equipment can be leased for a small donation. Some even offer used hearing aids and glasses. If they don't offer this service, they frequently know of someone who does. A social worker at your local hospital may also know of organizations that offer secondhand equipment.

3. **Senior Discounts.** It's smart to ask whether or not a business offers a senior discount rather than assume that they don't – those "10 percent off" offers can add up. Ask every business that your parent frequents – restaurants, banks, dry cleaners, pet stores – if they offer a senior discount. Many grocery stores are now offering senior-discount days and free delivery to regular customers, which also saves on gas. During peak seasons of cold and hot weather, many utility companies will allow seniors on fixed incomes to pay their bills over longer periods of time.

4. **Free Health Care Screenings and Shots.** Flu shots can literally be a lifesaver for your parents, especially if they have lung problems. Most senior centers, state

health centers and a good number of hospitals offer flu shots as a community service to seniors. Prior to flu season, call your local Area Agency on Aging to find out who is offering free flu shots in the area. You can call the Eldercare Locator to track down the agency closest to your parent at 1-800-677-1116. Your Mom and Dad can also receive free screenings and health education programs at health fairs sponsored by local hospitals or local malls. Go to the information desk at the mall to get a copy of their Calendar of Events and call the local hospital to get theirs. These free screenings, however, shouldn't be seen as a replacement for routine physicals with a physician.

5. **Generic Drugs.** Generics can cost about half as much as brand-name drugs and they must be approved by the FDA as being therapeutically equivalent. So, have your parents ask their doctor about getting a generic and tell the pharmacist they want it. Your parents can also ask the doctor for samples to make sure that they react well to the medication before buying a 30-day supply. If samples aren't available, they can ask the pharmacist for a one-week supply.

6. **Discount drug programs.** The drug companies offer discounts and free drugs for people who cannot afford certain medications. Go to The Partnership for Prescription Assistance at www.pparx.org or call toll-free 1-888-477-2669. Also ask your local pharmacy if they offer any discounts.

7. **Volunteer Services.** Your local Area Agency on Aging, senior center, United Way, church or synagogue will most likely be aware of volunteer programs and community- based services. Before your parents pay for companion services, cab rides, respite care, home-delivered meals, chore services or minor repairs, call one of these organizations.

Q: Should my Dad drop his auto insurance while he recovers from a stroke?

A: If your Dad does drop the coverage, he will likely trigger a series of actions that will fall under the category of "lapsed coverage." Insurance companies are very wary of drivers who have had a period of lapsed coverage. After all, it's in their best interest to insure drivers who regularly pay their bills, have had continuous coverage and good driving records.

An individual who does not have a record of continuous coverage raises red flags: Could they have had an accident while they were not covered? Could their lapse be due to a poor payment history? Were they dropped by another carrier for risky behavior? Continuous coverage provides insurers with a record that they can verify, rather than wondering whether or not "uninsured" periods were risk and arrest-free.

Chances are your father has enjoyed a good history on all counts and he is in the "Preferred Driver" category, which yields him reasonable insurance rates. If he takes a break from paying auto insurance because he isn't driving during his recuperation, he will likely lose his preferred status and land in the "higher risk" category. This holds true even if he goes to a new insurance company, as most will request a *Driver's History Record* from your state Department of Transportation before they grant insurance to a new applicant.

The bottom line? The money saved by not paying the premium for several months of coverage is no match for the dramatically higher insurance rates he'll pay when he tries to reinstate his policy. By some estimates, his rate could quadruple when he involuntarily joins the higher risk crowd! If you want to save money, you could look into reducing his liability insurance to the minimum level required by law and removing his collision coverage while he is not driving the car. Also, note that your Dad's insurance company is required by law to notify your state Department of Transportation when an insurance policy is cancelled by the insured or the insurer. So, if you stop paying the bill, within 60 days his insurance company will notify the state, which will likely send your father a *Letter of Inquiry* to determine why the policy was cancelled. If you don't respond to the letter, they may suspend his vehicle registration.

A greater concern is whether or not he should resume driving. After medical assessments, you and he should have candid discussions with his doctor, physical therapist and occupational therapists to determine whether or not he has recovered his functional abilities to safely drive. During his therapy he may find it motivational to have a goal in mind like driving, however, at the end of the day he must acknowledge his capabilities and limitations following his stroke. After personally experiencing the rigors of rehabilitation, surely he would not want to place other innocent people at risk for the same by getting behind the wheel when he's no longer a safe driver. Hopefully, things will go well for him and he'll soon be back in the driver's seat, getting his life back on track.

Q: What is the difference between Original Medicare versus a Medicare Health Plan?

 Medicare offers consumers an option as to how they'll receive their Medicare benefits. They can opt for the Original (traditional) plan or go with an approved Medicare Health Plan which consists of managed care plans like Health Maintenance Organizations (HMO) or Preferred Provider Organizations (PPO).

Original Medicare is a traditional, fee-for-service plan in which Medicare pays a set fee for covered medical services. You pay a premium (deducted from your Social Security check) for Part A, which covers hospital costs (e.g. a room in a hospital, rehab, or skilled nursing facility) and Part B, which covers medical costs (e.g. doctors' visits, home health and outpatient services). You should also have a Medi-gap policy to cover the 20 percent difference between what Medicare covers and the provider charges. You may go to any hospital or physician you want, where and when you want, and Medicare pays them directly.

With a Medicare Health Plan, you can save money. You won't need to pay for a Medi-gap policy; instead, you pay a lower monthly premium to the Medicare Health Plan provider. You also pay a modest co-pay (usually around $5 to $10) for doctor visits. Original Medicare doesn't cover annual check-ups with your doctor or gynecologist, so this savings can really add up. Medicare gives the Medicare Health Plan company a fixed amount of money for the year to take care of you. Whatever you don't cost them, they get to keep. Thus, their focus both philosophically and financially is to keep you well. So, you'll get plenty of preventive care. The other benefits are: they usually handle all of the paperwork, and are very good about flu shots, mammograms, hearing and vision care. At a minimum, they must offer everything that the original Medicare plan offers. Generally, people can join a Medicare Health Plan at any time; however, from November 15 through December 31st of each year, the law requires that the plans must accept new members.

If you have complex needs and have been seeing specialists that you really like, you might want to think twice about joining a Medicare Health Plan. Make sure your specialists are in their network – can you accept using their physicians, specialists and hospitals rather than freely finding physicians on your own? Here are some questions you should consider when looking at a Medicare Health Plan provider:

> Are your current specialists and primary care doctor in their network?

> Is your favorite hospital in the network?

> Where do you go for emergencies? Is there a procedure you must follow?

> How easy will it be for you to see a specialist? Do you need a referral?

> Can you change doctors if you don't like your assigned primary care doctor?

> If you live a few months of the year at a second home or travel, how are you covered?

> What skilled nursing homes are in the network?

> What will your out of pocket expenses be (e.g. for prescriptions, doctor visits, hospital stays or outpatient surgery)?

> What are the monthly premiums and exactly what do they cover?

There's a terrific resource to help you decide whether or not you should switch from Original Medicare to a Medicare Health Plan, and it is available on Medicare's website at www.medicare.gov. Click onto "Medicare Basics" and scroll from there to find the information you want. You'll receive comparisons of benefits, monthly premiums, co-payments, quality measures, and patient satisfaction surveys among managed care plans available in your particular region. There is also a guide on what to look for in a plan.

One final word of caution: Medicare Health Plans can drop out of the Medicare program any time they want; so look for a plan with a solid financial history. On the other hand, you can leave a Medicare Health Plan at any time, for any reason. If you choose to go back to Original Medicare, call 1-800-MEDICARE to re-enroll. If you need more information, call your local Area Agency on Aging at 1-800-677-1116 and ask to speak to the State Health Insurance Program representative. They'll let you know which senior centers provide volunteer counseling to help you sort through how different plans match up with your particular needs.

: Who can help me figure out these confusing Medi-gap policies?

 : Trying to figure out which is the best Medi-gap policy for yourself or whether you should opt for a Medicare Health Plan versus Original Medicare is pretty daunting. Add the decision about buying long-term care insurance to the mix and you can feel downright overwhelmed.

But thanks to a federal program known as the State Health Insurance Assistance Program (SHIP), every state in the country offers trained counselors to answer questions regarding health insurance in an objective and easy-to-understand manner. All services are free and the information is kept confidential. The counselors will provide brochures that explain your benefits under various health insurance programs. Contact your local SHIP program by calling the Area Agency on Aging at 1-800-677-1116. There are eight ways that a SHIP volunteer provides guidance to help you:

1. Decide whether a Medicare Health Plan provider (e.g. Health Maintenance Organization or Preferred Provider Organization) is right for you by explaining the way their network operates compared to traditional Medicare.

2. Understand your Medicare benefits by explaining the way each network operates.

3. Select a Medi-gap insurance policy by explaining the benefits offered under each of the insurance plans and provide a list of companies selling Medi-gap insurance.

4. Reviewing with you programs to help pay for your prescription drugs and helping you sign up for Extra Help with Medicare Part D plans.

5. Find programs that will pay for your Medicare deductibles, co-pays and premiums and assist in your applications.

6. Understand and review long-term care by examining, reviewing and selecting the best government assistance programs and private long-term care insurance policies.

7. Understand all of the new options that will be available in the future.

8. Process and resolve disputes by being your advocate if they have a problem with Medicare or your Medicare Health Plan provider.

Q: My Mom moved in with us on the understanding that my siblings would share in the costs, but now they're not. What should we do?

A: Perhaps everyone's expectations were not "out on the table" and discussed before the big move. There must have been a number of factors that led your family to believe that your mother was no longer able to live alone. So, let's go back to that place and time where you all agreed and work our way back from there.

First, everyone should make a list of your mother's needs that they believe necessitated her moving in with you. For example, does she need someone to either remind her or give her daily medications? Does someone need to prepare meals? Does she suffer from any form of dementia that causes her to be confused and unable to be left alone for any period of time? Does she have a number of doctor's appointments that she must keep on a regular basis? Can she no longer handle her finances? Does someone have to help her with the tasks of daily living (grooming, getting dressed, bathing, using the toilet, eating)?

Once everyone has identified these needs, go over them and eliminate the duplicates to make a final list. Make three columns headed, "Who," "How much Time" and "Costs." Enter who will perform each task and the number of hours per week you think it will take. Then, enter an estimate of how much this service would cost. Even if you and your siblings will perform the task, assign a dollar value to it anyway. For example, most of the tasks are probably non-medical and on average people are paid between $12 to $15 an hour for this type of service.

Since your mother lives with you, I suspect that many of these tasks will be performed by you. By adding up the amount of work and assigning a price to it, your family will be in a better position to objectively see the costs associated with your mother's care. In addition, your siblings will become much more appreciative of how much you do. However, I strongly encourage you – right from the start – to get your siblings involved in sharing some of these tasks. Do not fall into the trap of a "solo act," as it will wear down you and your marriage faster than you can imagine.

The next step is to assign a dollar value to your mother's housing. For example, if one of your six rooms is now hers, you might "assign" one-sixth of your housing costs to her. In addition, any costs associated with modifying your home to meet your mother's needs (e.g. building a ramp) would be fair game for your siblings to share. Since the move is about helping Mom, then you should certainly pay a share of her housing expenses. In other words, if you have three siblings then I'd take all of these costs and divide by four.

You also need to spell out what contributions you expect from your mother toward her housing and care. Will she pay a portion of the mortgage commensurate with her living space in the house? Will she pay for her share of the groceries? Will she pay for medications, health care supplies and her phone, cable and laundry bills? The more

businesslike and objective you are in your approach, the less chance of emotional conflicts between you and your siblings over what's fair and what's not. This same strategy applies to you and your mother. If you think that your relationship is too strained to do this family exercise by yourselves, seek an outside facilitator, such as a geriatric care manager (you got it: split the cost by four) or clergy person. You're obviously a family that cares deeply about what's best for your mother. You'll find your way by going back to what brought you here in the first place.

 We are thinking about a reverse mortgage. Is there a place we can get some free advice before we go to a lender?

 The National Council on Aging (NCOA), a non-profit service and advocacy organization for older Americans, charges a fee of $125 for their Reverse Mortgage Counseling Services. There is no fee unless you choose to apply for a reverse mortgage. Also, this fee is waived for older homeowners who either face foreclosure or have modest yearly incomes of $20,000 or less for singles, or $30,000 or less for couples. Homeowners must be at least 62 years of age to sign-up for a session, upon

which they'll learn about different kinds of reverse mortgage loans and how community programs and other options can help them remain in their homes. Or, thanks to a new provision, they can use the funds to buy a new home without hefty mortgage payments.

Experts expect a surge in older homeowners looking into reverse mortgages and home equity conversions due to hard economic times and newly enacted changes that include higher loan limits, lower fees, a new home purchase component, co-op eligibility and stricter consumer protections that make consumers more comfortable with the product.

If you are interested in a reverse mortgage counseling session offered by the NCOA, go to www.ncoa.org. Enter *"reverse mortgage"* in the search bar and follow the prompts for more information. Once you read over the information, you can call to schedule an appointment, which will take place over the phone. You can also visit NCOA's website at www.ncoa.org to download their excellent consumer booklet, *Use Your Home to Stay at Home*, which is also included in the packet.

 : Is a reverse mortgage a good idea for my Mom?

 : A reverse mortgage is essentially a loan against your Mom's home that she doesn't have to pay back for as long as she lives in it. Thus, she can turn the value of her home into cash, giving her the ability to afford the remodeling she needs or maybe long-term care services that are not covered by Medicare. When she moves, sells the home or dies, the money is then paid back.

The loan can be paid to your mother in various ways: she could receive it as one lump sum, as a regular monthly cash advance like a paycheck, as a credit line that she draws against whenever she needs the funds, or a combination of any of these methods. One word of caution: If she receives public benefits such as SSI, make sure that her new income doesn't throw her over the eligibility limits. Check with your local Area Agency on Aging to make sure she'll still be eligible.

Reverse mortgages are available to people who are 62 years of age and older and own their home. The major benefit with this type of loan is that your mother doesn't have any monthly payments to make and she won't need a certain income to qualify.

Here are some of the basics of reverse mortgages: There will be financing fees such as closing costs and interest. Your Mom will remain the owner of her home; thus she's responsible for property taxes, repairs and insurance just as she always has been. When the loan is finished, your Mom or her heirs must pay back all of the cash advances plus interest. The lenders aren't interested in owning and selling her home; they just want their money back.

One of the most important features of a reverse mortgage is the "non-recourse" limit. This means that the lender does not have any recourse to secure payment for the loan from any other source – your mother's heirs, assets or income. The only legal recourse they have is limited by the value of your Mom's home. This is an important protection: your Mom will never owe more than what her home is currently worth when the loan is to be repaid.

There are three major kinds of reverse mortgages. Some state and local governments offer *single purpose loans*, for example, to pay property taxes or to make home repairs, but there are usually income caps to qualify. *Multipurpose loans* can either be in the form of federally-insured Home Equity Conversion Mortgages (HECM) offered by banks and mortgage companies, or more expensive "*proprietary*" reverse mortgages, offered by private companies. These would enable your mother to use the money to, for example, both repair her home and receive a monthly income.

As with any decision of this magnitude, take the time to research all of your options. AARP has done an outstanding job of pulling the information together in a handbook, *Home Made Money,* and you can receive a free copy by calling 1-800-424-3410, or go to their website at www.aarp.org/revmort/ for the same information, along with a host of links.

The National Reverse Mortgage Lenders Association has set best-practice benchmarks for their members, and you can find out who has met these guidelines by either calling them at 1-866-264-4466 or visiting their website at www.reversemortgage.org. Not until you've done your research will you know whether or not it's the right choice for your mother.

Q: How do I talk to my parents about protecting their assets?

A: As many surveys have proven, most families tend to avoid the subject or wait until a health crisis hits to finally get their affairs in order. But, when emotions are running high and you're fighting for your health, you couldn't pick a worst time to think through how to protect your assets and distribute them among family members. Some parents may hesitate to talk about a will because it's a sign that their roles in the family are changing, or they may interpret the discussion as a signal that they are becoming more dependent. They may simply feel it's rude to talk about their personal finances. But wills are about a lot more than money: They are about values, meaning, relationships, and how family members see each other. It's no wonder so many people avoid the conversation. But, **not** having a will can spell a lifetime of heartache for those left behind. Here are tips to help you get the conversation started and what to discuss once you begin:

- Start the conversation by telling your parents that you want to know what they want. Try something like, "Mom and Dad, I really want to carry out your wishes, but I need to better understand them. What should I know? How can I help?"

- Acknowledge that you realize that this is *their* money – not yours.

- Let them know that advance planning through a will, living will and durable health care power of attorney will keep them in *control*. This is not about you taking over.

- Stay focused on your parents' concerns, not what you want from them.

- Approach the issue by sharing what you're doing about your will. Perhaps you've learned some strategies from your lawyer to better protect your assets, or you've read an article that you can share with them. They'll get the message that you practice what you preach.

- Advise them to identify who gets what heirlooms through a "Letter of Instruction," to keep peace in the family.

Many an estate lawyer will tell you that the bitterest family feuds are over seemingly insignificant items like a small piece of furniture, a set of dishes, or an inexpensive piece of jewelry. It is usually something family members feel attached to because it brings back fond memories of their loved one. If your parents have thoughtfully identified something that they want each family member to have to remember them by, it will help their children remain friends rather than arguing over who gets the ceramic frog collection.

- Emphasize that they should use their assets to enjoy a good quality of life and to care for each other, should either of them become sick. It is sad to see older people not spend their money to make the quality of their life better or for needed health care because they want to leave it all to their children.

- If they are uncomfortable talking about this with you, share some names of elder law attorneys.

And finally, remember to keep in mind through all of your discussions with them on this topic, that an inheritance is a *gift*, not a right.

Section Two
Legal Issues

Q: I suspect that the prizes my Mom keeps winning are scams; how do I know and what do I do?

A: You're right to suspect that something might be up – and it's not your Mom's luck. There are an estimated 14,000 illegal telemarketing operations fleecing at least $40 billion out of unsuspecting Americans every year. More than half of the victims are among the elderly.

Why older people? They were raised to be polite and, as a result, are very reluctant to just hang up. Many live alone, so they are accessible by phone, and they welcome almost any human contact. The telemarketers are very friendly, polite and act like they're looking out for the older person. Many older people have difficulty hearing and so may agree to something they didn't understand. And, like all of us, they're all drawn to winning something.

There are warning signs that you should look for when you visit your Mom or Dad. The National Fraud Information Center, run by the National Consumer League, warns that your parents might be a target if they are:

› Receiving loads of junk mail for contests, "free trips," prizes and sweepstakes.

› Receiving frequent calls from strangers who promise valuable awards, great moneymaking deals, or requests for charitable contributions.

› Having payments picked up by a private "courier" service.

› Receiving lots of cheap items (prizes) such as costume jewelry, beauty products, or small appliances. In some cases, your parent might have bought these to supposedly win a bigger prize.

› Receiving calls from organizations that say they will recover money (for a fee) that your parent paid to a telemarketer.

Besides these warning signs, you should be highly concerned if your parent is having trouble paying bills, has written numerous checks or made withdrawals for escalating amounts of money to unfamiliar companies.

If you see these warning signs, what do you do? First of all, don't blame your Mom or make her feel that she's been foolish. If you do, she might fear that if she tells you everything, you might take away her financial control. Instead, let your Mom know that you suspect that these people might be taking advantage of her honesty, politeness and trusting nature. She needs to know that this is robbery; the thief has merely used a phone instead of a gun.

Now, you need to act. Help your Mom assemble all of the information surrounding the scam. If you're not sure whether it is a scam, counselors will help you to sort this out at the National Fraud Information Center. You can reach the NFIC by calling 1-800-876-7060 or file an Online Incident Report by visiting the website at www.fraud.org. You also can call your state's Office of the Attorney General; most have a consumer hotline. Both groups really encourage you to report scams, so they can prevent these guys from taking advantage of others.

Once someone has entered one contest, or has taken the bait from one scam, these companies create "mooch lists" and, you guessed it, sell them to one another. So, if your Mom has been seriously harmed by these telemarketers or she's receiving far too many calls, you might want to consider equipping her with caller ID, signing her up for the Do Not Call List and/or getting her to hang up.

Here's a list of tips from the NFIC to keep your parents out of harm's way. According to them, it's probably a scam if:

> You have to take the offer immediately.

> The caller refuses to share written information before you commit to anything.

> You can supposedly make huge profits in an investment with no risk.

> The caller insists that you pay by a private courier who will come to your house and pick it up.

> You need to make payments on your winnings for processing fees, customs, taxes or any other reason.

> The caller wants cash.

> The caller wants your social security number, credit card number or any other financial information.

> The caller asks for a charitable donation but won't give you any information on how to verify the charity.

> The caller never accepts no for an answer – and keeps calling.

You can help your Mom get her phone number listed on the national Do Not Call Registry by calling 1-888-382-1222 or go online at www.donotcall.gov.

Q: My mother called me the other night excited that she won a free vacation on a cruise ship. I'm worried that it may be a scam. What should I do?

A: It's a shame that far too often these days, "winning" something can turn out to be a hoax and actually cost you money. Sometimes, a lot of money. The Federal Trade Commission (FTC) has a name for these so-called free vacations as, "trip traps." You'll receive these offers by way of post cards, phone solicitations, faxes, internet ads or pop-ups, and email. Maybe your Mom wrote her name and address on a contest entry form at a special event or at a store for a chance to win some sort of product. The contest may have just been a ploy to find a way to contact her and hundreds of others for their vacation get-away.

One of the more common practices you'll find is the sales pitch for what sounds like a very nice vacation; however, the scam artist leads you down a path of upgrades. They'll convince you that for just a few hundred dollars, you'll be able to stay in a four-star cabin on your free cruise vacation. Pay a little extra and you can add another island stop to the tour. And, by the way, the travel dates you want are rarely available so that, too, will cost a little more. Your Mom will be asked for her credit card to reserve this special offer and once she's handed that over

to them, she can be out thousands. Or, they could simply call announcing the prize and ask your mother for a one hundred dollar handling charge to book her reservation.

The FTC claims that travel fraud is a thriving business evidenced by thousands of complaints filed every year, bilking between four and five million dollars out of the pockets of would-be travelers. Unlike the telemarketers who try to con people into large investments schemes that scam you out of thousands of dollars, travel traps go after smaller amounts pitching lower price vacations. They also like to promote vacation club memberships that offer discounts and vacation packages at condos and resorts. But, even those who have actually won a vacation report back from their get-away that they were given substandard accommodations that could have cost a lot less had they booked the vacation themselves.

Here's what the FTC would tell your Mom on how to protect herself from a "trip trap:"

▸ Don't fall for great deals at unbelievably low-prices. Few legitimate businesses can afford to give away products and services of real value to you at such prices.

- A legitimate business will not expect you to make an immediate decision to book the trip. Never buy anything from anyone who uses high-pressured tactics.

- Get the details: what exactly is covered and what is not – such as airfare, hotel, and transport fees. Ask for the name of the hotels, airports, airlines and restaurants that are included in your vacation package. Ask about cancellation policies and refunds. If the salesperson doesn't know the answers or won't give you this information, then hang up. If they do tell you, then contact these businesses directly to verify the arrangements.

- Find out the name of the travel provider - the company that acquires your reservations and tickets which is often separate from the telemarketer.

- Get all information in writing before you agree to buy. Once you receive the written information, make sure it reflects what you were told over the phone and the terms you agreed to. Again, directly contact hotels, cruise lines and airlines to verify if what appears in writing is true.

- Stay clear of buying just a part of the package – like the air fare or hotel stay - separately from the whole package because refunds may be only tied to the whole package, not parts of it.

- Don't give your credit card number or bank information over the phone to a telemarketer, even if they tell you they just need it for verification purposes to send you your free vacation package.

- Do not pay with cash, check or money order. When you pay with cash or a check, rather than a credit card, you lose your right to dispute fraudulent charges under the Fair Credit Billing Act. The law gives you up to 60 days after the bill's statement date to dispute the charge.

- Contact the Attorney General in your state or where the company is located to see if any complaints have been lodged against the travel firm or the travel provider. You can also check out the Better Business Bureau at www.bbb.org or call the Western Regional office at 1-412-456-2700 or their Eastern Regional Office at 1-570-614-4222. Be aware that fraudulent businesses often change their names to avoid detection.

Your state Attorney General or the Attorney General in the state where the company is located usually has a division that deals with consumer protection issues. The American Society of Travel Agents, Consumer Affairs, at 1101 King Street, Alexandria,VA 22314, may also be able to mediate your dispute with an ASTA member. You can also email them at consumeraffairs@astahq.com. Visit their website at www.travelsense.org.

Bottom line: Trust your instincts, if it sounds too good to be true, it probably is.

: What are the most common scams targeting the elderly?

The National Association of Adult Protective Services estimates that there over a half million such scam cases each year. This number doesn't even include all of the consumer fraud complaints that are often filed with state attorneys general offices for telemarketing fraud. Your parents are susceptible to a wide and ever-growing range of ways to swindle them of their life savings. Here's a brief rundown of some of the more common ways that scam artists are making their mark:

Stock Offerings: Your parents may receive a call from a telemarketer telling them of a great chance to buy stock in a small, promising company just before it goes public. They'll be told that, by getting in on the ground floor of this "Initial Public Offering" (IPO), they'll yield high profits with little risks. If your Mom or Dad is internet savvy, they'll get these offers via emails – they are extremely risky and many are simply bogus.

Faith-based schemes: Over a hundred thousand trusting souls have lost billions in faith-based investments. Swindlers offer investments that prey on the older person's religious beliefs by telling them that their investment also helps a social cause, or that some of the funds will go to a church. Some scam artists scan obituary notices and show up at the widow or widower's door days later with a package in hand. Often it's a Bible or religious symbol they claim the deceased ordered – of course, for a high price. (Yes, it was a popular scam back in the Depression and it's still going on today.)

Credit Card Insurance: Cashing in on the protective and cautious nature of many older people, telemarketers will offer them credit card insurance that they don't need (since federal law protects consumer exposure to no more that $50 of unauthorized expenses when a credit card is stolen). Or, telemarketers will tell people they've won a prize and a three-year credit protection plan. Once your parent hands over his or her credit card number to be "protected," the telemarketer accesses the account and enjoys a spending spree.

Home Repair: A very common tactic is for a home repair person to approach your parents and tell them that, while they were working on someone else's home in the neighborhood, they noticed a leaky roof or some other construction problem at your parent's home. Since they have some extra material from their other job, they'll do your parent's at a discount. Sometimes, they'll ask for the money upfront and never return, or they'll perform poor quality work and overcharge; once they're in the door, they'll sometimes keep "discovering" new things that must be fixed.

Unfortunately, the list of scams numbers in the hundreds, from door-to-door sales, sweepstakes, gifting clubs, travel/vacation offers, and credit repair to loans that are too good to be true. For an excellent overview of most scams, check out the Federal Trade Commission's website at www.ftc.gov. Enter the word, "scams" in the search bar for a list of the latest nationally identified scams, and enter the word, "seniors" to find an extensive listing of articles written about senior scams in particular. Just scrolling through the lists gives you an appreciation of what your parent is up against.

Another smart resource is AARP's website at www.aarp.org. Enter the word, "scams" in the search bar and you'll find an extensive list of current and past scams, warning signs for scams, tip-offs to family members that your parent is being scammed and links to excellent sites on consumer protection related to seniors. You can also check out the AARP website for downloadable publications on the topic. And, if you want to check out a business before your parent commits to their service, call the Better Business Bureau at 1-703-276-0100, or visit their website for a national search at www.bbb.org.

 : I worry that scam artists could take advantage of me and my husband. What should we watch out for?

 : Because older people are generally polite, have good credit and a savings that is immediately accessible, they are the best prey for scam artists. And it shows: Consumers lose over $40 billion a year to telemarketing fraud alone and more than half are older victims. Here is how you and your husband can outsmart the predators:

1. **IRS impersonators.** Be wary of people who present themselves as tax preparers who are not affiliated with a reputable company, such as H&R Block, or AARP volunteers. If you use email, also be careful of email addresses that look like they are coming from the IRS (such as tax-refunds@irs.gov) telling you that you have a tax refund. They'll ask for your Social Security number and your credit card number to credit your refund. Do not

respond; instead call the IRS at 1-800-829-1040 to find out if this is legitimate.

2. **"Phishing."** This is a gimmick used to get personal financial information from you, such as a Social Security Number, banking accounts and credit card numbers, under the guise of either updating or validating your billing information.

3. **"Congratulations, you've won…"** If you get a call saying you've won something and you need to secure the prize by giving the caller a credit card number or pay a delivery fee or taxes, it's a scam.

4. **Credit Card Insurance.** Cashing in on the cautious nature of older people, telemarketers offer credit card insurance either as a prize or special offer. This is insurance you do not need, as federal law protects consumer exposure to no more that $50 of unauthorized expenses when a credit card is stolen.

5. **Home Repair.** In this scam a home repair person approaches a homeowner telling them that, while they were working on someone else's home in the neighborhood, they noticed a leaky roof or some other construction problem on yours. Since they have some extra material from their other job, they'll do your work at a discount. They may ask for the money upfront and never return or perform poor quality work and overcharge.

6. **Work-at-Home.** Retirees can be attracted to scams that offer a large monthly income while working at home. The catch is that they have to pay for up-front supplies, training and materials that they rarely recoup.

7. **Seminars.** Be wary of free seminars that promise to help with estate planning and finances. Some offer free lunches and prizes, but they also present various investment scams. They usually try to secure your financial records, as well.

8. **Stock Offerings.** Either through phone calls or email, you will be offered the chance to buy stock in a small, promising company just before it goes public.

Stop unwanted calls from telemarketers by calling the National Do Not Call Registry at 1-888-382-1222 (Toll Free) or go to www.donotcall.gov. Reduce the number of pre-screened credit and insurance offers by going to www.optoutprescreen.com or call 1-888-5OptOut (1-888-567-8688).

Q: My Dad wants me to manage his Social Security benefits and I have power of attorney, but the SSA won't let me. What's their problem?

A: The problem for SSA is that they are the ones who are held responsible for the proper receipt and use of a beneficiary's funds, so they need to be absolutely sure that whoever is managing the money is working on behalf of the beneficiary. They also have to contend with strict privacy laws.

Before we go into being a Representative Payee, for those of you who simply want to ask questions of SSA on behalf of your parent, the easiest way is to be with your Mom or Dad when you place the call and have them give permission to SSA to talk with you. If you live long distance, I'd suggest doing a three-way call. To protect beneficiaries and themselves, SSA requires that a Representative Payee be appointed for an individual receiving Social Security who is not able to manage their own money. A capable beneficiary like your father can appoint a relative or trusted friend to handle the funds and ask questions of SSA on their behalf. A Representative Payee does not need to be a lawyer, nor do you need a lawyer to process this request. You will, however, need to go to the SSA office nearest you to apply to be a payee and fill out an application form "Request to be selected as payee"

(SSA-11-BK). Be sure to bring documents to prove your identity, along with your father's physician contact information. SSA requires that the payee application must be completed in a face-to-face interview. They will review your application and contact your Dad's physician to assure them that he is capable of designating you as a Representative Payee.

Once you've been approved by SSA, you'll be in a position to manage your father's Social Security income, but this doesn't give you legal authority to manage non-Social Security income or medical matters. Your main job is to manage the money in the best interest of your father, as you are acting on his behalf. Pay his bills, purchase goods and services that meet his standard of living and address his needs. SSA recommends that you set up an account with you as the financial agent. They suggest two ways to title the account:

1. *(Beneficiary's name)* by *(your name)*, representative payee.

2. *(Your name)*, representative payee for *(beneficiary's name)*.

Be sure to ask a bank officer to assist you in setting up the account correctly. As a

Representative Payee, you are responsible for keeping records and reporting on how you spend the benefits by completing a Representative Payee Report (Form SSA-623, SSA-6230 or SSA-6233). SSA will send you the appropriate form to fill out about once a year. You can not pay yourself a fee for acting as your father's Representative Payee, however, you can be reimbursed for out-of-pocket expenses such as transporting your Dad to medical appointments or being reimbursed for postage to pay bills. For more information, call SSA at 1-800-772-1213 (TTY 1-800-325-0778) and at the voice prompt say "Become a Payee," or call the local office to get a copy of *A Guide for Representative Payees* (Publication Number 05-10076, February 2006). You can also view this guide online at www.socialsecurity.gov/pubs/10076.html.

Q: Is being an Executor of my parent's will an honor or just a huge headache?

 A: For many people, being named an executor of an estate is a sign of trust. However, many people will also tell you that being an executor can be hard work and some would say it's more of a headache than an honor.

When your parent dies, you'll need to take his or her will to your local county government office that handles probate. Some counties call these offices probate court, registrar of wills or surrogate's office. You'll need to bring an official copy of the death certificate and your personal identification when you present the will. The court will look over the papers and confirm that they are valid and you, indeed, are the executor. All of the stakeholders of the will – creditors, heirs and beneficiaries – will be given notice that probate has begun. The next step is an inventory and appraisal of the estate. Everyone who is due money must be paid and, as you might guess, creditors and the IRS get first dibs. An accounting of the estate's remains is completed and then the heirs receive their inheritance. Here's a list of some of the things that an executor does:

- Inventories all of the assets

- Identifies and lists all of the debt

- Arranges to have all assets and debts appraised

- Notifies creditors that they need to file their claims for payment and pays all creditors

- ▸ File claims with insurance companies

- ▸ Opens a checking account from which to pay bills and deposit assets

- ▸ Closes old bank accounts

- ▸ Pays taxes to the state and federal government and files a final income tax return

- ▸ Decides whether or not assets must be sold to satisfy debts

- ▸ Distributes the assets as directed by the will

Depending upon how large or complicated your parent's will is, this process can literally take years; most families report that it takes a full year to execute the will. In many states the executor is given some financial compensation out of the estate and this amount is set by law. Some executors hire people to complete many of these tasks, especially if they have a busy career and live out of town. There's an excellent book on what to do when you're an executor titled, *The Inheritor's Handbook* by Dan Rottenberg. A terrific website that will also be of assistance to you is www.nolo.com. Just click on wills and estate planning and you'll find great resources and answers to frequently asked questions.

: How do I talk with my parents about their will?

:
Let's start with why people write a will or create a trust in the first place:

- ▸ They want to plan ahead for the costs of incapacity – for example, nursing home care – and let others know their wishes.

- ▸ They want to pass their assets on to family members rather than let the government take the assets.

- ▸ They want to keep peace in the family by identifying who gets what.

Keeping these in mind should help bring some focus to your conversation. You could begin the discussion with something like, "Dad, I really want to carry out your wishes, but I need to better understand what they are: Do you want to pass down property to the family? Would you like to use money from your assets to help take care of you and Mom if either of you need care? Have you thought of ways to avoid paying high taxes and staying out of court?" This gives you the opportunity to identify what they have or have not done to meet their needs.

Let your parent know that you fully understand that this is their money and that advanced planning means they stay in control. If you sense they need to better understand how to protect their assets, recommend they see a professional to guide them through the options that are best for them. You may also want to broach the subject by sharing strategies you've used to write your own will. Or, you might simply relate some information that you've learned, as in "Mom, guess what I discovered the other day? If I set up a trust, I can ..." Sharing information during the course of everyday life makes the topic less threatening. However you approach the topic, remember that an inheritance is a gift, not a right. For an excellent website on general legal issues and frequently asked questions about wills, go to www.nolo.com or give Nolo Press a call at 1-800-992-6656 and ask about their publications.

Q: How do I use the Family Medical Leave Act to take care of my Mom?

: Just as soon as the days of carpooling, PTA meetings and life-on-the-run with the kids are winding down, here comes Mom...runs to the pharmacy, doctor's appointments for every body part and then a surgery that's going to require rehab and tender loving care to get her back on her feet. Up until now you've been piecing it together, but eventually, something slips up: Mom misses a crucial doctor's appointment, you're late on making a deadline at work, and time spent on the phone with Mom and all of her specialists becomes noticeable to your co-workers. Pretty soon you're showing up late for work and your reputation as a top-rate employee starts to take a beating. It's time to take a deep breath, look at your options and go to your boss.

So, what are your options? Well, the law's on your side, for starters. You can take advantage of the Family Medical Leave Act, since the law applies to taking care of your parents as well as you, your spouse and your kids. The law states that employers with 50 or more employees must allow them at least 12 weeks of unpaid leave for a family member who is seriously ill. Grandparents don't count, nor do your in-laws. To qualify, you must have worked for the company a minimum of 24 hours a week for at least one year. Your company must continue providing your full health benefits during your leave and you're entitled to get your old job back or another position with equivalent duties, along with your same salary and benefits. You do not have to take the full 12 weeks off at once. You can break it up during the year. Remember that this is not paid leave, which is the prime reason people don't ask for it, even though they need it.

Many companies provide more than the law requires. Family-friendly companies will even offer geriatric care manager services to help you organize and identify the services your parent needs, others help subsidize adult day services or arrange for care during the day so you can work. Providing you with flex-time or job sharing are other options that a helpful employer may offer.

The lesson? Don't assume your employer will fail to respond or understand. With Baby Boomers dominating the work force and finding themselves sandwiched between caring for kids and parents, look for more progressive elder-care benefits to be offered by many employers. Before you go to your employer, however, do the research: find out what vacation and sick-leave is owed you, make a list of your parent's caregiving needs, and have a frank discussion with the doctor to get a sense of how much time is needed for your Mom or Dad to recover. Realistically assess what your siblings can do and then

determine how much time you'll need to take off.

Your next step is to go through the requirements of FMLA. Go to the U.S. Department of Labor website at www.dol.gov. Click on "Regulations" and follow the prompts to the FMLA page. They provide all the information you need and a list of Frequently Asked Questions. You can also ask your employer for a copy of the FMLA fact sheet that your employer must display. Whatever you do, don't keep your caregiving demands a secret. Co-workers and employers can be very sympathetic if they know what's going on in your life. Think of all the understanding we shower on parents of a newborn, knowing they haven't had a good night's sleep in weeks and understanding their need to check in with the babysitter every chance they get. Parents with newborns don't keep their caregiver role a secret. Nor should you.

Q: What's the difference between living wills and durable health care power of attorney?

 A living will and durable health care power of attorney come under the general heading of "advance directives," as they provide guidance on what people want in advance of a particular situation. Living wills focus on end-of-life decisions enabling you to state your wishes about medical care, in the event that you develop a life-ending condition or enter a state of permanent unconsciousness, and can no longer make your own medical decisions. The living will takes effect when a doctor determines that death is fairly certain or that the person is in a persistent state of unconsciousness. The living will directs a physician to withhold or withdraw life-sustaining treatment that serves only to prolong the process of dying. However, the directive also states that measures should be taken to provide comfort and relieve pain. Most living will documents state whether the individual does or does not want any of the following forms of treatment:

- Cardiac resuscitation
- Mechanical respiration
- Tube feeding or any other artificial or invasive form of nutrition (food) or hydration (water).

- Blood or blood products
- Any form of surgery or invasive diagnostic tests.
- Kidney dialysis
- Antibiotics

The living will declaration becomes effective when your doctor receives a copy of it and determines that you are incompetent and in a terminal condition or a state of permanent unconsciousness. In most states, you must sign the document in front of two witnesses who are 18 or older.

The living will does not have to be notarized or executed by a lawyer. Be sure to give copies of it to physicians and the hospital. You can also name a surrogate in the living will who is authorized to make end-of-life decisions on your behalf. Aging with Dignity offers an excellent "Five Wishes" living will that is very complete and helpful. You can order a copy at www.agingwithdignity.org or call them at 1-888-5WISHES (594-7437). Many hospitals also offer copies of living wills at admission.

In some states, a living will is not effective in the event of a medical emergency involving ambulance personnel; paramedics are required to perform CPR unless they are given separate orders that state otherwise. These orders are commonly referred to as "non-hospital do-not-resuscitate orders" and are designed for people who are in such poor health that there is little benefit from CPR. These orders should be sought directly from a physician.

Durable health care power of attorney is broader than a living will. It empowers an "agent" appointed by the individual signing the document to make health care decisions on his behalf should he become incompetent. This agent can make decisions on admissions to and discharges from health care facilities, what to do with medical records, whether to make organ donations, whether or not to move the patient, arrangements for home health care and accepting or refusing treatment that affects the physical and mental health of the patient. These medical decisions come into play at all levels of health care – not just when death is imminent.

You don't have to be a lawyer to be designated as having durable health care power of attorney. The word "attorney" simply means "designated agent." The power of attorney does not kick in until an individual is legally incompetent. For example, you may not be able to communicate following a stroke or are too confused following surgery to make decisions. However, as soon as you have recovered and are competent, you resume your power to make your own health care decisions. Your must sign the durable health care power of attorney when you are competent and in front of a witness.

Every adult should have both a living will and durable health care power of attorney. It's far better to thoughtfully and openly consider these issues while you're well rather than in the midst of a crisis.

Q: What is "HIPAA" all about?

A: The Health Insurance Portability and Accountability Act (HIPAA) created the first national standards to protect an individual's medical records and other personal health information. Congress passed this law in response to numerous abuses of personal health information being given (without a patient's permission) to mortgage lenders, credit card companies and employers who, in turn, used this information against the interests of the patient. With medical records moving across hospitals, doctors' offices, insurers, third party payers and state lines, advocates cried out for national standards to protect health care consumers.

As a result of HIPAA's Privacy Rule, consumers have the right to:

> Review their health information

> Obtain a copy of their health information

> Request that their health information be amended or corrected

> Request that their health information NOT be disclosed

> Request that their health information be given in an alternative way (e.g. fax or email) or at an alternative location in a confidential manner (note that The Privacy Rule does allow health care providers to impose a reasonable fee to cover copying and postage.)

If you have a durable health care power of attorney for your parent (or anyone else), you are authorized to receive health information, however, a general power of attorney will not allow ready access to another's health information. I recommend that anyone who regularly needs access to their parent's health care information should ask their parent to write a letter authorizing them to receive it. If you're being told that

you or another doctor cannot receive your parent's records because of HIPAA, keep prodding. According to the American Medical Association, "Doctors can share protected health information when it is in their patients' best interest."

A word on faxes: it is not against the federal ruling to fax medical records to you; however, the doctor's office must make sure that the fax number is valid and will go to a secure place to reach the authorized recipient. Many doctor's offices will not fax records to patients due to lack of support staff to handle the requirements and the volume of requests. But, as we move towards electronic health records, the days of the fax will go by the wayside. If you'd like to learn more about HIPAA rules and how they may affect you and your parents, go to the website of the Office of Civil Rights at www. hhs.gov/ocr/hipaa and click on "*Frequently Asked Questions* (FAQ)."

Q: My Dad was just fired. How does he file age discrimination charges?

A: The U.S. Equal Employment Opportunity Commission (EEOC) reports an average of 23,000 age-related filings each year with numbers expected to rise. The law that applies to your father's situation is the Age Discrimination in Employment Act of 1967 (ADEA), the bedrock to all age discrimination cases. It protects anyone who is 40 or older from employment discrimination based upon their age. These protections apply to both employees and job applicants. According to ADEA, it is "unlawful to discriminate against a person because of his/her age with respect to any term, condition, or privilege of employment – including, but not limited to, hiring, firing, promotion, layoff, compensation, benefits, job assignments, and training."

The ADEA applies to employers with 20 or more employees nationwide, including federal, state and local governments, school districts, employment agencies, and labor organizations. Another law, the Older Workers Benefit Protection Act of 1990 (OWBPA), amended the ADEA to prohibit employers from denying benefits to older employees. They can, however, reduce the benefits based on age only if the cost of extending the reduced benefits to older workers is the same as the cost of providing benefits to younger workers. So how does your Dad know whether or not he has been "let go" because of his age? Here are a few telltale signs:

> The employer has recently asked, "When are you planning on retiring?" or has shown an added interest in his retirement plans.

> The employer replaced him with a younger person who has less experience, fewer skills and/or less education.

> The employer has recently given him a poor performance evaluation without any basis, or after years of good performance evaluations, and all of sudden finds fault in his work and cites this as a reason to demote or fire him.

> The employer does not send him to training courses to develop new or updated skills and then uses his "outdated skills" against him as a reason to fire him.

Employers sometimes believe they will save money hiring younger workers because they'll have fewer health care and Worker Compensation claims, fewer vacation days to cover and lower pension pay outs. However, on the opposite side of that coin, employers who hire older workers say that older workers actually cost their companies less because they are more reliable, loyal, and punctual, and have higher attendance rates.

So, how can your Dad file a claim if he thinks he has been unjustly fired because of his age? He must first file a charge of age discrimination with your state's Human Relations Commission (HRC). You cannot go to court with a private lawyer until AFTER you have filed with them. If your Dad worked in a company that has more than 20

employees nationwide, then he can file a complaint with the federal agency of the Equal Employment Opportunity Commission. The HRC covers employers with four or more employees and they will file your father's complaint with the EEOC if it is covered by the federal agency. Your Dad will need to file his complaint with the HRC's regional office for the region where he works, not where he resides.

You must file your complaint within 180 days of the "alleged act of harm," in other words, when your Dad was fired. The HRC will help him prepare his complaint and he is not required to have a lawyer represent him. Be aware that the Commission investigator must be neutral during the investigation. So don't think that the Commission's investigator is acting as your Dad's legal representative. Employers receive notice of the complaint within 30 days and they must respond 30 days later, however, they can be granted another 30 day extension. Your Dad must be granted a copy of the employer's response to his complaint.

If the HRC dismisses his complaint within one year of the date of filing the complaint, or if the complaint is still open after one year, your Dad can file a lawsuit in his local Court of Common Pleas (if his state has such a court), or in civil court in the county within which he resides. For more information on filing age discrimination complaints, check out the Equal Employment Opportunity Commission's website at www.eeoc.gov or give them a call at 1-800-669-4000. To find a lawyer specializing in this field, go to the National Employment Lawyers Association at www.nela.org or make a written request for your state's listing of lawyers by sending a self-addressed, stamped envelope to NELA, 44 Montgomery Street, Suite 2080, San Francisco, CA, 94104.

Q: My husband is only 55 years old and has been diagnosed with early onset Alzheimer's. Can he get disability payments from Social Security?

A: Thanks to a new ruling by the Social Security Administration (SSA), your husband can immediately apply for a fast track determination to qualify for Social Security Disability Income (SSDI). The agency recently included "early onset," also known as "younger onset," Alzheimer's disease affecting people under 65 years of age on their "Compassionate Allowance List." This means that individuals with certain diseases or conditions are eligible for benefits based on the disease itself, rather than the applicant having to prove that it has disabled him so he can no longer work.

Applicants, of course, must still meet other SSDI criteria, but at least people suffering from early onset Alzheimer's won't have to endure the long, drawn out process of waiting to see if they qualify for benefits. In the past, it wasn't uncommon for someone with this disease to wait up to three years to receive a ruling from Social Security, while in the meantime; they lost their jobs, endured a severe emotional toll and racked up expensive medical bills. The other advantage of being determined eligible to receive SSDI, is that it will allow your husband to receive Medicare benefits, as well.

Besides early onset Alzheimer's, SSA has added four other related dementias to the Compassionate Allowance list: frontotemporal dementia (FTD), Pick's disease, Creutfeldt-Jakob disease and mixed dementia. Experts claim that there are at least a half-million people in the United States in their thirties, forties and fifties who suffer from Alzheimer's or a related dementia. Overall, there are 5.3 million Americans with Alzheimer's disease and nearly 11 million family members and other informal caregivers provide over 12 billion hours of unpaid care for them. It now ranks as the seventh leading cause of death.

Now that your husband has been given a medical diagnosis of early-onset Alzheimer's, you should immediately apply for SSDI benefits by going to his local Social Security Office. It's best to apply in person, however, so call ahead to schedule an appointment by calling 1-800-772-1213. There is a significant amount of information you'll need to provide and forms to fill out. You can acquire a list and complete some of the forms online by going to www.socialsecurity.gov/applyfordisability/adult.htm. At the site you can download a "Starter Kit," a Check List and other forms.

You and your spouse would do well to call your local Alzheimer's Association Chapter to find out about services available in your community and how to join a support group. You can visit www.alz.org for terrific resources and find a local support group or call 1-800-272-3900.

The Alzheimer's Association fought long and hard for this new ruling from SSA and deserve a great deal of credit. The Alzheimer's Association celebrated the ruling by claiming "Now, individuals who are dealing with the enormous challenges of Alzheimer's won't also have to endure the financial and emotional toll of a long disability decision process."

: What are professional health advocates?

: Over the last few years there has been a new crop of for-profit companies known as "health advocacy firms" that navigate the health care system for you. They'll sort out medical bills, find doctors and specialists, arrange for second opinions, track down clinical trials, scope out nursing homes and negotiate with insurers if you've been denied coverage. And, that's just for starters. Their brochures often boast of helping their customers understand tests and treatments prescribed by their physicians, coordinate a myriad of healthcare providers treating a complex medical condition, arrange in-home care following a hospitalization, broker the transfer of medical records among physicians, coordinate and make appointments for diagnostic tests, facilitate transfers between facilities and arrange conference calls among multiple physicians caring for one person.

These companies bank on the fact that the American health care system isn't going to be easier to navigate anytime soon. If anything, it's getting more complicated, leaving frustrated consumers hungry for the equivalent of "Onstar" to pilot them through the healthcare maze.

Currently, there are four major healthcare advocacy for-profit companies, all of which are national. However, Care Counsel out of San Francisco only deals directly with employers who purchase the service for their employees. So, if you are employed, then your first step is to contact your Human Resources department and ask if they provide an elder care service as part of their employee assistance plan. In fact, most of the health advocacy firms get the bulk of their clientele from employers. Three of the largest companies offering direct consumer services are Pinnaclecare, headquartered out of Baltimore, and two companies based in and near Philadelphia, Healthcare Advocates and Health Advocate.

This new type of business is not regulated, so be sure to find out how long they've been in business (most have started within the last five years) and ask about the expertise of the founders and staff who will be working with you.

Other than these types of companies, you can also hire geriatric care managers who will help coordinate your health care and offer similar health advocacy services. Many of them are nurses or social workers who work as part of a group or act on their own as consultants. They usually conduct an assessment for a fee and then charge for services rendered. You can find geriatric care managers by going to National Association of Professional Geriatric Care Managers site at www.caremanager.com or find them listed in the Yellow Pages under social workers or home health care.

And don't forget, if you have questions about Medicare claims, Medi-gap policies and long term care insurance, call your local APPRISE program offered through your state unit on aging at 1-800-677-1116.

Q: What paperwork should I have prepared in the event of a health crisis?

A: Regrettably, most of us wait until a crisis before we start thinking about caregiving issues facing our parents. But, making high-stake decisions while your emotions are on over-drive can almost always guarantee poor, uninformed choices.

There are a number of pro-active steps that I encourage all families to take to make sure your loved one gets the best possible health care when a crisis hits. It's also a way for your parents to prevent conflicts among you and your siblings since no one will have to "guess" at what Mom or Dad wants when they're in no position to act for themselves. Here is what every parent should do:

➤ Fill out a Living Will (also known as an Advance Directive) so that everyone will know what you want regarding end-of-life decisions. Your local hospital can provide you with a copy or call Aging with Dignity for their easy-to-understand *Five Wishes Living Will* at 1-888-5WISHES (594-7437).

› Fill out a Durable Health Care Power of Attorney. This is broader than a living will. It empowers someone you trust to make health care decisions on your behalf any time you become incompetent.

› Make a list of all of your physicians and identify the hospital of your choice in the event of an emergency. Share this list with your family members.

› Play "IF" scenarios with your loved ones: IF you should have a stroke or break your hip, what rehab or nursing home facility would you like to go to for your recuperation? IF you're sick and need home health care, what agency should be called? IF it's not safe for you to live alone, what assisted living facility would you like to live in? IF you can't get around

and do for yourself but can still remain at home, what kind of services would you like to help you?

› To help you play out your IF scenarios, go visit assisted living, rehab and nursing home facilities while you are well and then decide which ones you'd like if you ever need them. Interview home health agencies, and find out what services are available from your local Area Agency on Aging (1-800-677-1116), from your local church or synagogue and senior care agencies. Make a list of your top choices with contact information for each.

› Create a "Rainy Day Folder" for all of your directives and the results of your research from steps 4 and 5. Be sure to make a duplicate folder and give it to the family member you've appointed as your durable health care power of attorney.

Unplanned decisions are uninformed decisions, and in the heat of a crisis, they are rarely in *anyone's* best interest.

 : My father is seriously ill and has asked me to help him get his affairs in order. How do I begin?

 : First off, I'm very sorry to hear about your father's health. I remember being with my brother when he was told that he had a life-limiting diagnosis of cancer. He asked me to help him, as well. I learned throughout his illness that helping him tend to legal and financial matters gave

him a sense of control. He was determined to leave his young family financially secure and his wife free from dealing with the dissolution of his small business. This is what gave him peace of mind. He was going to be a protective Dad until the end. Tragically, he only had twelve weeks with his family from the day of his diagnosis.

Emotionally, there's so much coming at you right now that it might not seem that dealing with these matters is the best use of the precious amount of time you have left with your Dad. But, helping him gain control and giving him the peace of mind, as it did my brother, that his loved ones will be taken care of when he's gone, is a priceless gift you can give your father. I recently came across an extremely well-done publication by the American Bar Association commissioned by the National Hospice and Palliative Care Organization titled, *Legal Guide for the Seriously Ill: Seven Key Steps to Get Your Affairs in Order*. The hospice association found that family members and patients were at a loss – especially during a crisis – of what to do to protect their assets, how to finance their care if they weren't insured, how to draft a will, how to take time off from work for caregiving or treatment and how to plan for the future care of young dependents. As a result, they saw a need for a practical and easy how-to guide that could quickly navigate patients and families through the most essential steps of "getting their affairs in order."

The seven steps show you how to: pay for the health care you need, manage your health and personal decisions, manage your money and property, plan for the care of dependents, know your rights as a patient and an employee and complete various legal documents. The 50-page guide describes each step and then identifies decision points you should consider. Alongside it is a list of resources and tips with direct links to their websites to assist you with completing each action step. Unfortunately, the ABA did not have enough funding to print hard copies of the guide, though they hope to do so by the end of the year. Thus, you'll need to go online to access the guide. To make it easy for you, just go to my website at www.lindarhodescaregiving.com and click onto *"Caregiving Tip of the Week."*

Here are a few tips you'll find in the guide:

› You're eligible for hospice care if you have Medicare Part A (hospital insurance) and your doctor certifies that you have a life-limiting illness that is expected to result in death in six months or less. By being part of hospice, pain management and outpatient medications will be covered.

› There are a number of ways to financially piece together paying for your care beyond health insurance or Medicare. Look into: veterans benefits, Social Security disability, Medicaid, Accelerated Death Benefits, reverse mortgages, tax deductions and credits and in a worse case scenario, bankruptcy.

- Review all of your retirement accounts and annuities. Make sure that whoever is identified as the beneficiary upon your death is still the person you want to receive the benefit.

- Some estate planning tools to consider are: Giving property away before your death, forgiving loans upon your death and creating joint ownership of bank accounts or other property with a "right of survivorship."

You also may want to consider going to your local bookstore to find one of the many how-to books on legal matters or seeking the advice of an elder law lawyer.

 : How can I prevent my parents from becoming victims of identity theft?

 : Identity theft among the elderly is skyrocketing: According to the Federal Trade Commission (FTC), in just one year the number of identity thefts among those over the age of 60 rose by 218 percent. Older consumers make perfect targets because they are likely to have higher credit lines, greater home equity and better financial resources than the rest of the population. Besides shredding unsolicited credit applications, outdated checks, statements and unessential financial information, the FTC and the American Bankers Association offer the following steps that your parents can take to protect their credit identity:

- Never give out identifying numbers or financial information on the phone unless you prompted the call and know the person or organization being called.

- Know the due dates of your bills and statements. If a regular bill or statement fails to reach you within a week of the usual time, contact the company to find out why. Thieves often re-route mail to themselves to avoid alerting victims.

- Stop receiving most pre-screened credit card offers by calling 1-888-OPTOUT (1-888-567-8688).

- Call the National Do Not Call Registry 888-382-1222 or visit their website at www.donotcall.gov and sign up to stop receiving most telephone solicitations.

- Do not carry your Social Security card in your wallet, put the number on your driver's license or use it for personal identification numbers.

- It's wise to review a copy of your credit record once a year to see who has been asking about your credit, which can give you an early warning of potential trouble. Visit www.AnnualCreditReport.com or call 1-877-322-8228 to order your free credit report. You also can write: Annual Credit Report Request Service, P.O. Box 105281, Atlanta, GA 30348-5281.

- Cancel credit cards you don't use and only bring credit cards you really need when you shop and use direct deposit whenever possible.

- Do not leave financial information lying-out in the open that would tempt hired help or even financially-strapped or unscrupulous family members to accessing your accounts.

And, what if your parents are victims? They should act immediately! The Federal Trade Commission's website (www.fts.gov) offers several excellent publications available by download. Go to the *Consumer Protection* tab and then click on "ID Theft, Privacy & Security" in the menu. You can also call them to receive this information or report a theft at 1-877-438-4338.

The FTC recommends three immediate steps: First, contact the fraud departments of the three major credit bureaus, one of which is Experian (888-397-3742) and they will contact the other two. Get them to flag your file with a "fraud alert," requiring creditors to get your permission before opening any new accounts in your name. When fraud is suspected, the bureaus must give you free copies of your credit report.

Secondly, the FTC suggests that you contact all creditors with fraudulent accounts or

charges in your name. Ask for someone in the security or fraud division and tell them what you know. Follow-up with a letter and be sure to list all charges that you did **not** make.

And third, file a report with the police in your community and/or where the identity theft took place. Keep copies as proof to creditors that you are doing what you can to catch the thief. Under the voluntary "Police Report Initiative," credit bureaus will automatically block the fraudulent accounts and bad debts from appearing on your credit report, but only if you can give them a copy of the police report.

Q: I think my friend's mother is a victim of domestic violence. Do I report it as elder abuse – and how?

A: Mistakenly, too many people think that "elder abuse" is not connected to domestic violence and that it's something that just happens in nursing homes. But, as you are finding with your friend's parents, elder abuse can be a family, domestic matter. All too often, older women are ashamed and embarrassed to seek help. They frequently live on fixed incomes and feel that they have no option but to stay in an abusive relationship or setting. The numbers are very unsettling: One in three women is a victim of domestic abuse, and nationally 4,000 women on average die every year from domestic violence. Among those victimized by elder abuse, women in their mid-seventies are the most frequent victims, and most of them are injured by a male family member.

According to research on elder abuse, signs of abuse are: bruises or grip marks around the arms or neck, bruise marks that look old, rope marks or welts on the wrists and/or ankles (caused by tying people to wheelchairs and beds), repeated unexplained injuries, a dismissive or evasive explanation about injuries and refusal to go to the emergency room for repeated injuries and black eyes. If your friend's mother also acts uncommunicative, fearful or suspicious of your interest in her, shows lack of interest in social interaction, and/or becomes isolated by her caretakers, then she might also be experiencing emotional or psychological abuse.

Family situations that contribute to elder abuse include: discord in the family accelerated by illness and care needs, caregiver stress, marital stress and a history or pattern of violent interactions within the family. Sometimes, a woman who may have been abused for years may turn her pent-up rage on her frail and sick husband, or an adult child who has been badly treated by his or her parents now begins to neglect and abuse his parents when the tables are turned.

So, what do you do about your concerns and possible suspicions? Inform your friend that you visited her Mom and report what you saw. She may have a medical explanation for it. But if there isn't an explanation, then continue to pursue it. If you feel comfortable and the opportunity presents itself, ask her Mom what happened and use your judgment as to her response and explanation. Let her know that if she would like to talk to you, you are there to listen and assist her. Professionals advise that you should not confront the alleged abuser, as you may place the victim in a more vulnerable position.

If your suspicions are confirmed or you see more symptoms as I've described, then encourage your friend to seek professional help right away. Here's what both or either of you can do:

> Call the Domestic Violence Center hotline at 1-800-799-SAFE (7233) and a Crisis Advocate will help you assess and respond to the immediate situation. Once the immediate situation is stabilized, they offer counseling for the victim and create a safety plan with her and family members. She could also receive emergency shelter, if she needs to be removed immediately.

> Call the Area Agency on Aging Protective Services program. They guarantee confidentiality and are professionally trained to determine whether or not abuse is taking place. The social workers can also assess the entire situation and help create a less stressful caregiving environment, if that is contributing to the problem. You can find the Area Agency on Aging closest to you by calling 1-800-677-1116.

No matter what, don't ignore what you saw. As one Crisis Advocate told me, "If you, a doctor or family member sees bruises on a woman of any age, please ask questions. Let them know you're there for them and so are a lot of resources. You just need to ask."

 My son is divorced and relocated for a job. His wife has custody of the children and we live near them, but she won't let us see our grandkids. Do we have any legal rights?

 It's always sad to see children caught in the cross-fire of divorce. Exposing kids to the fall-out of anger, bitterness and jealousy from a broken marriage sure doesn't add up to wanting your children to grow up healthy, happy and strong. Grandparents' rights to visitation of their grandchildren are governed by the Pennsylvania Custody and Grandparents'

Visitation Act. Grandparents and great-grandparents may seek visitation through the courts when: The birth parent is deceased, parents are divorced or separated for at least six months (even if they were never married) or when the child has resided with the grandparent or great-grandparent for twelve months or more, during which time the child was removed from them. Grandparents have no rights under the act for visitation if both parents reside together with their children and they object to the grandparents visiting their children. The only exception to this rule is if the child recently lived with the grandparents or great-grandparent for twelve months or more.

The court will make its decision based on what the law refers to as "the best interests of the child." In other words, this isn't about you and your needs. It's about serving the child's best interest to maintain, preserve and foster relationships that are meaningful and beneficial to them – so, let this be your focus in pursuing visitation rights with your grandkids. According to elder law lawyer, Jan Brown, of Jan Brown and Associates in Harrisburg, the Pennsylvania courts do value the relationship between grandparents and their grandchildren.

But, before you venture off to the court system, Brown would tell you, "Absolutely take the mediation route first. It offers the best chance for all sides to understand each other's positions, which means they'll more likely come to a resolution that works for everyone. Coming to an understanding that all parties have been a part of is more likely to work than a parent feeling they are being forced to do something they oppose." It also means grandkids escape a tense hand-off whenever a visit does take place.

Based on Brown's experience, she's found that parents and grandparents who use mediation end up with a bonus – as a result of going through the process, they learn how to resolve differences, which make them better prepared to solve the ever-changing visitation and custody needs of the grandkids themselves.

Elder law and family law lawyers who are "certified mediators" are an excellent source for you to work things out with your daughter-in-law. They'll know the law and can help you think through the circumstances surrounding the on-going and future needs of your grandchildren. If done well, they can save you a lot of time, heartache and money. If you can't afford a lawyer, then find a local legal aide clinic by calling the Pennsylvania Legal Aid Network at 1-800-322-7572. (Press 1, then remain on the line).

No matter what you do, continue to reach out to your grandchildren by writing them letters, sending photos and care packages that remind them of their relationship with you. Ask your son to set up a "three-way" call so he can connect you on the phone when he talks to the kids. Keep track of everything you're doing to maintain a relationship with your grandchildren should the mediation route not work. But, whatever you do, don't place any pressure on the grandkids that make them feel they are part of the tug-of-war between their Mom and you.

Section Three
Benefits & Resources

Q: How does my Mom apply for Social Security benefits?

A: The traditional way is to make a visit to your local Social Security Office, but the process is much easier on the internet (see the following). There are 1,300 offices nationwide and you can call 1-800-772-1213 to find the office nearest you. If you go to the local office to apply for benefits, you and your Mom should bring her:

▸ Social Security Card

▸ Birth certificate

▸ Proof of U.S. citizenship

▸ Spouse's birth certificate and Social Security number (if she's applying for benefits based on her husband's record)

▸ Marriage certificate

▸ Military discharge papers if she served in the military

▸ W-3 form from last year or her latest tax return

The time to apply for benefits is four months before the date she qualifies. Presently, early retirement can begin at age 62. If your Mom was born before 1938, her full retirement age will remain at age 65; however, the full retirement age is moving up for those born after 1938. Be sure to check with the Social Security Administration as to your full retirement age based upon your birth date. (For example, Baby Boomers born between 1943-1954 will not reach full retirement age until they are 66 years old.) If you have access to the internet, you can go to Social Security's excellent website at www.ssa.gov.

The SSA has been in the forefront of offering a range of services on the internet. If you lose your Social Security card or Medicare card, you can apply for new cards online. You can email questions and add your name to a list to be updated on the latest new rules given a topic of your choosing. You can even submit a request to receive a Social Security statement identifying all of your contributions throughout your working life and what you can expect to receive upon retirement at different ages. You can also search for your full retirement age based upon your birth date. Here are a few guidelines for submitting your Mom's Social Security retirement application online:

▸ You'll need a printer because, once you've entered the information and sent it to SSA, you'll also need to print the application, sign it and mail it to the address provided.

- › The internet service isn't available 24/7, but close to it, so be sure to check the hours listed on the benefit application page before you start.

- › You must agree to direct deposit to make an online application, so have your Mom's bank account number and her bank routing number on hand (and direct deposit is a good idea for security purposes, anyway).

- › You'll need to know her earnings for the past and current year.

- › You'll also need to enter other basics, such as her married name, Social Security number, and date of birth.

- › SSA lists what you'll need to know before you start the online application. As with all applications, you will need to mail in some original documents that SSA will mail back to you.

The website can answer just about every question on Social Security and benefits. You'll find a Women's Page filled with financial tips and benefits advice for women of all ages. (If you're a teacher, note that there's also a terrific Kid's Page.)

Q: What does Medicare cover when it comes to medical equipment, devices and supplies?

Medicare actually covers a great deal under this category known as Durable Medical Equipment, Prosthetics, Orthotics, and Supplies (DMEPOS). Let's take a moment to break down each term: Durable Medical Equipment is medical equipment that can be reused, such as walkers, hospital beds and wheelchairs. In many cases, the equipment is rented by Medicare and when you are finished using it, you return it to the supplier. Prosthetics (devices that substitute for a removed body part) cover such items as cochlear implants, limb, facial, breast and ocular prostheses. Orthotics includes custom made foot ware, diabetic shoes, and insoles. And finally, supplies cover materials often used just once in conjunction with other devices such as test strips and lancets used with home blood glucose monitors or supplies used with respirators and wound care.

To better protect Medicare beneficiaries, the Centers for Medicare and Medicaid Services (CMS), recently required that any vendor who wishes to act as a Medicare Supplier be accredited by a professional entity like the Joint Commission or the Community Health Accreditation Program (CHAP) and have a surety bond. CMS took this action to prevent fraudulent companies from taking advantage of unsuspecting customers.

When it comes to receiving any of the equipment, devices or supplies covered under the DMEPOS benefit be sure to take these three steps:

1. If your physician or other treating licensed professional, such as a Nurse Practitioner or Physician Assistant, writes a prescription stating that the supplies and/or equipment you need in your home are medically necessary; then ask if they will also be filling out and submitting a "Certificate of Medical Necessity" form so you can receive Medicare approval. Your claim will not be covered by Medicare if you do not have a prescription stating that it is medically necessary and approval from Medicare.

2. Ask if the supplier is enrolled in the Medicare program and has a Medicare number. If they are not enrolled, then Medicare will not pay your claim. So, absolutely make sure they are enrolled.

3. Ask the supplier if they accept "assignment." This means that the vendor has agreed to accept whatever Medicare assigns as payment in full. This is a good thing. It means that the supplier can not come back to you to pay a balance between what they charged Medicare versus what Medicare actually covered.

You can find out which suppliers in your area have received approval from CMS and were awarded a Medicare Number by going to www.medicare.gov, looking under "Resource Locator" and clicking on "Medical Equipment Suppliers." You'll receive the name and contact information of suppliers in your area once you have entered your zip code. Even though you may have looked up a supplier online, always ask their sales person if they have a "Medicare Number" to verify that they can bill Medicare. If you can not go online to find a supplier, then call 1-800-MEDICARE (800-633-4227) to find those vendors who participate.

Generally, you will pay 20 percent of the Medicare-approved amount for the product you receive, while Medicare pays the remaining 80 percent. However, most people have a Medi-gap policy which may pick up their 20 percent portion. DMEPOS benefits are paid through Part B of your Medicare plan after you have met your annual deductible. Check your "Medicare and You" Handbook mailed to you each year to find out what is covered under this benefit.

Q: Are VA benefits automatic for my Dad or does he have to enroll?

A: Several years ago, Congress passed the Veterans Health Care Eligibility Reform Act, stating that any veteran who wants to receive VA health care services must now enroll. Your Dad needs to fill out Form 10-10EZ and there are three ways he can get it:

1. Visit, call or write a local VA care or benefits office listed in the blue pages of the phone book under federal government.

2. Call the VA Enrollment Center at 1-877-222-VETS.

3. Simply download the form and file it electronically by going to the VA website at www.va.gov.

Hopefully, your Dad kept his Honorable Discharge Certificate (DD-214) because he'll need to give them a copy. Once your Dad enrolls, he'll be assigned one of two eligibility categories: must-do or may-do. The VA must provide hospital and outpatient care to veterans in the "must-do" group, consisting of veterans who have a service-connected disability, former POWs, World War I veterans and low-income veterans. Depending upon funding, the VA may also offer some nursing home care to this group. The VA may provide health care services to the "may-do" group, depending upon the resources available to the Department of Veterans Affairs. These veterans will have to pay a co-payment for the care.

In addition to an eligibility category, your father will be assigned to one of seven priority groups. Vets with a service-connected disability that is 50 percent or more disabling are given priority one status. Most veterans of WWII fall into priority group five – they don't have a disability connected to the war, but their annual income and net worth are considered "low income" as determined by the VA system. Those who have higher incomes can still receive services, but they pay a higher co-pay.

Veterans accepted for enrollment in the VA health care system can receive inpatient and outpatient services, including preventive and primary care. Prescriptions are covered when veterans receive their treatment from a VA medical facility. Most of the time, the veteran will be asked to pay a $2 co-pay.

If your Dad qualifies, he could receive primary care from outpatient clinics, community-based care, some nursing home care, home-based primary care, adult day care, rehabilitation, diagnostic and treatment services, and hospital (medical and surgical) inpatient care. If the VA doesn't operate a facility where your father lives, they can send him to one located nearest to him or subcontract with another provider to give him the service. It's certainly worth the effort for your father to enroll and find out what kind of health care he could receive in return for his service.

: What are some of the best websites dealing with aging parent issues?

: The internet is downright amazing, if not overwhelming, when it comes to spewing out all kinds of information on just about every topic imaginable. As baby boomers age and become internet savvy, the websites on aging are popping up faster than the speed of light. A simple keyword search on *elder care* will call up millions of hits. Where to begin? Here are five core websites that will get you well on your way to navigating the resources that await you in cyberspace:

National Council on Aging
"Benefits Check-up"
www.benefitscheckup.org

Simply fill out a simple online questionnaire and immediately find out if your parent qualifies for benefits and prescription discounts. The site provides forms and contact data once you know you're eligible for a benefit.

Medicare
www.medicare.gov

Medicare is the centerpiece of your parents' health care. What's covered and what's not are always changing. But, the feds did a nice job in making it understandable by putting up an online guide on just about every question you might have on Medicare. They also provide ratings and comparison shopping reports on nursing homes, home health care agencies, hospitals, medi-gap policies and drug plans. For example, if you're looking for a nursing home, you can find the results of the latest inspection report on every nursing home in the country and see how many stars Medicare awarded the facility according to their five star rating system.

Locating eldercare services nationwide
www.eldercare.gov

If you're looking for community-based services in another state, this site is a one-stop shop. Go to their Quick Index so you can easily hyperlink to all of the services offered by the Administration on Aging. You can track down the Area Agency on Aging closest to your parent(s) and access other caregiving websites.

MedlinePlus
www.medlineplus.gov

MedlinePlus answers a wealth of questions on hundreds of health conditions and thousands of medications, including herbs and vitamins assembled by trusted authorities from the National Library of Medicine, the National Institutes of Health, other government agencies and health-

related organizations. You'll also find an illustrated medical encyclopedia, interactive patient tutorials, and the latest in health news.

AARP
www.aarp.org

Even though this is a commercial website, when it comes to senior issues, it is top-notch in giving you easily understandable consumer information from A-Z. They provide you with the latest news, helpful links and printable versions of many of their excellent publications. You don't have to be a member of AARP to use it.

Q : What are home care agencies?

A : Home care agencies, also known as non-medical senior care, personal care or home care aide agencies provide care that does not require a licensed professional or a physician's prescription to receive the care. Let's say your Mom needs help with toileting, preparing meals, getting in and out of her chair or bed, bathing, getting dressed, being reminded to take her medications or someone needs to keep

up with light housekeeping or take her to a doctor's appointment – then you need to approach a home care agency. Because this is not medical care, this type of care is not covered by Medicare. If your mother has long term care insurance, then they may cover the care, but again, call them to find out. This type of care is sometimes referred to as "custodial care" or assistance with Adult Daily Living tasks (ADL) or Instrumental Adult Daily Living Tasks (IADL) such as paying bills, housekeeping, and meal preparation.

Home care agencies, because they are not providing medical care, are not licensed in many states (only thirteen require some sort of licensure). Those states with laws do require agencies to let you know whether or not the direct care worker is an employee of their agency, is covered by workers compensation, is covered by professional liability insurance or if they are NOT an employee. For example, if you've contacted an agency that is a Registry, they do not employ the people they send to you, so you must withhold and report the worker's state and federal income tax, Federal Unemployment tax, Social Security and Medicare taxes.

Examples of home care agencies are: Home Instead Senior Care, Visiting Angels, Comfort Keepers, Senior Helpers, and a host of others that can be found in the Yellow Pages under home care, senior care, and personal care.

Q: My friend has been getting aging services for her Mom from the "AAA." I know she can't be talking about the auto club, so what is she talking about?

A: Your friend's Mom is referring to Area Agencies on Aging (AAA) that receive funding from state funds and the federal Older Americans Act. They act as your county's centralized advocate for issues facing older people and chief planners for aging services in your community. They also act as a major provider and sub-contractor of aging services dedicated to giving older adults the options to live at home and remain in their communities. Senior centers, home delivered meals, and shared ride programs receive funding from your local Area Agency on Aging. And, it's your AAA that acts as a watch-dog protecting vulnerable elderly from physical, mental or financial abuse and neglect rendered by family members, strangers or in a care facility. Here are just three of the major ways you can take advantage of your local Area Agency on Aging:

Information hub. Since the agency is responsible for planning aging services for the whole community, they'll know just about every program in the region. Many of them offer guidebooks of all the services available. Most have websites that you can track down by going to www.eldercare. gov. Just enter your parent's county and click on *General Information and Assistance* on the search bar. The local AAA can tell you what services are available, advise you on eligibility criteria of various programs and give you contact information. You can also call 1-800-677-1116 to find the closest agency to you. Nearly every county has an Area Agency on Aging. You can also find them listed in the Blue Pages of your phone book.

Family Caregiver Support Program. This is a terrific program funded by the state and federal government for caregivers and care receivers (60 years-plus), who are related by blood or marriage and live together. So, if your Mom lives with you and you're caring for her, you may qualify for financial help to cover out-of-pocket expenses and receive a grant to modify your home or purchase helpful devices to meet your parent's needs. Some families have used the money to install a stair climb or modify a bathroom. The age restriction of 60-plus is removed if your parent suffers from dementia. The program operates on a sliding fee scale, so it's not a poverty-restricted program. You can obtain a family consultation, legal advice, needs assessment, respite care, caregiver education and training along with help on out-of-pocket expenses.

Care management. The goal behind this service is to enable your loved one to live at home for as long as possible, even if they would qualify for nursing home care. If your parent has a modest income, he may qualify for a caseworker and a team of professionals skilled in geriatric social work and nursing

(provided either by the Area Agency on Aging or one of its subcontractors) to help manage his care. They'll assess your parent's needs and bring together the services required to take care of your parent and help him or her remain in the community. For example, they may arrange for adult day services for a loved one with dementia while their caregiver is at work, send in-home delivered meals and arrange for a caregiver to come in three times a week along with a weekly nursing assessment. Each plan is tailored to an individual's needs. The Area Agency on Aging also provides geriatric assessments to determine whether or not your parent needs nursing home care or assisted living. Each program has eligibility guidelines.

So, go ahead and take your friend's lead. If your Mom is in need of aging services, call ElderCare Locator at 1-800-677-1116 to see if the AAA's robust network of services can help you and your Mom.

Area Agencies on Aging

Q: Is there a one-stop shop to find out what benefits my parents can get?

A: For many benefits, age sixty-five is the magic number for eligibility, but you should be aware that some benefits can be secured as early as age sixty. Here are two major resources to navigate your search for benefits:

The National Council on Aging (NCOA) offers a helpful screening service that will help you find and enroll in federal, state, local and private programs that help pay for prescription drugs, utility bills, meals, health care and other needs. Go to www. benefitscheckup.org and fill out their questionnaire that only takes 10 to 15 minutes to complete. You'll enter basic information on your parent, including income, all of which remains confidential. Once you've entered the data, the "Benefits Checkup" will search thousands of benefits against your parent's information. Within seconds, you'll receive an "Eligibility Report" that will identify potential benefits for which your parent may be eligible. The report will include all of the information that you will need to contact the local agency to determine whether or not your parent actually qualifies. You will be given local names, addresses and 800 phone numbers, along with application forms that you simply download and send in

to the appropriate agency. This resource is a great timesaver, so if you don't have internet access, it's worth a trip to the library to get online.

The NCOA website also allows you to apply for Medicare's "Extra Help Prescription Drug Coverage" for people with lower incomes who qualify for Medicare Part D co-payments. And, if your parents can't afford to keep good food on the table, they can apply for the Supplemental Nutrition Assistance Program or "SNAP," formally known as the Food Stamp Program. The Benefits Checkup website is especially helpful if you live in a different state than your parents, as it searches thousands of programs by state and gives you local numbers to contact.

Finally, the **Area Agency on Aging (AAA)** is another valuable resource for advice on what services are available and if your parents qualify. You can find your parents' local AAA by calling the Eldercare Locator at 1-800-677-1116. To learn more on Area Agencies on Aging, read the previous Question and Answer.

: How can my Mom apply for handicapped parking tags?

: Your first step is to contact your state's Department of Motor Vehicles, as each state has its own laws and regulations governing parking tags. Most states now refer to these as a *Person with Disability Parking Placard.* In general, the following people qualify for this type of placard allowing them to park in the handicapped parking spaces with the wheelchair symbol.

Anyone who is:

1. Blind.

2. Does not have full use of an arm or both arms.

3. Not able to walk 200 feet without stopping to rest.

4. Not able to walk without the use of or assistance from: a brace, cane, crutch, another person, prosthetic device, wheelchair or other assistive device.

5. Restricted by lung disease (usually specified levels measured by a spirometry test.)

6. Using portable oxygen.

7. Affected by a cardiac condition to the extent that the person's functional limitations are classified in severity as Class III or Class IV according to the standards set by the American Heart Association.

8. Severely limited in his or her ability to walk due to an arthritic, neurological or orthopedic condition.

If your parent has a 100% service-connected disability that is certified by the U.S. Veteran's Administration, or the same disabilities as listed above, but they are service-connected rather than due to aging or injuries, then your parent can apply for a "Severely Disabled Veteran" placard, which provides the same benefits as the Person with Disability placard. Now, how about getting a *Person with Disability* placard? Here's how:

Many states now allow you to download copies of their application forms, or you can go to a local Motor Vehicle Office of the state department of transportation. If you are a member of the AAA (American Automobile Association), they too, have copies of the forms and some can help you apply and process your state's application. In most cases, the applicant must be the person with the disability – not you, even if you are going to be driving her everywhere in your car. In other words, the placard is for the person, not the vehicle.

Your next step will be to take your state's form to your mother's physician. He or she must certify which conditions make her eligible for this parking privilege. Her doctor must sign the form and enter his or her medical license number. In some states, a police officer may also certify that someone is eligible if the applicant "does not have the full use of a leg or both legs, or is blind," as evidenced by use of a wheelchair, walker, crutches, cane or other prescribed device. Once a physician or police officer

certifies that your mother is eligible and signs the form, she may need to get the form notarized.

If your parent is applying for a "Severely Disabled Veteran" placard, then the Veterans Administration Regional Office must certify and sign the form. According to most states, placards are to be used only when the vehicle in which it is displayed is parked and is being used for the transportation of the person with the disability. You don't get to use it if your mother is not in the car. The placard qualifies you to park in areas designated for use by persons with disability only. It does not give you license to park where parking is prohibited.

 : My Mom keeps confusing Medicaid with Medicare. Just what is the difference?

 : There is a world of difference between the two programs. Medicare is a federal health insurance program for those 65 and older: Part A essentially covers hospital expenses and Part B covers physician and outpatient services and Part D covers prescription benefits. Everyone receiving Social Security at age 65 automatically receives a Medicare Card. This is Medicare in a nutshell; for lots more on the subject go to www.medicare.gov or read

over the annual guide Medicare sends to your parents, *Medicare & You*, that highlights a Summary of Medicare benefits, coverage options, rights and protections, and answers to the most frequently asked questions about Medicare.

Medicaid, by contrast, is a health insurance program run at the state level for people living at or below the poverty line. The federal government shares the cost with the state. Many older people who qualify for

Medicaid are also eligible to receive a federal supplement to their Social Security check known as SSI. Medicare is automatic and you do not have to meet income eligibility limits. In contrast, Medicaid has stringent income eligibility rules and you must apply. If your mother qualifies, she would be able to receive health care services from physicians who accept Medicaid, and her hospitalizations and prescriptions would also be covered. If she's 65 or over, she'd receive Medicare as well. The two are not mutually exclusive. Depending upon her financial circumstances, Medicaid may cover her premiums for Part A and B, along with the deductibles.

Most people start looking towards Medicaid when they are facing nursing home costs that can easily reach $6,000 per month. Her state Medicaid program will review all of your mother's "countable income," such as wages, self-employment income, pensions, interest, dividends, annuities, entitlements and benefits. If the countable income is less than the nursing home costs, then your mother would likely pass the income test. But, she'll also have to meet medical requirements that prove she needs skilled nursing care in an approved long-term care facility.

You'll often hear the term "spending down" associated with Medicaid and nursing homes. Many people pay for a nursing home using their savings, assets and income to meet the monthly bill, eventually spending their assets down to a level where they meet federal poverty guidelines. At that point they apply to Medicaid. Years ago, people

had to spend down to such an extent that the nursing home resident's spouse would be impoverished by the time Medicaid would help out. But today, federal law protects spouses from becoming impoverished. Medical Assistance Offices calculate a monthly "Community Spouse Resource Allowance" and if the spouse is living in the home, it will not be considered a countable asset, nor will the household goods or the car. The state Medicaid office will determine the allowance based upon an eligibility formula. Some people think that they can game the system by transferring all of a parent's income and assets to the children as a way of "spending down," so that the parent will immediately qualify for nursing home assistance. You should know, however, that any assets transferred within five years prior to nursing home admission are NOT exempt from the asset eligibility test. This is often referred to as the "look back" provision. The Medicaid program also requires re-payment of medical assistance for nursing home care from your mother's estate after she dies, or from her husband's estate if he outlives her. Contact your local welfare office listed in the Blue Pages of your phone book to determine if your Mom would qualify. It may also be wise for you to see a certified Elder Law attorney; you can find one in your local area by going to www.naela.com.

Q: A friend of my mother's rarely has any food in the house and we know she's not eating well. Do you think she could get food stamps?

A: You've really touched on a topic that many older people either misunderstand or shy away from. The United States Department of Agriculture (USDA) reports that nearly a million and a half elderly households do not have enough of the right types of food needed to maintain their health or simply do not have enough to eat. We've all heard the stories about older people being forced to choose between spending money on their prescriptions or groceries. It's a trade-off they should never have to make.

Yet, of all the benefits out there for the elderly, my guess is that food stamps are the most underutilized. A great many people qualify and simply don't know it. Others fear they'll be embarrassed handing over food "stamps" to a cashier in front of a bunch of judgmental onlookers. But the days of "stamps" are long gone: your Mom's friend would be handing over an electronic card that looks just like a plastic credit card. So, who's to know? If you don't have a problem accepting Medicare – a government subsidized program – why walk away from this benefit? There are actually five programs available: Supplemental Nutrition Assistance Program (SNAP), which was formerly known as "Food Stamps," Commodity Supplemental Food, Senior Farmers' Market, Congregate Meals, and Home Delivered Meals also known as "Meals on Wheels." So, let's go over each:

SNAP Program (Food Stamps): Generally, all persons who live together and prepare meals together are grouped as a "household" under the food stamp program. An adult sixty and older, however, can be considered a separate household even if living with other family members. These "elderly" households must meet the "net income test," which is gross income minus certain deductions, such as medical expenses; and they may have up to $3,000 in assets. The older person's home, lot, and pension funds are not included in the $3,000 limit. Your mother's friend would apply at the local county board of assistance office. If it is difficult for her to go there, she can be interviewed by telephone. To find her local office, look in the blue pages of your phone book under "Government Services."

Commodity Supplemental Food: This program offered by the USDA provides a free box of commodities up to once a month. Anyone at least 60 years of age and with an income at or below 130 percent of the federal poverty level can qualify. Nearly eight out of ten participants are elderly, so your Mom's friend certainly wouldn't be alone. Typical boxes include pasta, rice, beans, butter, cheese, canned meat and poultry, along with canned fruits and vegetables. Oftentimes, the state agency receiving the commodities from the federal government contract out to non-profit groups like food pantries to distribute the food. Give your local Area Agency on Aging (1-800-677-1116) a call to find out about eligibility and who distributes the food.

Senior Farmer's Market: This is another program offered by the USDA for folks 60 years and over whose income is less than 185% of the federal poverty guidelines. If her friend qualifies, she'll receive coupons worth an average of $70, which she can take to local farmer's markets to buy fresh produce. Again, give the Area Agency on Aging a call to see if the program is offered near her.

Congregate Meals: This program is offered at no cost to seniors and there are no income guidelines. Many people, however, give a small donation. Perhaps your Mom can take her friend to a local senior center a few times a week to receive a very good hot meal and the added benefit of socialization. Senior centers are listed in the blue pages of your phone book usually under "Aging Services," or give the local area agency a call to track down the closest center to your friend.

Home-Delivered Meals: Chances are the same senior center offering congregate meals will also have a group of terrific volunteers who will deliver meals five days a week. This program is for those elderly who are homebound and is of no cost to seniors sixty years and older. There are no income eligibility limits, but because resources are limited, there may be a waiting list and most people who use the program do have a modest income.

With all of these resources available, your mother's friend shouldn't be hungry, or worse yet, at risk of being malnourished. Good nutrition is critical to an older person's health. You'll be saving her from a lot more than hunger pains – so trust your instincts and get involved.

Q: Can you tell me if the new health care reform law affects Medicare?

A: Yes, it does and by all accounts from the Centers for Medicaid and Medicare (CMS), it is positive, however, there is concern because there is an expected $500 billion dollars in spending cuts over the next ten years. CMS argues that this will be achieved by aggressive efforts to reduce fraud and waste, not through a reduction of benefits.

One of the most welcomed changes is dealing with the infamous "donut hole" under the Medicare Prescription (Part D) benefit. Currently, if you have enrolled in a Medicare Part D plan, you've learned that after your plan has paid a set amount for your prescription drugs, you enter a coverage gap wherein you must pay 100 percent of your prescription costs until you reach a certain threshold when the coverage kicks back in again. This is known as the "donut hole." For thousands of people, this means falling off a financial cliff or making another harrowing choice by not buying their medications and waiting until a new year begins.

But now (2010), if you do reach the coverage gap (donut hole), Medicare will send you a one-time rebate check for $250, but only if you are NOT enrolled in the Medicare Extra Help program. Checks will be mailed directly to beneficiaries throughout the year, soon after they have reached the coverage gap. There are no forms to fill out. Medicare will automatically send you the check. So, don't believe scam artists who may call you asking you for private information so they can help you get your "$250 rebate check."

In 2011, those who reach the coverage gap can expect to receive a 50 percent discount on all of their brand medications and by 2020 there will no longer be a coverage gap in Prescription Part D programs. Between now and then, Medicare beneficiaries will continue to learn of discounts being offered to those reaching the coverage gap.

Here are some more benefits you can expect:

› Medicare will cover an annual physical by your physician.

› Coverage will remain the same under the Original (traditional) Medicare and Medicare Advantage Plans.

› By 2014, the new law requires that at least 85 percent of every dollar spent by Medicare Advantage plans is spent on health care services rather than administrative costs or insurance company profits.

- A new voluntary long term care insurance program was created called CLASS to help pay for long term care in facilities and at home.

- In 2014 insurance companies will be banned from denying coverage to adults due to a pre-existing condition.

Another positive development is the passage of the Elder Justice Law as part of the Affordable Health Care Act. You can expect to see a much more aggressive program to identify and prosecute health care waste and fraud, along with more programs to address elder abuse and neglect.

 My husband wants to retire at 62 years of age, but he's worried his company might drop their retiree health benefit. Does the new health reform law help?

It could help, if his company participates in a new benefit provided by the "Affordable Care Act." The new health reform law will be phased in over a four year period. But, the "Early Retiree Reinsurance Program" under the law already began on June 1, 2010. Given past trends, your husband has had every right to be concerned. Over the past twenty years, the number of employers who provide medical coverage to early retirees has dramatically dropped by 50 percent. Today, less than one-third of large employers provide health care coverage to retirees aged 55 to 64 years and their families. This is a critical gap in coverage for workers who don't yet qualify for Medicare at age 65 years and are at risk for a host of chronic conditions ranging from diabetes, hypertension to heart disease and cancer.

Congress is hoping that by allocating $5 billion dollars as a subsidy to employers – public, private, unions and non-profit – then companies will be convinced and able to keep offering early retiree health care benefits. Experts report that three out of four of the nation's large employers are planning to apply for the funds as soon as they are available. This means that those companies that qualify will realize a savings averaging between $2,000 to $3,000 per early retiree or an overall savings of between 25 to 35 percent of what they usually spend to insure their early retirees. It also means that early retirees should eventually see a reduction in their premiums.

Health care coverage that qualifies for the subsidy includes medical, surgical, hospital, prescription drugs and other benefits that cover the retiree, their spouse or surviving spouse and dependents. Companies that self-insure or purchase insurance plans for their employees qualify. If an employer does not offer early retiree health care benefits, but would like to do so, they must wait to apply until January 1, 2011.

The first thing your father should do before he opts for early retirement is to talk with his Human Resources representative to find out whether or not they will continue to offer health care benefits until he reaches Medicare eligibility age (in his case, three years from now). He could also ask if they are going to apply for the "Early Retiree Reinsurance Program," which gives you an indication of their plans to offer the benefit.

For those early retirees who will not be receiving a health care benefit, they can look to the law to allocate another $5 billion dollars for states to create "high risk" insurance pools through "Health Insurance Exchanges." Individuals can qualify if they have been uninsured for the past six months and have a pre-existing health condition. There is no age requirement to qualify. The new law will also offer standardized, easy-to-understand information on these insurance plans to make it easier for consumers to shop and compare the best policy for them. This program is set to get underway in July and should offer affordable premiums for the uninsured. The law also requires that a member's out-of-pocket expenses will be capped at $5,950 per year.

If you'd like to learn more about what is covered under the new health reform law, (The Affordable Care Act) go to <u>www.HealthReform.gov</u>.

 : I think my Dad may be a victim of a Medicare scam. Can you describe some typical scams and what you can do about them?

 : If more consumers became aware of all the ways that Medicare is being scammed and reported it, we'd have up to 70 billion dollars each year of "stolen" dollars from Medicare to spend on the growing number of elderly who need medical care. Scams and fraud against Medicare are basically divided into two categories: schemes that misrepresent services delivered to beneficiaries making false claims to Medicare for payment; and plots that trick beneficiaries into giving out their Medicare ID and Social Security Number (SSN), along with financial information.

The most frequent kind of Medicare fraud involves health care providers who invent ways to improperly bill Medicare for services or products. Here's how they do it: use improper coding on the claim so they'll receive a higher payment known as "upcoding," bill for unnecessary medical supplies, order excessive lab test or x-rays, and other radiology exams that aren't needed, or they'll make claims for products and services that were never received by the beneficiary. In these instances, they figure most people don't look over their Medicare Summary statements, so they never catch on.

The second type of scheme is to come up with a ruse to acquire a beneficiary's Medicare number, along with any other personal and financial data they can get. Not only can they bill Medicare for services never rendered, but they can also enjoy all the "benefits" of identity theft. The National Consumer Protection Technical Resource Center for the Senior Medicare Patrol program identifies the most common scams used to get someone to give up their Medicare number:

> You'll be offered free products or services, such as a grocery or gas gift card, if you simply fill out a survey on the Medicare program. The promoter often visits senior centers and adult retirement communities to make the offer. The survey form requires that you enter your Medicare ID and SSN.

> A promoter, often under the guise of a medical equipment company, tells you that you qualify for free equipment like an "Arthritis Kit" or TENS unit to help with pain, along with supplies from Medicare. Of course, they need your Medicare ID number to fill out the paperwork.

> A promoter calls you offering free medical evaluations and testing, or they send coupons to your home asking you to call to set up an appointment. Some actually set up a testing site, giving you very basic services, but before you receive them, you must fill out a form giving your Medicare ID number and SSN. Others, just get the information over the phone and tell you they'll call back to confirm the date and time.

> Telemarketers call your home telling you that they represent the government or a private insurer and that they need to make some correction or offer you a specific service and they need your Medicare ID number to do so.

> You receive a phone call offering you a Prescription Drug Plan approved by Medicare and you only have to make a one-time payment of $299 or $399 with no co-pays or monthly premiums for unlimited drugs. Besides wanting your Medicare ID number, they'll also need your bank account information so they can make a one-time withdrawal.

The rule of thumb is to never give out private financial and insurance information to a stranger, especially anyone offering you something for free. A Medicare representative will **not** call you; if someone says they are, don't believe them. Keep track of the tests your doctor has ordered for you, and equipment or supplies ordered through a Medicare-certified durable medical goods company. Check them against your Medicare Summary Notices each month to make sure some "vendor" isn't being reimbursed for goods or services you've never received. If you suspect you've been a target, call the Health and Human Services Office of Inspector General at 1-800-HHS-TIPS.

Q: Are there any centralized resources to help me find public programs to help with caring for my mother?

A: When I first entered the field of aging about 35 years ago, it was easy to keep up with new developments and age-related services, but today, just enter the words "elder care services" or caregiving" for a Google search on the internet and you'll receive hundreds of thousands of responses. So, let me make it easier for you and narrow it down to five core resources that can assist you in caregiving.

1. **Family Caregiver Support Program**
   This national program is offered in every state through your local Area Agency on Aging. If you are taking care of a loved one 60 years of age and older who lives with you and have a moderate income, you may qualify. Many programs pay $200 a month for families to spend on services and supplies to help them keep a loved one at home. Some programs also offer up to $2,000 in home modifications so that a ramp or stair climb, for example, can be installed. To find a local Area Agency on Aging nearest you, call: Eldercare Locator at: 1-800-677-1116 or go to www.eldercare.gov.

2. **Benefits Checkup**
   This screening service is free from the National Council on Aging. Fill out their online forms and learn if you qualify for any of the hundreds of state, national & private programs in their database. You can also find out if your mother qualifies for Extra Help for Medicare Part D, Food Stamps, and assistance with health care, home care, meals, utility bills and more. This is a web-based service only at www.benefitscheckup.org. If you don't have access to a computer and the internet, it really is worth a trip to your local library to take advantage of this service.

3. Medicaid Waiver Programs

This state program offers lower-income individuals who are ill enough to qualify,  nursing home care and the services to enable them to remain at home instead. Services like home care, assistance with daily living tasks, nursing care, care management, respite care, adult day services and supplies may be covered. Contact your local Area Agency to find out if you qualify. If you can't find your local agency in the blue pages of your phone book, call the Eldercare Locator at 1-800-677-1116 or go to www.eldercare.gov.

4. Medicare

Medicare's official website has recently been redesigned and it's much easier to navigate. They have added a new section on "Caregiver Resources" that's very user-friendly because the information is organized from the perspective of what a caregiver might ask, especially in terms of what services are covered. For this specialized section of their website, go to www.medicare.gov/caregivers/.

If your mother is a Medicare beneficiary, it's worth taking the time to review the annual "*Medicare & You Handbook*" mailed to her home every year that describes her benefits and what is covered. If you go to the website, you can also compare nursing homes through Medicare's five star rating program, and compare hospitals, home health care agencies, Medi-gap policies, prescription plans and durable medical equipment companies at www.medicare.gov or call 1-800-MEDICARE.

5. Partnership for Prescription Assistance

If your mother isn't eligible for Medicare, yet needs vital medications that she cannot afford, then check out The Partnership for Prescription Assistance sponsored by the association of drug manufacturers. This program helps qualifying patients without prescription drug coverage acquire the medicines they need for free or nearly free. To find out if your Mom qualifies, call 1-888-4ppa-now (1-888-477-2669) or go to: www.pparx.org.

Of course, there are many other resources available to you, but tapping into these five should help get you well on your way.

: ## What is the Family Caregiver Support Program?

One of the most helpful resources for families providing care to a relative is the national Family Caregiver Support Program administered by each state. For thousands of families this program can spell the difference between their older relative staying at home or going to a skilled nursing facility. If you're caring for a relative who is 60 years of age or older who lives with you and they have a moderate income, you may qualify.

Even though each state may tailor the program to meet their older populations' unique needs, you'll find that most programs offer:

> Information to caregivers about available services.

> Assistance to caregivers in gaining access to supportive services.

> Counseling and training to assist caregivers in making decisions and solving problems related to their caregiver roles.

> Respite care to temporarily relieve the caregiver. For example, they can help pay for adult day services, intermittent or overnight respite care during an emergency or in-home respite care.

> Supplemental services to complement the family caregiver's role. For example, they can provide funds for home modifications (like installing a ramp or a stair climb), assistive technologies, equipment supplies, emergency response systems, or transportation.

The program also provides caregiver support services to grandparents 55 years and older raising fully-dependent grandchildren and older adults raising a dependent disabled (mental and/or physical) adult child. To find a local area agency operating the program near you, call Eldercare Locator at 1-800-677-1116.

Q: How can I easily find devices to help with the activities of daily living?

A: What's known as the "assistive device" industry is pumping out thousands of products to make the activities of daily life easier. Yet, far too many people don't know about them and then there's the trick of hunting them down. The design of these products basically has one purpose in mind: rid day-to-day activities from becoming an Olympic sport. Here are a few examples:

About to stumble every time you put on your socks? There's a stocking aid with long strings that keeps you steady and gets them on. Is juggling a cane and a flashlight making you unsteady? There's a "path light cane" that lights your way to where you're going. About ready to throw out your shirts or blouses because buttoning them has become an anger management issue? There is a simple button hook that makes buttoning up your shirt as easy as a snap. The examples are endless.

So, how do you go about finding these nifty little life savers so helpful for independent living? The most objective and comprehensive list of assistive devices is compiled by ABLEDATA. The program is sponsored by the National Institute on Disability and Rehabilitation Research

(NIDRR). The best thing to do is to go to their web site at www.abledata.com, where you can search products among 19 areas ranging from "Architectural Elements," that make the built environment more accessible (lighting, sensors, lifts, ramps) to "Transportation," making getting around in cars much easier. You can access customer reviews of products and link directly to the manufacturer to buy the product. All you do is enter a word or phrase in the search box and in seconds you'll find plenty of products to choose from. If you can not access the website, give them a call at 1-800-227-0216. They do not send out catalogues, but for a small fee they'll print out copies of what you may be interested in and send it to you. You don't have to pay anything for them to search products for you over the phone. An example of a commercial company selling assistive device products is Senior Emporium and you can reach them by calling 1-888-299-5232 or visit them at www.senioremporium.com.

To get a better assessment of what you need, you might approach your physician to see if he or she would prescribe Occupational Therapy. Occupational Therapists (OTs) help people perform the activities of daily living (eating, bathing, using the toilet, cooking, dressing, and doing basic household chores.) A therapist can come to your home and identify ways to make living at home easier and safer. The therapist could also show you how to use adaptive equipment and devices along with getting you involved in creative activities to help you with daily functioning. OTs have received special training and are licensed.

Medicare helps pay for medically necessary outpatient physical and occupational therapy when a physician prescribes it and the therapist sets up the plan of treatment under his or her review. Hospitals, home health agencies, and rehabilitation agencies that are Medicare-certified often provide

Occupational Therapy, as do private practice therapists. To find out more call 1-800-MEDICARE (1-800-633-4227).

Community services may also help you: Check out the local Easter Seal Society and Blind Association as they may provide services to help you learn about and receive assistive devices. Your local senior center is also a good resource to find secondhand equipment and devices that can either be given, loaned to you or purchased for a very small fee.

Have fun shopping!

 : How does the PACE prescription plan in Pennsylvania work?

 The Pennsylvania Pharmaceutical Assistance Contract for the Elderly (PACE) is one of the most generous and long standing state run programs in the country, providing prescription help to older people. You're eligible if you meet certain income thresholds, are 65 years of age and older and have been a resident in Pennsylvania for at least ninety days prior to submitting an application. Hundreds of thousands of Pennsylvanians receive benefits from the PACE program every year.

The program offers comprehensive prescription coverage to older Pennsylvanians and covers most prescription medications, including insulin, syringes and insulin needles.

It does not cover over-the-counter medicines, medical equipment or doctor, hospital, dental or vision services. There is no application fee. Once you are enrolled in the PACE program, a benefit card will be sent to you, and you will pay modest co-payments based upon a 30-day supply

The program offers two levels of enrollment, each with different income eligibility criteria based upon your previous calendar year's income. Everyone, however, must meet the age limit of 65 years and older and the residency requirement. Here is a recap on each:

PACE: You cannot be enrolled in the Department of Public Welfare's Medicaid prescription benefit. For a single person, your total income (2010) must be $14,500 or less. For a married couple, your combined total income must be $17,700 or less. Once you are enrolled, you will receive a benefit card and you will pay no more than $6.00 for each generic prescription filled and no more than $9.00 for each brand name prescription filled at your pharmacy. The program will automatically enroll you into a Medicare Part D prescription plan and will cover your monthly Part D premium up to the regional benchmark (in 2010 this figure was $32.09). If you opt to sign up for a Part D program on your own, it must be a plan with a signed agreement with PACE.

PACENET: You cannot be enrolled in the Department of Public Welfare's Medicaid prescription benefit. A single person's total income can be between $14,500 and $23,500. A couple's combined total income can be between $17,700 and $31,500. Again, once you are enrolled, you will receive a benefit card and you will pay no more than $8.00 for each generic prescription filled and no more than $15.00 for each brand name prescription filled at your pharmacy.

Unlike the PACE program, however, if you are **not** enrolled in a Medicare Part D Plan, then you must pay a nominal deductible each month (in 2010 the rate was $32.09) at the pharmacy in addition to the co-payments. If the deductible isn't met each month, it will accumulate. On the other hand, if you've signed up with a Medicare Part D plan that has a signed agreement with PACE, then the deductible is waived and you'll pay toward the monthly premium of the Part D plan. This is in addition to the generic and brand co-payments of eight and fifteen dollars respectively.

One of the greatest benefits of both programs is that beneficiaries will be covered during the "donut hole," when Medicare Part D programs do not cover prescriptions.

The PACE program does not automatically enroll beneficiaries in Part D programs if they do not have Medicare Part A or B, receive drug coverage through employee retirement plans or are members of Medicare Advantage Plans. Of course, if you notify PACE that you do not want to be enrolled in a Part D plan, then your wishes will be followed.

If you're interested in the program, you can apply online at www.pacecares.fhsc.com or give them a call at 1-800-225-7223. The website also lists all of the Part D plans that have signed agreements with PACE. Local senior centers and pharmacies often have PACE applications available, as well.

Q: I heard about a benefits book for older people in Pennsylvania. Do you know what it is and how I can get a copy?

A: What you are referring to is a guide book published by the Pennsylvania Department of Aging that identifies a wealth of programs, services, and benefits that are available for residents of Pennsylvania sixty years and older. The book, titled *Benefits and Rights for Older Pennsylvanians* is published annually and has been a mainstay in the field of aging for nearly thirty years. Every program available through Area Agencies on Aging is described, along with services offered by other departments in state government that are targeted for seniors. For example, the shared ride program operated by the Pennsylvania Department of Transportation is cited in the book along with information on PennDot's Reduced Motor Vehicle Registration, how to obtain Identification Cards, Parking Permits for Persons with a Disability and Auto Insurance Discounts.

The 145 page guide book covers such topics as Veteran's Services, Volunteer Opportunities, Housing Programs, for example Reverse Mortgages and Continuing Care Retirement Communities, Recreation and Leisure Activities including how to contact one of 600 senior centers across the state, Home and Community- Based Services, Employment Programs for Seniors, and Health Insurance.

The "rights" portion of the guide book focuses on consumer protection issues affecting seniors and how to take action if your rights have been violated. You'll find a quick definition of each topic covered and basic contact information on how to access the service through 800 phone numbers and web site addresses.

You'll also find information on the PACE/ PACENET prescription program, how to apply for property tax and rent rebates, and how to receive free insurance counseling through the APPRISE program.

There are four ways to gain access to the book. You can go online and download the guidebook at www.aging.state.pa.us and go to "Brochures." You can order a printed copy of the book for free by writing to: PA Department of Aging, Healthy Aging, Education, and Outreach Division, 555 Walnut Street, 5th Floor, Harrisburg, PA 17101 or give them a call at (717) 783-8975. And finally, most state legislator's district offices have copies on hand for their constituents.

It's a gem of a book that makes you really appreciate the advantages of being older in Pennsylvania.

Caregiver Resources

ELDERCARE LOCATOR

Area Agencies on Aging (AAA) offer a wide range of community based services, care management, information and referral, protective services and other benefits that can help your loved one stay at home and remain active in the community. Call 1-800-677-1116 to find the nearest agency to you or visit www.eldercare.gov.

FAMILY CAREGIVER SUPPORT PROGRAM

This national and state program is offered in every state through your local Area Agency on Aging. It provides assistance to families caring for a loved one in their home who is 60 years and older. It also provides support for grandparents raising grandchildren. Call 1-800-677-1116 to find your local AAA or visit www.eldercare.gov.

BENEFITS CHECKUP

The National Council on Aging offers a free screening service that can identify what benefits you may be eligible for that are provided by local, state, and federal agencies, along with non-profit organizations. They also identify prescription benefits that you may be qualified to receive. This is a web-based service only at www.benefitscheckup.org.

MEDICARE'S WEBSITE

Every year Medicare beneficiaries must decide whether or not they want to stay with "Traditional Medicare" or opt for a managed care plan. They must also choose a Medicare Part D prescription plan and Medi-gap policy. At www.medicare.gov you can compare plans, learn what Medicare covers, research quality care reports on nursing homes, home health agencies and durable medical device and equipment companies. Or, you can call at 1-800-MEDICARE. For a specialized section on Caregiver Resources, go to www.medicare.gov/caregivers/.

OFFICE OF LONG TERM LIVING

The Office of Long Term Living is administered by the PA Department of Aging and it wraps together a wide range of services that enable people sixty years and older to live at home as an alternative to living in a nursing home. It also does the same for people who are younger who have long term needs due to a disability. You can call the Long Term Living Helpline at 1-866-286-3636 for more information or visit their website at www.ltlinpa.org.

SOCIAL SECURITY ADMINISTRATION

Call them to arrange for direct deposit of checks, ask about benefits, request a copy of your Social Security Card, determine eligibility for disability or SSI, use their "Retirement Estimator" to find out the amount of your monthly check based on different ages of retirement, and apply for Social Security and Medicare online. Call them at 1-800-772-1213 or visit their website at www.ssa.gov.

MEDLINEPLUS

Produced by the National Library of Medicine under the United States National Institutes of Health, you can easily access a wealth of information on 800-plus diseases and conditions with links to resources, explanations and side-effects of thousands of prescription drugs and supplements, contact information on clinical trials for cancer patients, a medical encyclopedia and a medical dictionary, easy-to-understand tutorials on common conditions, tests, and treatments both in English and Spanish. The website offers reliable, up-to-date health information all of which is for free and there is no advertising. Go to www.medlineplus.gov.

ABLEDATA

This website has a huge database of assistive devices, technology and equipment to make the tasks of daily living easier to foster independent living. Description of devices, some consumer reviews and contact data to purchase the product is given. The site is sponsored by the federal National Institute on Disability and Rehabilitation Research (NIDRR) and it does not commercially sell any of the products, nor do they receive any funds from the companies listed. It is a free, objective information source for consumers. Go to www.abledata.com or call 1-800-227-0216.

PENNSYLVANIA'S PACE PRESCRIPTION PLAN

The Pennsylvania Pharmaceutical Assistance Contract for the Elderly (PACE) offers comprehensive prescription coverage to older Pennsylvanians and covers most prescription medications, including insulin, syringes and insulin needles. You're eligible if you meet certain income thresholds, are 65 years of age and older and have been a resident in Pennsylvania for at least ninety days prior to submitting an application. You can apply online at www.pacecares.fhsc.com or give them a call at 1-800-225-7223. The website also lists all of the Part D plans that have signed agreements with PACE.

FAMILY CAREGIVER RESOURCES

There are three major websites that offer information and resources to family caregivers. All of them are non-profit organizations and each offers some of their own unique resources for caregivers. Here they are: National Alliance for Caregiving (www.caregiving.org); Family Caregiver Alliance (www.caregiver.org)or 1-800-445-8106; and the National Family Caregivers Association (www.nfcacares.org) or 1-800-896-3650.